sexWATCHING
Looking into the world of sexual behaviour

This book is lovingly dedicated to my wife Kit and our four daughters: Hinda, Irene, Sara and Leah.

sexWATCHING
Looking into the world of sexual behaviour

MILTON DIAMOND

GUILD PUBLISHING
LONDON

This book was devised and produced by
Multimedia Publications (UK) Ltd

Editors   Anne Cope, Judy Martin
Production   Arnon Orbach, Judy Rasmussen
Design   Millions Design
Picture research   Frances Vargo, Paul Snelgrove, Helena Beaufoy
Indexing   Paul Barnett

First published in Great Britain in 1984 by
Macdonald & Co (Publishers) Ltd

This edition published 1984 by Book Club Associates
by arrangement with Multimedia Publications (UK) Ltd

Origination by D.S. Colour International Ltd, London, UK
Typeset by Text Filmsetters Ltd, Orpington, UK
Printed in Italy by Amilcare Pizzi SpA, Milan

Contents

For initiating and motivating me to write this book I must particularly thank Dr Leonard Kristal of Multimedia. The encouragement, support and patience of the Multimedia team at all stages of production were warmly appreciated. Hearty thanks are also due for the technical and personal help given by editors Anne Cope and Judy Martin.

Introduction

I have been fortunate in having lived and travelled in many parts of the world, in North and Central America, England and Europe, Japan, Southeast Asia and Polynesia. My present home is multicultural Hawaii. I am doubly blessed in that I have a profession – that of teacher, researcher and counsellor in the area of sexuality – which not only allows but demands involvement with a subject of universal interest, sex. Wherever I have travelled or lived I have kept my eyes and ears open to sex. I have been sexwatching for most of my life; perhaps more so than most. And it has been and continues to be a fascinating experience.

Every culture has rules for dealing with everyday needs such as eating, working and socializing. Sexual exchanges and sexuality pervade these everyday activities. The perhaps unremarkable observation I have made is that, despite apparent differences in sexual expression among different societies, there are many, many commonalities. At the same time, although other societies may seem exotic, our own Western society displays some of the most interesting patterns.

However this book is more than a sexual travelogue. It is a resource as well, a resource for understanding and dealing with sexual questions and issues basic or common to most people in their everyday lives. I would like people to have a greater understanding of this complex subject and to feel more comfortable with it. That is one of the reasons why I have, in the main, steered clear of clinical and sexological jargon, and kept controversial debate to a minimum. My reflections will, I hope, stimulate the reader to think more deeply about his or her own beliefs, attitudes and behaviour.

All too often sex is viewed through keyholes, figuratively if not literally. People look furtively when they would love to stare, peep when they would like to read and view at leisure. And most unfortunately, in Western culture, they are often barred from seeing some of the most wondrous and beautiful events of life, such as childbirth and joyful loving coitus. In this book I want to make visible the myriad aspects of sex that go unnoticed or are unnecessarily hidden.

To those who prefer mystery, I firmly offer the wisdom of Henry Thoreau: 'I lose my respect for the man who can make the mystery of sex the subject of a coarse jest, yet when you speak earnestly and seriously on the subject is silent!' or of Dr C.G. Lang, former Archbishop of Canterbury: 'I would rather have all the risks which come from free discussion of sex than the great risks we run by conspiracy of silence'.

Milton Diamond, Ph.D.
1984

What is sexwatching?

Anyone interested in sexwatching, that is in taking a multifaceted look at sex, must decide what phenomena qualify as sex and what the scope of the watching is to be. A moment's reflection will show sex to be an immensely broad subject, certainly not limited to what people do in bed. Sex and its many manifestations are all around us but most of us have been taught not to notice or publicly examine them.

Of course sex includes what happens when two people are together in genital play or coitus, or when they strive for reproduction, but it is explicit and implicit in a much wider range of activities. It is present when we dress in the morning for work or in the evening for play; when we greet or see others; when we think of and deal with ourselves. Sex is part of everyday existence, public and private. One can certainly exist without coitus, but not without sex – to be human is to be sexual.

One difficulty in looking at or thinking clearly about sex is the lack of a precise and rich common vocabulary with which to express our sexual experiences. Many of our sexual perceptions are not adequately expressed in the words available to us. The word 'sex' itself is convenient shorthand for all the physical, emotional and social facts of being male or female. 'Coitus' specifically refers to inserting a penis into a vagina, but for most people the word is clinical and the concept limiting. 'Intercourse', a term less rigidly defined, refers to any type of genital activity, but it too seems narrow, impersonal and lacking in emotion. Vernacular alternatives – balling, screwing, and fucking – are often used derogatorily, though the situation or tone of voice used can make them more or less acceptable. 'Having sex' is a more socially acceptable expression, but any emotional connotation remains safely disguised in the mind of the speaker. 'Making love' is a euphemism with very broad appeal; associating love with sex seems to reduce discomfort and begins to convey something of the richness of the experience. Nevertheless much sex lacks love and much love exists without sexual intent. 'Lover' is a synonym for 'sexual partner' but not all sexual partners are loved.

The purposes of sex

While a great deal of sexual activity directly or indirectly relates to reproduction, having children is not the purpose of most sexual activity. And the ubiquity of self-stimulation from birth to tomb is testimony that sexual pleasure does not always require a partner. Prostitution, masturbation, daily male–female teasing and flirting, and even most coitus within marriage, do not have reproduction as their goal. Indeed the probability of children would deter most people from these activities. If reproduction were the only goal of sex, coitus among sterile couples or after the menopause would not occur, sex before marriage would scarcely be a subject for debate, and prostitution and pornography would be non–existent. Nevertheless it is procreation, the thought of progeny, that gives the sex act much of its potency, resonance and mystery.

To the biologist, procreation is the fulfilment of an evolutionary imperative. To many men or women who believe in God, in an all-pervading life force, procreation is a sacred obligation. Indeed for some individuals coitus is synonymous with the intention to procreate and not indulged in otherwise.

It is because sex serves so many non-reproductive purposes that sexual behaviour is so ubiquitous, so pervasive. It seems to provide a social cement, a medium of exchange which most people use, sometimes willingly, sometimes not.

Sex gives pleasure – for most of us genital stimulation and response, close body contact and even flirting and teasing are inherently pleasurable. Sex provides release from tension – intercourse, masturbation, dating and other social interplay can defuse sexual and non-sexual tensions and frustration. Sex is stimulating – any satisfactory sexual experience can heighten perception, alleviate boredom, awaken new interests. Sex offers companionship and intimacy – most of us are afraid of loneliness, and want to be known fully and deeply by at least one other person. Often bodies come together in the hope that hearts and minds will follow, but sometimes body intimacy is the most that can be achieved. When there is a meshing of physical and mental intimacy a substantial relationship has developed. Sex is also a commodity – even when it is not blatantly bought or sold, as it is in prostitution, it can be used as an inducement to buy or sell, as in advertising. Often sex is

Is the making of children the grand purpose of sex or simply the result?

To share our life with someone who meets our sexual needs is probably one of the most satisfying experiences we ever have.

11

bartered in exchange for goods or services, even for love. But often the barter is an 'apple for oranges' deal: a fair exchange is hoped for but often the items traded are not equivalent or clearly understood.

Sex is also a form of recreation, available to all classes and conditions of people – 'swinging' or the swopping of sex partners, pornography, blue movies and 'dirty' jokes are significant forms of entertainment. Sex is also a means of communication – physical contact, or the lack of it, conveys strong messages about mood, arousal and feelings. Sex can also be a weapon – desired behaviour can be coerced by withholding sex as a punishment or offering it as a reward.

In most of the world today, and certainly in the West until thirty or forty years ago, sex is seen as a marital duty. Traditionally within marriage partners have the right of sexual access to one another, whether sex is a pleasure or not. Despite recent court cases alleging rape within marriage, the tradition of sex as one of the duties of marriage is likely to persist. If one performs other marital or family duties faithfully, such as caring for children or elderly relatives, why should one not do one's sexual duty? 'He never has to look elsewhere' and 'She is always satisfied' are remarks made with

some pride. On the other hand for many the call to such duty is a source of deep anger and resentment.

The picture then is complex but clear. Sex is an infinitely flexible medium which answers different needs and serves different purposes at different times. If sex did not exist something like it would have to be invented. With such a powerful medium at our disposal we surely owe it to ourselves to know as much about it as possible.

Early ideas about sex
There are many different frameworks for thinking about sex, each with its advantages and disadvantages, proponents and opponents. Interest in sex is as old as human life. For our cave-dwelling ancestors its mysteries

Above *Male and female symbolized in enduring granite. Stone Age monument at Men-an-tol, Cornwall, England.*

Can one ever have too much of a good thing?

were naturally tied to the cycles of life and death. Like other important matters sex was ruled or influenced by the stars, and by gods and spirits. It remains that way in many non-technological societies today.

In the ancient world many competing philosophies and religions regarded sex as having spiritual meaning, as being central to an understanding of human existence. But integration of sex with religious beliefs and practices was by no means consistent. The cultures in which Judaism developed ranged from the sensual to the ascetic. Some early religions called for celibacy, even castration; others not only allowed but encouraged heterosexual and homosexual acts in their temples; some practised prostitution in the service of the gods.

Physical passion, without emotional entanglement, was not suspect or disapproved of in ancient Greece. Here two young men enjoy and are enjoyed by their hetairai, *female companions. Attic vase, 500 BC.*

Greeks and Romans

The religious practices of Greece and Rome are of particular significance to present day Western societies. They, more than Judaism, strongly coloured the development of Christianity and are now part of the collective unconscious of much of the industrialized world.

Greece of the sixth century BC saw the rise of the Orphic religion. This gave to the world a dualistic view of human existence: trapped inside a mortal body was a troubled immortal soul. Thinking and knowing were conceived of as qualitatively different from imagining, feeling and experiencing. The Greek insight was that ideas are independent of things and people; things and feelings are temporal, but ideas are eternal. If, they reasoned, the human mind is capable of understanding eternal ideas the mind itself must be capable of eternal life. This version of the mind they called the soul.

According to Orphic beliefs, one's proper task in life was to achieve peace in the present world and prepare for a future one. This was best done by leading a pure life and performing certain rituals. The exact recipe for a pure life, however, was much argued about. Pythagoras (582–500 BC), remembered best for his mathematical theories, taught that leading a pure life involved repudiating sexual desire, a 'fury of the soul', and escaping domination of the flesh. Orgasm being the prime self-indulgence, mastery over sexual desire was an important form of self-improvement. Pythagoras did not advocate total abstinence himself but several of his followers did.

Plato (427–347 BC) adopted certain aspects of Pythagorean thinking. Though he rejected the cultic aspects of the Orphic religion he dwelt much on the dualism of Ideas (soul) and Matter (body) and taught that the soul was superior in character to the body but was hindered in its performance of the higher psychic functions by physical needs and desires. One of the higher functions of the soul was to reason. Ideas were perfect, but matter could never be. Only the world of ideas contained ultimate reality.

Similar dualistic thinking was applied to the phenomenon of love. There was sacred love and profane love, *agape* and *eros*, the one spiritual, the other physical. Plato believed that true happiness could only be found through *agape*, non-physical love. This higher love, Platonic love, could lead to self-mastery and an end to the disease of physical craving. 'Copulation' Plato wrote 'lowers a man to the frenzied passions characteristic of beasts and for this reason sexual desire belongs to the lowest element of the mind.'

Later Greek, Roman and then Christian philosophers followed Plato's lead. Diogenes the Cynic (412–322 BC) taught that all desires and appetites not absolutely necessary to maintaining life were to be renounced: sex was not necessary. Zeno (342–270 BC), founder of Stoicism, was less extreme. He taught that instincts and emotions were not antagonistic to right living provided they were kept within bounds. Marriage was acceptable provided its purpose was procreation, but passion in marriage was suspect. Seneca (4 BC–AD 65) urged his Roman contemporaries to love with judgement not with affection. A man should 'control his impulses and not be borne headlong into copulation'. Plotinus (AD 203–62), founder of Neoplatonism, preached that the key to human virtue lay in detachment from worldly (evil) desires. His more extremist followers considered all pleasure sinful, not only sex but also theatre-going, horse-racing and meat-eating.

Bas relief from a Roman funerary urn. In the Roman world prudence, moderation and judgement were respected in domestic and public life. Between husband and wife companionate love, not romantic love, was the ideal.

15

Accompanying these antisexual philosophies of the pre-Christian and early Christian era was a high degree of misogyny. Someone close at hand had to be blamed for the temptations of the flesh, and who better than woman? Eve is the prototype scapegoat. She and her descendants have lured men into evil ways. The idea of woman as tempter still resonates through Western sexual thought.

Jewish thought

Developments in Judaism were quite different. The Jews believed in one God, not in a pantheon, and in a unity of body and mind. For a satisfactory life body and mind had to be in concert; one could not dominate the other. While the Greek philosophers were city people, the Jews, as originally agricultural people, saw sex as a natural and indispensable part of life, for themselves as for their herds. In sharp contrast to the asceticism and antisexual pronouncements of the early Greeks, the Jews saw sex as a vitality in life to be enjoyed as a right for husband, wife, and even concubine.

There was no separation of the sexes at the time of the First Temple. The Old Testament states that man cannot live a satisfactory life alone; he needs a companion and helpmate, an equal partner – a woman. Sex segregation in worship developed not as a result of hostility between the sexes but for just the opposite reason; they were too friendly. The religious historian Louis Epstein writes of arrangements in the Temple at Jerusalem:

> For ordinary worship and sacrificial rites the teachers were satisfied that mingling of the sexes would cause no immorality. But they were disturbed by the levity of men and women crowding the Temple to witness the festival celebration . . . The festival was joyous to the point of hilarity and, in the minds of the teachers, created temptations for sexual improprieties among less scrupulous men and women.

It is notable that men and women were held equally to blame for breaches of decorum.

As the Jews became urbanized they adopted some of the attitudes of their Greek neighbours. It was right to resist the temptation to do evil and constantly strive to do good, but the Jews held to their belief that the rewards of a righteous life come in this world, not in the next. Other than in a minority of splinter groups (the Essenes were one such), the

Jewish religion never denounced the pleasures and virtues of sex or downgraded women.

The Jews, as did the followers of Aristotle, preached moderation in all things. As Maimonides wrote later: 'The Torah has intended natural man to eat moderately of what he has, drink what he can in moderate amount, and enjoy legitimate sexual pleasure in moderate measure.' In medieval times the rabbi Nachmanides wrote: 'The Lord created all things in accordance with his wisdom, and whatever he created cannot be shameful or ugly . . . When a man is in union with his wife in a spirit of holiness and purity, the Divine Presence is with them.'

Adam and Eve in a Garden of Eden created by the sixteenth-century painter Lucas Cranach. Through Eve – curious, disobedient, weak-willed – the human race 'fell' into an uncomfortable state of knowledge, simultaneously aware of its godlike origins and its miserable inadequacies.

Christian traditions

From these conflicting currents of Jewish and Greek thought Christianity emerged, attempting to distinguish itself from its Jewish heritage, believing Jesus to be the Messiah, intent on salvation in a world to come, taking a generally ascetic view of sex and other pleasures. Abstinence for the short duration of life on earth was fair trade for eternal celestial bliss. This antisexual attitude was reinforced by the spread of Manichaeism during the late third and fourth centuries. The doctrine of Mani (crucified in Persia in AD 276 for his opposition to Zoroastrianism) was based on the struggle of two eternal and conflicting principles, God and light, matter and darkness. Coitus was an act of darkness; even to contemplate it was evil. However, the Manichaeans accepted that not everyone was strong enough to deny the sexual impulse. Before his conversion to Christianity, St Augustine (died c.605) was a Manichaean and had lived with a mistress, and his struggle to subdue his sexual urges continued throughout his life. The only rationale for sexual activity, he finally decided, reconciling his Christian and Manichaean ideas, was the Old Testament injunction to 'go forth and multiply'. An earlier convert, St Paul, had expressed a similar opinion: 'It is good for a man not to touch a woman. Nevertheless . . . it is better to marry than to burn.'

As the historian Vern Bullough wrote:

With Saint Augustine the basic sexual attitudes of the Christian Church were set. Virginity was the preferred state of existence, but for those unable to adapt to this state, marriage was permitted. Within marriage intercourse was tolerated, but only for the purpose of procreation . . . Christian ideas on sex, however, were not primarily derived from any biblical teaching but were based upon the intellectual and philosophical assumptions of the period of its birth . . . Inevitably Christians became – in spirit if not always in practice – ascetics, justifying sexual activity only in terms of progeny. Inevitably any kind of sexual activity not resulting in procreation had to be condemned.

The glib assumption that a common Judaeo-Christian heritage is responsible for today's sexual attitudes is wrong. Jew and Christian went their separate ways. Though some Jewish communities may have been sexually conservative or ascetic, and some Christian communities liberal or sensual, Judaism retained a generally positive attitude towards sex and Christianity a generally negative one.

Alliance between Church and State

With minor turns and digressions it was the limited Augustinian concept of sex that prevailed from the seventh century onwards and became incorporated into Western civil law. With both Church and State to contend with, critical and unbiased investigation of sex was a very difficult undertaking.

The tie between Church and State still leaves its mark. The medieval notion was that the State should be an agent for moral good by making illegal those activities that the Church pronounced sinful. So the State became

responsible for punishing any sexual activity not tied to procreation, a role it is only slowly shedding to this day. It must also be said that throughout history the State has used religion as an excuse to make laws for civil or political purposes. For example, for reasons still not fully identified, the sixth century Christian emperor Justinian placed all homosexual activities in the same category as adultery. Punishment for homosexual acts ranged from doing penance to castration or death. It was Justinian's law that introduced the notion of homosexuality as unnatural. The wording 'acting contrary to nature' is still used in legal codes today.

A jealous husband stands guard over his wife while her lover prowls outside. A scene from Chaucer's Miller's Tale *depicted in a late fifteenth-century French manuscript.*

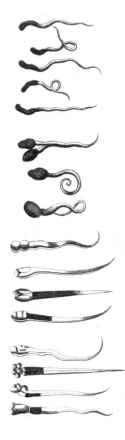

Late eighteenth-century microscope drawings of the sperm of (top to bottom) a cockerel, a ram, a dog and a rabbit. The first accurate description of spermatozoa was given in 1677 by Antoni van Leeuwenhoek of Delft.

Challenges to the old order

The re-urbanization in Europe that followed the great plagues of the fifteenth and sixteenth centuries – one of which was syphilis, called 'the great pox' because its spread was more devastating than the scourge of smallpox – changed many people's sex and family lives. As the State began to wrest power away from the Church, more and more natural philosophers (the scientists of their day) questioned the established order. They and the ever practical farmers began to experiment with breeding and to investigate the reproductive system and its mysteries.

In England William Harvey discovered how the blood circulates, and in the 1650s he also investigated the hatching of chicken eggs. In Italy in the mid 1500s Vesalius and Fallopius studied the female reproductive system. In the Netherlands in the seventeenth century Leeuwenhoek and de Graaf and in the nineteenth century von Baer explored the conjunction of sperm and egg. Slowly the mysteries of reproductive biology were submitted to scientific analysis. Though some natural philosophers considered study of the sexual organs, even those of plants, blasphemous and obscene, others justified it in terms of making human reproduction safer and more efficient.

The Reformation also modified views of sex and marriage. Martin Luther and John Calvin, for instance, did not regard sex within marriage as sinful. 'God winks at it!' said Luther. It was 'pure, honourable and holy' said Calvin. Even the Puritans, returning to Old Testament fundamentals, praised marital love and marital sex, though they strictly censured sexuality outside marriage.

In the latter part of the eighteenth century, as the American colonies and France broke free of their monarchic pasts, thinking about human sexuality began to change. Influential philosophers like Jean-Jacques Rousseau and Denis Diderot called for a return to nature; not to Greek or Catholic ideas of nature as an amalgam of the laws of logic and mathematics, but to nature as the play of emotions, feelings and instincts. As Diderot wrote: 'Religious institutions have attached labels "vice" and "virtue" to actions that are completely independent of morality.'

The philosophers of the Age of Reason offered two important new attitudes. First, they cast aside the belief that physical impulses were necessarily destructive and to be controlled. They said, in contrast, that instincts were good and should be expressed and that it was society's restrictiveness that subverted human joy and perfection. Second, they did not believe that one came closer to God by rejecting natural desires.

While these ideas were not to everyone's taste, they offered a blend of reason and optimism. Through scientific experiments and a critical examination of experience men and women might come to discover truths about the world around them, and about themselves. Poverty, famine, plague, war, inequality and eventually human behaviour were susceptible to scientific study. Divine ordinance was no longer an acceptable explanation of anything and everything.

The beginnings of sexology

Deep-rooted social attitudes do not change overnight. Prior to and throughout the nineteenth century most education and scientific research took place in colleges and universities associated with religious institutions. Few strictly public and non-religious universities existed. But slowly and surely investigators began to ask questions specifically related to sex. Much of what they wrote and said we now know to be incorrect but the real significance of their work was that they overcame the prejudice that any study of sex independent of its moral trappings was wrong. They began to sweep aside the old view that reproduction legitimized sex and that the reproductive system was the only aspect of human sexuality that justified study.

It was partly the social problems of the nineteenth century, which included rampant venereal disease, illegitimacy, and the widespread abandonment of families, that encouraged such enquiries. Investigators came from many disciplines and many countries. For the most part they focused on social and marital problems rather than the seeking of knowledge for its own sake. Sexology as a science in its own right had not yet emerged.

At the turn of the century Krafft-Ebing (1840–1902), a German neurologist and psychiatrist, made an attempt to categorize the sexual pathologies he saw in his patients. Paolo Mantegazza, in Italy, contributed anthropological studies of sex. In France Jean Charcot wrote of psychiatric and sexual problems and Auguste-Henri Forel published a

Three of the founding fathers of sexology. All three made enormous contributions to sexual understanding but were not immune to biases of their own. Richard von Krafft-Ebing (left) believed that masturbation led to 'degeneration'. Havelock Ellis (centre) had an interest in unusual sexual patterns, undoubtedly influenced by his own enjoyment of them. Magnus Hirschfeld (right) remarked that 'the sexual sadism of women' was 'invariably totalitarian'.

biological and moral review of sex. Two Englishmen, Richard Burton and later Havelock Ellis, published reports of exotic Oriental sexual practices, in real life and in literature. In Spain and the United States other researchers began to make their mark. But, as the historian Erwin Haeberle has pointed out, the true founders of modern sexology were a group of German Jews: Iwan Bloch, Magnus Hirschfeld, Albert Moll and Max Marcuse. Around the time that Sigmund Freud published his *Three Essays on the Theory of Sexuality* (1905), Bloch and the others were well embarked on the road to *Sexualwissenschaft* ('sexual science') and called for a broadly based and unified study of sexuality. Bloch himself published what was probably the first large scale review of sex titled *The Sexual Life of Our Time* (1912) and in it pleaded:

> *To do justice to the whole importance of love in the life of the individual and in that of society, and in relation to the evolution of human civilization, this particular branch of inquiry must be treated in its proper subordination as a part of general science of mankind, which is constituted by a union of all other sciences – of general biology, anthropology and ethnology, philosophy and psychology, the history of literature, and the entire history of civilization.*

While we know a great deal about Freud's entry into the subject of sex (he saw it as a window to understanding the mind), we can only speculate what prompted such an interest in Bloch. Perhaps he was impressed with the

misery caused by the venereal diseases he was treating. As a dermatologist he no doubt spent a large part of his time dealing with such problems. Before the advent of antibiotics venereal diseases filled more long-stay hospital beds than any other group of ills. Until the 1940s and the miracle of penicillin, dermatology was linked with syphilology much as we link obstetrics with gynecology today.

Bloch's call was quickly answered. In 1908 Hirschfeld founded the first journal devoted to sexology as a science. As early as 1897 he had founded a Scientific Humanitarian Committee which addressed itself to reforming attitudes towards sexual matters, including homosexuality. In the following year Marcuse also started a journal, this time for a wider audience. Albert Moll, already the author of a major monograph on homosexuality (1891) and another on libido (1897), followed with a comprehensive study called *The Sexual Life of the Child* in 1909. In 1912 he edited the first sexology handbook.

This small group of men were the begetters of many books and journals, and a great deal of research and therapy. They even made educational films about syphilis and homosexuality, putting the case for more research into venereal disease and for decriminalizing homosexuality.

In 1919 Magnus Hirschfeld founded the world's first Institute for Sexology in Berlin. This was followed in 1921 by the first sexological congress attended by scientists from Tokyo, Peking, Moscow, Rome, London, Copenhagen and San Francisco.

American Gothic,
*painted by Grant Wood in
1930. Puritanical attitudes
to sex persisted in the
United States until well
after World War I.*

American traditions

Developments in the United States were slower and different in focus. There was no central nucleus of scientific sex investigators as there was in Berlin. There were individuals devoted to reforming attitudes to sex, reproduction, women's rights, sex education and marriage laws, but encouraging research was not part of their enterprise. In late nineteenth- and early twentieth-century America – even more so than in Europe – nice people did not discuss sex. Certainly respectable professionals did not study the subject.

As the American author Harry Barnes

wrote in 1926 in an introduction to V.C. Calverton's *Sex Expression in Literature*:

Sex . . . is even taboo to intelligent discussion. It is a field which is arbitrarily declared to be vile by definition. Even physicians are not lacking who designate all types of sexual matters as nasty, without deeming it necessary to explain this arbitrary characterization. The sexual is looked upon as pre-eminently the field which must not be approached in a scientific manner.

In 1930 two professors at the University of Missouri were severely censured and penalized for collecting data from college students in an attempt to devise a system of sex ethics.

During the 1920s the climate began to change. As I see it, the credit for this was mainly due to four events. The first was the founding, in 1913, of the American Social Hygiene Association. Its purpose was to solve the social problems that accompany prostitution, venereal disease and illegitimacy. One of the first scientific studies of sex in the United States – a survey of the sexual behaviour of 518 college men by M.J. Exner – followed very soon after.

The second and third events were the rise of the Suffragettes – their call for women's rights included the availability of reliable contraception, safe and legal abortion and free love – and the blossoming of behaviourism, a new approach to the study of behaviour patterns based on observation, not assumption.

Fourth, and most important, was the impetus provided by a group of eminent biologists and psychologists (Walter B. Cannon, Frank R. Lillie, Robert M. Yerkes and Catharine B. Davis among them) who saw the need to encourage sex research. In 1921, with support from the Rockefeller Foundation and under the auspices of the National Academy of Sciences, this group formed the National Research Council Committee for Research in Problems of Sex. Their first resolution stated:

The impulses and activities associated with sex behavior and reproduction are fundamentally important for the welfare of the individual, the family, the community, the race. Nevertheless, the reports of personal experience are lacking and the relative few data of observation have not been collected in serviceable form. Under circumstances where we should have knowledge and intelligence, we are ignorant. To a large degree, our ignorance is due to the enshrouding of sex relations in a fog of mystery, reticence and shame. Attitudes toward the subject have been fixed by moral teaching, medical instruction and social propaganda, all based on only a slight foundation of well established fact. In the presence of this secrecy and prejudice scientific investigation would be difficult.

In 1938 the Committee started to fund the work of a then unknown entomologist called Alfred C. Kinsey.

One significant thing the Committee did was to foster sex research in many separate disciplines – anatomy, medicine, physiology, sociology, psychology, anthropology, law and philosophy – rather than create a unified field of study called sexology as the Germans did. This fragmentation, which still persists in the United States today, has some advantages but on the whole it is restrictive. An anatomical treatise on the genitals, for example, may be useful for comparing erection of the penis with engorgement of the clitoris, but it tells us nothing about the psychological or social dimensions of these processes.

Until the 1950s neither sex research nor sex researchers, whatever their country of origin, were taken seriously by the majority of physicians and scientists around the world and certainly not by the public at large. Even twenty years ago the term sexologist had a very suspect ring to it. The antisexual bias of history was slow in fading.

Attitudes in Britain and Europe

No British publisher would print Havelock Ellis' monumental seven-volume *Studies in the Psychology of Sex* written in 1896. The book was first published in German in Germany. The Library of the British Museum put it on its shelves but not in its catalogue. When copies arrived in London the distributor was prosecuted. Not a single physician or scientist of note came forward in court to defend the book or its publisher. The trial judge, Sir Charles Hall, suspended sentence but warned: 'It is impossible for anyone with a head on his shoulders to open the book without seeing that it is a pretence and a sham... do not touch this filthy work again [or] it will be my duty to send you to prison for a very long term.' The book finally appeared in English, in 1901, in Philadelphia but did not go on general sale; it was sold to professionals only. Publication in England had to wait until 1934. By that time it had become a landmark work in Germany, France, Spain, Italy and even Japan. In Japan in 1922, when biologist Senji Yamamoto and his student Tokutaro Yasuda, tried to publish sexological data collected from some 1146 volunteers, they too found the law against them. Their report was censured as 'an obscene document that would corrupt public morals'. Yamamoto paid dearly for his scientific daring: he was assassinated by fanatical nationalists who thought his findings defamatory to Japan.

A young woman publicly humiliated by the Nazis for having slept with a Jew.

The Nazis temporarily revived old prejudices against sex, except as a means of procreation. In those territories which fell under their sway they confiscated or destroyed all sexological material, forbade research and, in a gruesome return to the Dark Ages, systematically persecuted Jews and gypsies, and sent thousands of homosexuals to concentration camps and death. Even in countries outside German control attitudes towards sex research, grudging at best, became less hospitable. The world had more important matters to attend to.

Sex research after World War II

After the war, with the forceful and positive leadership of Hirschfeld and his colleagues gone, the focus of sex research moved to the United States. Alfred Kinsey and his collaborators published their classic study *Sexual Behavior in the Human Male* in 1948 and the volume on the female followed in 1953. By this time many academic, clinical and social disciplines, thanks to encouragement from the National Research Council, possessed experts on sexual matters. In Germany and Japan as well as Britain, France, Scandinavia, Czechoslovakia and other technologically advanced countries, the validity and usefulness of sex research was beginning to be accepted. But even today, despite the enormous scope for and influence of accurate sexual information, there are fewer than a dozen university departments in the world devoted to sexology. Some countries are without a single teacher or researcher qualified in this area. In the USSR and most of Eastern Europe there is a very notable absence of sex research.

But the scientific investigation of sex has had a negative side. Research findings are eagerly scanned for facts that can be lobbed into battles against the establishment, or against religion or against the opposite sex. In other words, sex has become a political football. At the same time the more the scientists discover the more esoteric the whole subject of sex seems to become. It is now being treated as a topic for experts rather than for people in general.

I would like to see the separate strands of research increasingly coming together, in the European mode, as the unified science of sexology, and I say that as someone whose work has received the support of the NRC Committee for Research in Problems of Sex.

In Europe, the lengthening shadow of Fascism and Nazism began to blot out the emerging science of sexology. In Germany Hitler saw the topicality of sex research, and the fact that the leading sexologists were almost all Jews, as inviting targets. Within four months of assuming power in 1933 he sent a Nazi mob to ransack the Institute for Sexology and publicly burn its books and papers. His rantings against Jewish science forced Hirschfeld, Moll and Marcuse to flee for their lives (by this time Bloch had died).

The calm before the storm: Alfred Kinsey (seated) and his colleagues (left to right Wardell Pomeroy, Paul Gebhard and Clyde Martin) on the eve of publication of Sexual Behavior in the Human Female *in 1953. Outraged critics told Kinsey he should have published his book quietly and for experts only.* Sexual Behavior in the Human Male *was published in 1948.*

Sex is something studied by experts but it is also contributed to and openly appreciated by the layperson; after all, ornithologists are complemented by bird watchers and astronomers by enthusiastic star-gazers.

Levels of complexity

Since sex is a complex subject we should build complexity into the way we think about it. Sex can be seen as a series of increasingly complex relationships, beginning with the individual, then expanding to the couple, the

Homo sapiens? *Cartoon by Zabransky.*

family and society at large. Understanding the behaviour of the individual makes it easier to understand interaction within couples, which in turn provides the key to understanding how families behave and how societies function.

And at each level of complexity sexuality can be viewed in several different ways: as a set of biologically or socially determined patterns of behaviour; as a set of physiological mechanisms; as a set of feelings about one's own sexuality; as a set of sexual relationships with people of the opposite or same sex; and as a set of events leading to birth and parenthood.

While these levels will be elaborated upon later, several very pertinent distinctions related to them need to be made at this stage if we are to become good sexwatchers. The layperson tends to see all sexual phenomena as interrelated, but the scientist observes that they are often independent. Take sex roles and gender roles. In Scotland gender roles for men include the wearing of a kilt. This would be inappropriate gender behaviour in Japan. But male sex roles in both Japan and Scotland are similar. A gender role is society's idea of how boys and girls, or men and women, should behave; a sex role is the acting out of one's biological predisposition. Gender has every-

Sexual identity is the sex you believe you belong to. Cathy Brown (right) was once Eugene Brown, but underwent surgery to become a woman. Her husband Christopher regards himself as male although he is still legally female. Their daughter is unaware of the switch and looks on Cathy as her mother and Christopher as her father.

thing to do with the particular society one lives in, and may or may not have much to do with biology. The distinction between gender and sex becomes particularly critical when discussing issues such as transvestism, women's liberation and also the development of sexual identity.

Next, let us be clear what sexual identity is. Early in life most of us know that we are male or female; accepting their gender roles, boys generally want to follow masculine pursuits and girls feminine ones. Occasionally, despite social pressures to conform to the physical evidence, a boy may be convinced he is a girl, or a girl that she is a boy. Our image of our sexual selves may or may not be in concert with our gender. Sexual identity is the inner conviction that we are male or female, whether or not that conviction reflects our physical appearance or the gender roles society imposes on us.

Sexual identity is often confused by the layperson with sexual orientation. Almost everyone at some time in their life is attracted to another person as a partner for love or sex. A very small number of individuals are attracted less to people than to objects (fetishism) or animals (bestiality). One's preference for men or women, or objects or animals, is one's sexual orientation. And as with sexual identity, orientation may or may not be in concert with sex or gender roles.

Getting the facts right

Organizing sexual thinking – whether on the basis of levels of complexity or along more traditional academic lines – is one thing, but finding the facts behind the thinking and using those facts honestly is another. How is sexual information gathered, analysed and used? How is sex research conducted? Sexology, the scientific study of sex, is perhaps more fraught with unintentional and occasionally intentional biases in information gathering and interpretation than the older sciences. Like politics, religion and history, it can be used to bolster prejudice and create fads.

Some time ago I formulated three rules about 'facts' uncovered in process of sex research. The first is that *facts are always accompanied by attitudes or emotions*. Data collected by a fundamentalist group may differ quite radically from data collected by a non-religious or less doctrinaire group. A writer for a men's magazine may select one set of facts for an article on vasectomy and his counterpart on a women's magazine a completely different set of facts. Polls taken by partisan groups are always suspect. The same set of facts, in different hands, can be used to 'prove' different points. Facts can also be suppressed if they are considered morally or politically unacceptable.

My second rule is this: *researchers talk about populations and trends, but their data are gathered from individuals*. Not only are the researchers themselves individuals but individuals also tend to look for themselves in others. For example, almost every survey ever conducted has shown that *most* women who have had abortions feel that overall they made the best decision. Nevertheless *particular* women may have been traumatized by the experience. The inevitable incompleteness of the researcher's own sexual experiences seriously colours his or her acceptance and interpretation of the data collected. As Alfred Kinsey, possibly the most thorough sexual detective of all time, once observed: 'The possibility of an individual engaging in sexual activity at a rate remarkably different from one's own is one of the most difficult things for even professionally trained persons to understand.' Someone who has one or two orgasms a year with a single partner has a very different view of sex from someone who has ten or twenty orgasms a week with as many different partners.

My third rule is, I believe, the most impor-

tant: *one must always distinguish between what is and what might or should be*. For example, as a husband and father of daughters I support women's claims to equal rights and opportunities with men, but as a sexologist I note that progress towards equality is patchy, extremely slow, and may never be attained.

Personal involvement can very easily lead one to mistake hopes, fears and ideals for actuality. More couples are now divorcing than ever before; that is actuality. But to say that this is a trend that will continue or go into reverse is speculation based on personal perspective. Throughout this book I will attempt to make clear what is actuality and what is speculation.

I believe, in spite of the fact that some statements of personal attitudes impinge powerfully on the public consciousness, that societies remain fairly stable in their fundamental sexual values and change them only with great effort. Culture, history, law and religion possess an inertia that resists change. If someone reports a dramatic break with tradition, I remain sceptical until evidence arrives documenting that the change is widespread and permanent.

The media and many individuals – for the sake of effect and because it is so much more gratifying to say something definite than something fuzzy round the edges – are fond of sensationalizing or prophesying by extrapolating from a few findings, or even one, and the unsuspecting are seduced and caught off guard. There has been news recently about syphilis being more common than ever before, about women and men switching roles to the extent that male and female

The American sex researchers William Masters and Virginia Johnson. Their collaboration began in 1954 and in 1966 they published Human Sexual Response, a report that exploded many fallacies and fantasies about sexual arousal and orgasm. Their report was based on the responses, in the laboratory, of 382 women and 312 men. Sex therapy as we know it today draws heavily on techniques pioneered by Masters and Johnson.

stereotypes no longer hold, about the ideal contraceptive being just around the corner, and about the coital rate among teenagers being at an all time high. All of these sensationalisms are false.

An additional fact is crucial to keep in mind in our sexwatching. The scientist refers to this as 'a disparity in KAP' (knowledge, attitudes and practices). People frequently know of, discuss, advocate, support or tolerate practices that they do not or would not allow themselves, and condemn in public what they practise in private. A man may preach fidelity but be cheating on his wife. Dentists can have toothache, marriage counsellors, sex therapists, psychologists and psychiatrists can have sex problems.

Sex surveys

My final caveat to the sexwatcher is this: remember that *sexual information is only as reliable as the research methods and samples used to obtain it*. Data gathered in 1984 from 2000 teenagers in London, England, may not apply to teenagers in Houston, Texas, or to teenagers surveyed in 1974 or 1994, or even to another 2000 teenagers sampled by another team of researchers. This may not preclude some generalization about teenagers throughout England or throughout affluent industrialized societies. But simply increasing the size of a sample does not guarantee accuracy. In 1936 *The Literary Digest* asked more than two million Americans to predict the winner of that year's presidential election; they gave the nod to Alf Landon, but Franklin D. Roosevelt won. *The Literary Digest* poll was unusually large, but it got the wrong answer.

Sex research is full of surveys – those of Shere Hite, *Redbook* and *Cosmopolitan*, to name a few – which suffer from sample distortion. *Redbook* and *Cosmopolitan* admit that their polls are valid only for their responding readerships; although both polls were answered by more than 100 000 women, these women represent limited and not necessarily representative slices of American womanhood. They may not even represent the total readership of either magazine. In 1982 *Playboy* conducted a large scale survey of American men and women. It received responses from some 65 000 men and 15 000 women. Surveys like these always stimulate great popular interest due to the personal nature of the questions asked and information given, but the

Shere Hite of Hite Report *fame. In 1976 and again in 1981 she played to a public eager to gaze at its sexual reflection.*

analyses applied to the responses given are often simplistic. What we are offered are conclusions inevitably drawn from a biased sample which is then further distorted by limited interpretation.

Hite, in her 1976 report on American women, solicited responses from more than 100 000 women. Only 3000 responded. No attempt was made to approximate these to the total population of women in the United States. The fact that 97 000 did not respond suggests that the 3000 who did may have been quite atypical. Similarly Hite's 1981 report on males was compiled from only 7200 questionnaires returned from 119 000 distributed.

The great appeal of both Hite reports was that they purported to be a comprehensive analysis of the sexual habits and attitudes of the majority of American men and women. Moreover both reports are a titillating mix of statistical tables, scientific evaluation, and lengthy conversational exposés. The 1981 report was castigated by one reviewer as 'a statistical disaster area' containing information of 'chronic imprecision', and praised by

another as 'a major contribution to the field of sexology'. Five years earlier the female report was simultaneously greeted as 'a most interesting look at the female sexual response' and as 'unpleasant and hardly credible'. My opinion of the Hite reports is that they were stimulating and clever pieces of popular journalism but invalid as scientific studies. Certainly they have been widely assumed to have more authority than they deserve. In fact they nicely illustrate the need for my three rules about evaluating sexological facts.

The most reliable facts are those gleaned from a sample population that mirrors the whole population under investigation. Suppose 59 per cent of a total survey population are adult, college-educated women of whom 87 per cent are married, 74 per cent are WASPs (White Anglo-Saxon Protestant) and 15 per cent are divorcees; in the survey sample one would try to match these percentages. If this matching is done skilfully, a sample of 5000 would be sufficient to reflect many millions. This is the ideal; unfortunately too many researchers settle for less □.

'Lights! Cameras! Love!' Drawing by Edward Koren © *The New Yorker Magazine.*

Whatever turns you on

What is sexually arousing? That is one of the most intriguing questions for any sexwatcher. Think for a moment. What characteristics do you find sexually appealing in others and what things do others find sexy about you? I have often thought that all those things that lead to one person coaxing another to bed, singling out that person from other friends or acquaintances, are more interesting that what they do together in bed. Bedroom play, while subject to all sorts of imaginative embellishments and elaboration, is a relatively limited part of sexual interaction when compared with the conscious or unconscious desires and strategies involved in arousal, initiation and invitation, persuasion and seduction. Stimuli to arousal are infinitely varied and mysterious.

The image makers of the film and advertising worlds carefully create scenes that portray seclusion, privacy, comfort, warmth, conditions which most of us associate with intimacy and the possibility of seduction. We are given the impression that time is infinite, that no cares or mundane necessities exist. A man and woman stand on a tropical beach at sunset, against a background of swaying palm trees

and a full moon shines on still waters. Another loving couple relaxes in a warm living room, with a flickering fire, soft carpet, music, candles, flowers, good food and wine. Invariably these ideal couples are in their twenties or thirties, relaxed and in good health, and of pleasing, if not exceptional, physical attractiveness.

Images like these are calculated to appeal to all the senses – sight, sound, taste, smell, touch and temperature (rarely is sexual arousal or fantasy associated with the cold). Fatigue and preoccupation, the two most common impediments to sexual arousal, are rarely portrayed in such tableaux. But many of us know from personal or vicarious experience that sexual arousal can happen in the most unlikely places, at the least expected times, and even with a complete stranger.

Chance encounters
Most surveys suggest that casual arousal is more a male than female experience, although the 1982 survey of *Playboy* readers found that among some 15 000 female respondents almost one in three had initiated sexual encounters with strangers they were attracted

A lovers' paradise: sun, sea, sand and time to spare. But sexual attraction exists outside the holiday brochures . . .

to and only 4 per cent had been turned down.

Sexual attraction does not rely only on physical beauty and on a sympathetic social situation. If it did sexual encounters would be a lot rarer. People who are disabled or deformed, people whose deliberate style is to be unkempt or unwashed, people of all conditions and classes arouse sexual feelings. A female physician on duty in an emergency room once described to me how a bloody and dishevelled accident victim brought in for treatment aroused her to such an extent that she had to excuse herself from the room. Jean Genet, in his autobiographical novel *The Thief's Journal*, speaks of being aroused by other men – ordinary men as well as sadists and criminals – in unlikely places.

Physical features

'Love at first sight' is not so much love as sexual attraction. A mere glance may be sufficient to draw two strangers towards each other. It is not difficult to accept that such glances lead to arousal if the people involved look like Robert Redford or Marilyn Monroe. But exactly what is sexy about our favourite actors and actresses? The stereotypes of thirty or forty years ago are not those of today. What do Meryl Streep and Joan Collins have in common, or for that matter John Travolta and Paul Newman?

Arousal might seem to come easily if the stimulus is obvious – the exposure of a firm

Paul Newman and Lana Turner, heart throbs to different generations of movie goers. What do the fans respond to? Perhaps something as simple and as complex as the ability to convey the message 'I desire you'.

breast or long smooth thigh, a hairy chest, rippling muscles, a bulging crotch. Sociobiologists, those scientists who study the links between social behaviour and biological phenomena, believe that secondary sex characteristics – body shape, hair, voice and so on – are attraction and arousal signals. Among our pre-speech paleolithic forebears these signals ensured that male and female came together for mating and reproduction. Our responses to these signals, so the theory goes, are innate. At a subconscious level we link secondary sex characteristics with fitness for reproduction and parenting. Subconsciously a man looks for health and child-bearing ability in a woman; she, in her turn, looks for his ability to protect and sustain a family. Desirable female characteristics would be youth, firm, adequate breasts and wide but not ungainly hips; male characteristics would include prestige within a social group and strength as

reflected in broad shoulders and a firm, muscular body. By extension, gestures that draw attention to the relevant features of both sexes – a woman swinging her hips as she walks or a man flexing his muscles – enhance our responses. So do activities that call attention to the genitals or mimic copulation. The exaggerated displays of a stripper are intended to be a turn-on. The gyrations of Elvis Presley and Mick Jagger on stage elicited frenzied responses from the audience.

Yet sexual attraction is not as simple as that. One can be strongly attached to someone whose secondary sex characteristics are not on display, someone who is – at least in the eyes of others – not worth a second glance. Often it is something trivial and accidental – the toss of a woman's hair or her smile, the sound of a man's voice or the way he laughs – which triggers sexual interest and a strong desire to follow up a chance encounter.

Pumping iron. In fact most surveys show that women are less than enthralled by muscles like these. Nice eyes, neat buttocks, slim build . . . now you're talking.

Concealment can be infinitely more exciting than blatant display when it stimulates the imagination.

General appearances

To men, looks are an important factor in sexual arousal. This has been confirmed by a great deal of well-conducted research as well as anecdotal evidence. In the 1982 *Playboy* survey 55 per cent of the thousands of male readers who responded ranked physical appearance as of prime importance. Only one in three women respondents felt similarly. The men ranked breasts, buttocks and eyes – in that order – as most important. The women who paid particular attention to looks ranked eyes first, buttocks second and lips and genitals in joint third place. Of course no one feature works in isolation. Usually it is the total im-

pression that counts, even if one or two especially fascinating features are emphasized. Generally women admit to being more stimulated by intelligence, common interests, sexual energy, money and power. While men appreciate such assets, they generally rank them less highly.

In a large study done by Karla Joy and Allen Young, North American male and female homosexuals were asked which physical or non-physical features they found attractive or unattractive in a sex partner. The most commonly preferred attributes specified by men were cleanliness and 'looks in general'. The most appreciated were, in order of importance, slim build, shapely physique and relative youth. The women put these same items top too – cleanliness and 'looks in general' first, followed by relative youth and slim build – but in general their responses were more varied than the men's. But for both sexes general attributes were more important than specific features such as eyes, hair, buttocks and so forth. Every culture has devised and accepted ways of enhancing general and specific attributes, through cosmetics, clothing and jewellery, the crucial assumption being that sexual interest is there to be tapped and intensified.

Why do we respond to sexual signals?

Even among the experts there is little agreement as to how sexual arousal or attraction comes about. The sociobiological view that it is an inborn, primitive mechanism related to fitness for parenting is a powerful argument but not universally accepted. It does not account, for example, for idiosyncratic preferences.

Some theorists claim that adult sexual arousal is carried over from events rooted in infancy and learned during development. The characteristics of one's parents, or one's interactions with them when a child, supposedly leave unconscious erotic programs that are then drawn on in adulthood. The stimuli to which we respond match fragments of previous sexual situations, real or imagined. For example, if the hero or heroine of your dreams has long hair or wears thigh-high boots, these may trigger off sexual arousal; if a stranger's voice or smile reminds you of a past lover, that too will stimulate arousal; so might a place or a scent or a tune associated with a previous lover or loved one.

Sometimes it is a certain type of interaction – usually one that boosts your ego, or makes you less anxious – that arouses sexual feelings. A knight in shining armour, or more likely an ordinary man who rescues a woman from a difficult situation, may trigger erotic thoughts. Nurses and doctors, because they are caring and relieve pain and anxiety, are often the subject of sexual fantasizing. People

Packaging our sexual signals. Clothes are, in themselves, a very subtle – or not so subtle – signalling system.

who share a common adventure or experience, especially if it is exciting or emotionally trying, find themselves erotically drawn to each other. Primatologists have found that rhesus monkeys reluctant to mate readily do so soon after they have been coaxed into taking part in aggressive behaviour towards a common enemy.

Another popular theory, credited to American psychologist Stanley Schachter, holds that since we tend to give specific emotional labels to any kind of physiological arousal – we call a dry throat and a trembling voice 'fear', 'anxiety', 'defensiveness', 'anger' and so on – under certain circumstances we tend to label physiological events as sexual attraction or interpret them as strengthening sexual feelings and perceptions we already have. Numerous experiments support this theory.

Links between anxiety, aggression and sexual arousal

In one study in which male subjects were led to believe they would be given mild or severe electric shocks the positive ratings they gave to randomly assigned partners of the opposite sex significantly increased. In another study, subjects obliged to make prolonged eye contact with a stranger, usually a situation that provokes anxiety, displayed greatly enhanced attraction to that person. Staring at a life-size photograph of the person elicited no such response. In everyday life we constantly, though not always consciously, feel stimulated and threatened by eye contact.

One intriguing study by Donald Dutton and Arthur Aron at the University of British Columbia tested this 'heightened emotion = arousal' theory under supposedly natural conditions. It was arranged that ordinary passers-by, all of them men, should singly encounter a man or woman (members of the research team) either on a suspension bridge swaying 230 feet above rapids, or on a solid bridge 10 feet above a tributary of the same river. The unsuspecting subjects of the experiment were stopped and asked to take a simple psychological test. This was a diversion from the real point of the experiment, which was to discover if the fear associated with the swaying bridge and the low level of anxiety associated with the solid one would directly influence subjects' later attempts to contact the interviewer. The interviewers routinely offered a telephone number to each participant, osten-

sibly so they could find out the results of the psychological test. Half of the participants interviewed on the swaying bridge telephoned the female interviewer, compared with only 15 per cent interviewed on the solid bridge. Very few bothered to contact the male interviewer, whether they had been interviewed on the swinging or the solid bridge. This finding, and other related investigations, seems to support the idea that there is definite link between anxiety and sexual attraction.

As a sidelight on this intriguing topic, consider the habits of the Gusii tribe of present-day Kenya, Africa. Among these people sexual arousal is said to occur *only* in combination with hostility and antagonism. Sexual training for girls involves being taught from childhood to encourage male advances while simultaneously frustrating them. Boys, in turn, are instructed to overcome female denial and demand or force coitus. The anthropologist William Davenport comments: 'Normal intercourse has to take the form of

The swaying bridge on which Dutton and Aron conducted part of their famous experiment. Feelings of anxiety and vulnerability can decrease or heighten sexual attraction.

ritualized rape if it is to provide mutual gratification.'

Rape, flagellation, and sadomasochism as sexual outlets in Western society reveal that sex with violence is not an aberration of primitive culture. Are these apparent links between arousal and aggression inconsistent with theories of interpersonal relations that predict greater attraction and arousal in situations of ease and comfort? Just as stress may enhance as well as diminish resistance to disease, mobilize or reduce our ability to withstand insult and challenge, so too it may affect sexual response. We are undoubtedly dealing with separate phenomena linked in ways we have yet to understand.

How do sexologists assess arousal?

The most obvious way to gauge a person's level of arousal is to ask them how they feel. They say such things as 'I feel horny', 'I get more excited with my lover than my spouse', or 'I find the blue dress more attractive than the green one', or even 'On an erotic scale of 1 to 10, I'd rate that person a 7.' More methodically, one can watch or even measure a particular aspect of behaviour. A number of measuring devices have been developed. In men erection can be monitored with a flexible ring-shaped gauge fitted around the penis. The gauge registers the expansion of the penis from flaccid to erect. In women tampon-like devices can be inserted into the vagina to record vaginal blood pressure, and pulse and blood volume; both measures correlate with vasocongestion and lubrication, considered to be the female counterpart to erection. In both sexes temperature-sensitive devices applied to the genitals, breasts, groin or elsewhere can be used to measure minute temperature changes associated with arousal.

Does body arousal match mental arousal?

Among sexologists it is well known that many women are not aware whether they have orgasm or not. Less known is the fact that a small number of men are not aware, without looking, whether they have an erection or not. For the vast majority of men, however, there is a good correlation between exposure to erotic stimuli, conscious feelings of sexual excitement and degree of physiological response. This is also true of many women,

though by no means all. It seems that for quite a large proportion of women the links between stimuli, feelings and physical response are not at all automatic. It is not uncommon for women to demonstrate a marked degree of vaginal vasocongestion and lubrication and yet report no feelings of sexual arousal. Laboratory data, combined with anecdotal and clinical reports, suggest that women need stronger stimulation before they become consciously aware of what their bodies are telling them.

An interesting fact emerged from a group of studies in which heterosexual men and women were shown films of various sexual

Pain and humiliation, given and voluntarily received, can be highly arousing. Sadomasochism (SM) is an occasional outlet for perhaps one in ten sexually active adults. Rituals and limits are usually agreed beforehand.

activities. In both sexes the strongest physiological reactions occurred in response to scenes of group sex. The second and third strongest responses from the men were to films of lesbian activity and films of a couple engaged in heterosexual sex; this order was reversed by the women viewers. Neither group showed a particular response to male homosexual activity, but both men and women were more aroused by watching women masturbating than by watching men masturbating.

Why did the group sex scenes cause most excitement among individuals of both sexes? Possibly for the majority of men degree of arousal is related to the number of women available (in this case on film) while for the majority of women arousal corresponds to the number of relationships witnessed that involve women. The men tended to fantasize more or less indiscriminately over all the

women in the films, while the women tended to concentrate their fantasies. The low response to male homosexuality may have a lot to do with the overt taboos against such behaviour that still exist in Western society; both men and women may have internalized these taboos to such an extent that they find homosexual male sex unappealing. Extrapolating from the film experiments, it is probably true to say that sexual stimuli and our physiological responses to them are interpreted as sexually arousing provided they are not in conflict with self-image and provided they do not provoke feelings of guilt. If we feel guilt and conflict, there may be no arousal or we do not interpret arousal as sexual.

Julia Heiman, who has done a great deal of research on the subject of arousal, studied both men and women listening to erotic audio tapes and monitored their physiological responses. Selecting those with the strongest physiological responses she found that every man recognized his feelings of sexual arousal. This was in striking contrast to the women, 42 per cent of whom said they felt no physical response, 54 per cent that they felt no vaginal sensations at all and 63 per cent that they were unaware of any lubrication. She writes: 'My research finds, indeed, that women like erotica as much as men do, that they are turned on by sexual descriptions, that their fantasies are as vivid and self arousing.' But, she adds, women may be 'slower to *admit* arousal'. Is this difference between the sexes innate or learned?

Some investigators claim that since men can feel and see their penises becoming erect, they learn to associate erection with subjective excitement. In women vaginal changes are less obvious and therefore more difficult to link with subjective impressions. Other researchers suggest an opposite view: it is the subjective or learned context of eroticism, they say, that leads to physiological arousal. Attempts to measure physiological and cognitive arousal simultaneously have indeed shown that physiological arousal seems to precede cognitive arousal, particularly in women. But it may be that certain physiological response thresholds have to be reached before cognitive thresholds are attained. During evolution the body must have had the means to respond to sexual stimuli long before the brain evolved to evaluate them.

Another theory holds that girls, more than

An ankle, by Jove! The fascination of the forbidden in an age when ladies' ankles were taboo.

Striptease in reverse. Now that society allows women to be more open and honest about their sexuality will the traditional wisdom that 'women are less quickly aroused than men' cease to be true?

boys, are taught to deny their feelings. They grow up more used to repressing socially unacceptable sensations when exposed to erotic stimuli. Supposedly this male–female difference is reinforced in adolescence and adulthood, when males traditionally encourage each other in overt sexual expression. We know that social expectations and traditional sex roles influence our emotional behaviour, but how and how much? I will repeatedly return to this intriguing topic when discussing the sexual response cycle and concepts of beauty and love.

The lure of the new and the forbidden

Novelty and variety are potent arousers. Even between regular partners new clothes, new hair-styles, new places and new interests can renew sexual interest. A new partner, in fact or

fantasy, is extremely exciting – sex with someone new is one of the most common fantasies reported by both sexes. The 'new partner = excitement' phenomenon is known as the Coolidge effect, after a story told of the thirtieth President of the United States, Calvin Coolidge.

The President and his wife, so the story goes, were touring a poultry farm, with Mrs Coolidge's party in the lead. As her group stopped to watch a highly aroused rooster at work a technician bragged that the bird could perform like that more than twenty times a day. Greatly impressed, Mrs Coolidge said: 'Please point that out to the President.'

In due course the President's party approached the same enclosure and the technician did as instructed. 'And does he do that with the same female all the time?' asked the President. 'Of course not! He does it with twenty different chicks!' came the reply. 'And will you please tell *that* to the First Lady', said the President.

Whether the story is true or apocryphal the Coolidge effect is real enough. It has been demonstrated in many species – fowl, rodents, primates. And while in almost all species, including humans, it is more common among males than females, it has been demonstrated in both sexes. Copulation frequencies among chimpanzees housed together for a long time rise dramatically with the arrival of new cage mates of the opposite sex. Among humans, the phenomenon is alive and well. Prostitution, and recreational and extramarital sex, are all evidence of it. According to an old Oriental saying: 'For a man the most arousing stimulus is another man's wife.'

How and why novelty fosters arousal is an intriguing question. Curiosity about the unknown is certainly a factor. There is also something attractive about the forbidden. As Freud said: 'Some obstacle is necessary to swell the tide of libido to its height; and at all periods of history whenever natural barriers in

the way of satisfaction have not sufficed, mankind has erected conventional ones to enjoy love.'

It was the dual force of attraction and repulsion present in sexual feelings that prompted Freud to coin the term *libido*. Though frequently equated with sex drive, libido is a wider and more complicated concept. It refers to the motivating force that leads one to sexual experiences, even when this is in conflict with the interests of the ego. In other words, libido may lead to socially and personally disapproved of behaviour, and therefore to a lot of subconscious anxiety and also conscious conflict. According to Freud our dreams provide us with a forum in which to act out the dictates of the libido without let or hindrance.

Anyone looking forward to a Saturday night date with all week to fantasize about it may reach a high level of excitement by the time the moment arrives. However, though both novelty and anticipation often breed desire, they also breed anxiety which can hinder performance. Clinically conditions such as impotence or premature ejaculation in men or vaginismus and anorgasmia in women often accompany a high level of anxiety. The plot thickens.

In sixteenth-century Europe the codpiece – ambitiously proportioned – was standard male attire. Detail from a painting by Brueghel the Younger.

Left *The 'tide of libido' swollen not merely by an intervening wall but by a peeping Tom.*

38

Social modification of innate responses

Some researchers claim that the triggers to sexual arousal are inborn and then become generalized to a certain extent. More people are heterosexual than homosexual probably because most men are predisposed to be aroused by female features such as breasts and vulva, and most women by such male features as broad shoulders and penis. Within these generalized preferences each society sets the degree of eroticism associated with the shape or style of these features.

Societies vary much more in their standards for women than for men. Some prize large breasts, some small, some drooping; some prefer long legs, or a vulva well covered with hair; in others large hips may be the erotic ideal, or a clean shaven pubic area. In men, broad shoulders, firm muscles and a tapered shape are almost universally appreciated, although there is less consensus in attitudes to body or facial hair, baldness, weight and so on. Societies certainly influence where, when and with whom an erotic response is appropriate. The attributes of a Sumo wrestler may not be attractive in a bank clerk; desirable features in a close relative provoke a different response when echoed in a stranger's face or physique. Our innate ability to be aroused is highly modified by codes of social behaviour.

It is interesting that in sexual matters familiarity does not necessarily breed contempt, or even indifference. The erotic appeal of breasts is not lessened, for example, in a society or in situations where bare breasts or scanty clothing are the rule. In situations sympathetic to sexual encounters breasts continue to exercise their fascination. This seems to confirm that certain parts of the body are built-in sexual stimuli.

Arousal thresholds

There is further evidence that arousal mechanisms are at least partly biological. In general, men are more easily aroused sexually than women – they have lower thresholds of arousal. Teenagers and young adults also have lower arousal thresholds than young children or elderly people. That is not to say that women, pre-teenagers and the over-60s do not become sexually aroused, just that it takes more to arouse them.

Thresholds to arousal are also affected by time. For example, a sailor returning from extended duty at sea might be attracted to women he would otherwise pass by. A woman deprived of male company for a long time might also find herself highly aroused by the first man she sees. Intervals without sex, whether one is single or in a stable relationship, can lead to heightened sensitivity towards new opportunities.

The hour-glass waist aroused the manly instincts of the Edwardians. A waist like this was achieved by ferocious corsetry and sometimes surgical removal of the lower ribs.

Sweet talk and music

It has been said that while men are turned on by what they see, women are turned on more by what they hear. An interesting conversation, further spiced with sweet talk and innuendo, can be highly erotic. Most women are particularly susceptible to the sound of a lover's voice offering sexual suggestion. Seductive talk was identified as a stimulus by almost half the women polled by *Cosmopolitan* in 1980: eight out of ten said they found music a very effective stimulus. This was also true of the vast majority of women studied by Kinsey in the 1940s and 1950s. In sharp contrast fewer than one in ten men of Kinsey's male respondents said they were aroused by music.

Odours and pheromones

Among animals sexual stimuli are usually quite specific and very powerful. The female gypsy moth's ability to attract a male from over a mile away is well known. She releases a chemical substance with an odour that he recognizes and finds irresistible. Similar odorous substances, called pheromones, are used as mating stimuli by many animals, even by species as highly evolved as ourselves. Vaginal and other body odours communicate sexual messages.

It is still debated whether female primates secrete special pheromones called copulins which signal to the males of their species whether or not they are receptive. It is not clear whether human females release copulins or whether human males can detect them. Nevertheless vaginal odours vary during the menstrual cycle and are least intense at ovulation when the likelihood of fertile copulation is greatest. Certainly many individuals in modern Western society find genital and body

Turn it on.

Turbo by Fabergé.
A very new fragrance for men.
It's supercharged!

FABERGÉ
COLOGNE
FOR MEN

turbo

Far left Sounds of love, a first broadcast of sexually explicit material on Carbone 14, a pirate French radio station. Tune in and turn on?

Promises, promises . . . Do aftershaves and perfumes deliver? Probably not. We are too complex to be hopelessly enslaved by scent alone.

scents erotically arousing, particularly during sex. The Roman poet Catullus wrote of vaginal secretions: 'When you smell it you will ask the gods to make you all nose.'

Here again, the variation among individuals is wide and many people find body odours offensive. Yet nature must have had a purpose in locating scent glands most numerously and prominently near the genitals, breasts and under the arms, and giving them wicks of hair to diffuse the odours.

Men generally have larger sweat glands than women and this correlates positively with the intensity of body odour, although intensity is not necessarily a factor in whether or not an odour is considered pleasant. Women, more often than men, even without training, can discriminate between the odours of males and females.

To date there is no really strong evidence that natural body smells are instinctively arousing for humans. Nor, as yet, is there any evidence of sex-specific preferences for particular odours analogous to those noted in animals. This has not deterred perfume companies from marketing cosmetics with hints that they are proven sexual attractants. These perfumes usually contain extracts of the scent

Right A smorgasbord of come-ons: provocative undress, a sidelong glance, good food, good wine . . .

glands of ungulates (musk), whale secretions (ambergris) or pig urine (androstendione).

Some researchers have speculated that the use of perfumes evolved not to attract sexual attention but to mask natural odours that were too erotic for social comfort. Cosmetic manufacturers have been very successful at encouraging us to mask our natural odours or substitute synthetic odours for them but the overall erotic effect of perfumes and deodorants is unknown.

Many people find body or genital odours offensive because they are associated with a lack of cleanliness. Filth is almost universally found repellent. Generally a clean, newly washed smell is considered attractive. It is interesting that the Japanese use the word *kirei* to mean either clean or pretty. Artificial perfumes add to clean smell but are not necessary or always appreciated. Certainly no one perfume has universal appeal.

There is of course a distinction between sexual signals that serve to attract and those that serve to arouse. One can be attracted to a pleasant odour but not sexually aroused by it. For the gypsy moth attraction and arousal are synonymous – as far as we know – but among humans and other mammals the situation is more complex. The stimuli that provoke sexual behaviour can be classified into three functional types: those that *broadcast* sexual interest and serve to attract or repel from a distance; those that *identify* a particular individual as a suitable or available partner; and those which *synchronize* sexual behaviours so the ready and available individual is paired with the one aroused. Perfume may broadcast sexual interest and style of dress may identify suitability and availability, yet neither necessarily arouse an intended partner. Breasts or broad shoulders are signals that can both attract and arouse.

Fetishism

Despite what society may say or biology dictate, certain stimuli remain highly individualistic and often defy rational explanation. The French psychologist Alfred Binet coined the term 'fetishism' for any unusually strong sexual attraction to an object or particular part of the body. The fetish is the trigger for sexual arousal and sexual satisfaction or gratification cannot occur without it. But such exclusive and specific conditions for gratification are rather rare.

Hormones as arousers

Several times in this chapter I have said that men seem to be more easily and more often aroused than women. Learning is certainly a component in this but there can be no doubt of the influence of androgens, a group of hormones produced by both sexes but in much larger amounts by males. Testosterone is the most important of the androgens. In men it is formed mainly in the testes; in women it is formed both in ovaries and adrenal glands. In both sexes its function is to enhance sexual interest and activity.

Castration (the removal of male or female gonads), a practice known since antiquity, not only leads to sterility and deterioration of the reproductive and sexual organs, but also to behavioural changes. Pet owners and those in animal husbandry use such knowledge every day. If castration is done before puberty, the effect is quite noticeable. Normal development, physical or behavioural, is inhibited. Done after puberty castration leads to lower levels of aggression, sexual interest and sexual performance.

From the studies carried out in the United States and Scandinavia, where castration was once a punishment or treatment for sexual offences or was necessary for medical reasons, we know that human behaviour after castration is similar to that in animals. Castration almost always leads to a decrease in sexual interest and potency though the rapidity of onset and extent of loss is quite variable. Nevertheless replacement androgens can restore this lost responsiveness and ability, in humans as well as animals.

The behavioural role that oestrogens play in females is less apparent when the organs that produce them, the ovaries, are removed. In animals removal of the ovaries quickly brings the display of sexual interest, receptivity and copulation to a halt but adequate doses of ovarian hormones soon restore them. In women, however, the effects of castration are generally much less noticeable. For one thing, in humans, removal of the ovaries is usually followed by a limited but compensatory output of oestrogen and androgens from the adrenal glands. The adrenals are the main source of androgens in women.

But reduced availability of oestrogens and progesterone, produced in largest quantity by the ovaries, causes the sexual tissues to decrease in tone and robustness. The vaginal

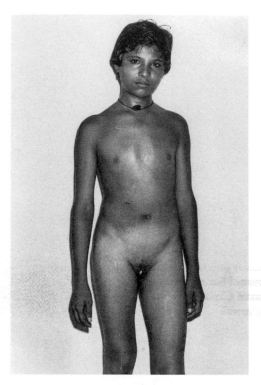

A 15-year old Indian boy after castration and penis removal and (right) wearing women's clothes. He is alleged to have been kidnapped and castrated by members of the eunuch community pictured below.

heightened arousal or increased sexual activity. Ironically, it is not only unlikely that they will gain any muscular benefit but also probable that their fertility will decrease. This is because the body has feedback systems that sense high testosterone levels thermostat-fashion and turn off testosterone and sperm production. A woman taking oral contraceptives is taking advantage of a similar feedback system. The extra oestrogen she takes inhibits ovulation. In some women, high doses of oestrogen increase water retention and the laying down of fat on the breasts, hips and buttocks.

Men and oestrogens, women and androgens

When men or women take hormones most appropriate to the opposite sex the effects are pronounced and have been known since the 1930s and 1940s. Basically men who take female hormones show a decrease in sexual interest and response and women who take androgens, with some exceptions, report an increase.

Over time men who take oestrogens and progesterone develop the secondary sexual characteristics of women, larger breasts and rounded hips. Muscles soften and hair and beard growth decreases. Potency and sex drive wane. And it takes very modest doses of female hormone preparations to initiate such changes. Even microscopic amounts of oestrogen inadvertently ingested by male workers in pharmaceutical companies have brought about such changes. This is one of the reasons that no effective chemical contraceptive is yet available for men. Hormone preparations may ensure infertility but they also have feminizing side effects.

One classic study of the effects of androgens on women was done in the 1940s by Udall J. Salmon and Samuel H. Geist. They were first alerted to the effects of testosterone in 1937. 'Our attention was first drawn to this phenomenon... by an ovariectomized woman ... being treated experimentally with testosterone propionate. During the course of treatment the patient volunteered the information that she had experienced resurgence of sexual desire after a period of quiescence of some ten years.' Their paper goes on to report on 101 women treated with testosterone for various gynecological disorders. Of 29 originally described as generally unresponsive sexually

tissues may become very thin, making coitus painful. All fat deposits, which are oestrogen-dependent, decrease. Breasts, hips and buttocks lose their roundness and firmness. There is often a concomitant lowering of sexual interest, but this seems a secondary rather than primary effect. Replacement oestrogens can reverse all of these processes, and also restore sexual interest.

What happens if the ovaries are left intact and the adrenals removed, as is sometimes necessary in treatment for certain types of cancer? Adrenalectomy removes a woman's main source of androgen and markedly lowers her sexual interest and responsiveness. Breast, uterine or even vulva surgery depress sexual interest to a much lesser degree, even though women typically have a heavy psychic investment in these organs. Most women have no idea what their adrenal glands are or what they do.

Androgens taken by normal men or oestrogens by normal women, do not have any consistent behavioural effects. The gonads and adrenal glands of healthy adults typically produce a sufficient supply of sex hormones and any excess is excreted. Healthy males who take androgens over a long period – male body builders for example – do not demonstrate

since puberty, 20 were considered to have developed normal erotic responsiveness, 4 improved their general responsiveness but remained anorgasmic, and of the other 5, 3 reported greater clitoral sensitivity but no other increase in responsiveness. Among the other 72 women treated with androgens only 8 reported no increase in sexual arousal and responsiveness. In this context an 'increase in sexual arousal and responsiveness' was defined as 'increased susceptibility to psychosexual stimulation', 'increased sensitivity of the external genitalia' and 'greater intensity of sexual gratification'. I should add that 20 of Salmon and Geist's subjects reported excessive arousability, although this subsided within several weeks of discontinuing androgen treatment.

Why, if they are so potent, have androgens not become standard aphrodisiacs? Because there is an exorbitant price to pay. There are unacceptable side effects. Women who take androgens become masculinized just as men who take oestrogens become feminized. Prolonged use leads to acne, muscle development, clitoral enlargement, growth of body hair, and a deeper voice. Before medical science understood the phenomenon and knew what to do about it, women who produced excessive amounts of androgen were

not uncommonly featured as 'she-men' or 'bearded ladies' in travelling circuses.

Although we know quite a lot about the anatomical and behavioural effects of sex hormones, we do not fully understand the mechanisms that translate hormone levels into action. No doubt these mechanisms are psychological as much as biological. Consider this illustrative case. A woman who had been taking 'medicine' (testosterone) for a cancer condition reported what for her was a most unusual occurrence: she was sexually aroused by the bus conductor and other men she saw in

From time to time athletes are accused of taking synthetic testosterone to increase muscle bulk and strength. In women extra testosterone produces an appearance of masculinity. Ironically there is no evidence that it actually improves strength. In the long run it can cause medical problems.

the course of her daily activities. This had never happened before her illness. A pious, churchgoing woman, she never followed through those feelings of arousal and indeed found them oppressive. The feelings only went away when the androgen therapy stopped. Sexual arousal had been fostered by the androgen but erotic behaviour had been inhibited by guilt feelings and the lessons learned in her upbringing.

Inhibited sexual desire

Despite the apparent ease of sexual arousal for most people there nevertheless remains a significantly large group of individuals who exhibit little or no ability to become sexually aroused. Clinicians sometimes refer to the condition as anarousmia or inhibited sexual desire (ISD). Kinsey found that low arousability occurred about twice as frequently among women as among men. Complaints of disparity in sexual interest or asynchrony of arousal are among the most common problems heard by marriage counsellors and sympathetic friends.

Lifelong lack of sexual desire or responsiveness is rare but not unknown. It is typically the result of a severely restricted, sex-negative upbringing. One particularly memorable case in my own experience involved a couple who came to see me at the husband's urgent request. The wife, who was twenty-two and had been a virgin when they had married two years earlier, engaged in sex because she felt obliged to please her husband but never more often than once or twice a month. A beautiful and intelligent woman in excellent health, she was not interested in more frequent coitus. He would have liked coitus four or five times a week. He substituted with masturbation, but finally persuaded her to come with him for counselling. Her background included a fundamentalist religious upbringing in which sex was equated with sin, and church attendance several times a week strongly reinforced the message. At the time they came to see me she taught in the church school, went to services on Sunday, attended a young adults' group one evening a week and went to choir practice on another. Her husband, brought up in another denomination, did not share her devotion to religion or her aversion to sex.

Lack of desire as a lifelong characteristic can also be the result of low androgen levels—as we have seen, the androgen testosterone fuels libido in both sexes. Various genetic conditions are also known to be associated with a low level of sexual interest, Klinefelter's syndrome for instance. Low arousability may also be associated with dysfunctions of the brain; in some men, for example, the culprit appears to be overproduction of prolactin by the pituitary. Prolactin is the hormone that stimulates milk production.

Anarousmia is occasionally an insidious accompaniment to disease, or may follow from feelings of helplessness, despair and depression, or sometimes from fear or misinformation. Believing, rightly or wrongly, that one's partner has a venereal or other infection or is uninterested in the proceedings can quite easily lead to a loss of sexual appetite.

Most often sexual indifference is something that develops gradually and usually it is the partner who retains sexual interest who brings up the subject: 'Are you seeing someone else?', 'Is it something I've done?' It is not always so simple. Feelings over non-sexual matters can build up to inhibiting anger, resentment or disappointment. As with all problems between partners, improving communication is a vital first step. Professional counselling may help, but success depends very much on motivating the uninterested partner rather than discouraging the interested one.

Understanding the responses of others

There being such a wide variety of specific and general stimuli that elicit sexual responses it is sometimes difficult to understand the preferences of others. But here again there is a discrepancy between the sexes. To quote Kinsey:

> *Even the sexually least responsive of the males can comprehend something of the meaning of the frequent and continuous arousal which some other males experience. To the third or more of the females who have rarely been aroused by psychological stimuli, it may seem fantastic to believe that there are females who come to orgasm as a result of sexual fantasy, without any physical stimulation, of their genitalia or any other part of their body.*
> [An occurrence for about one in 50 women but almost non-existent in males.]

Socially, the implications of these discrepancies are great. They go far beyond the fact that sexual partners may have to contend with quite different levels of arousal, excitement and desire. They reach into the wider world in which teachers, social workers, legislators and judges, on the basis of their own limited experience, make decisions of huge importance to many thousands of people. It is difficult to accept that other people may be very different from oneself.

Some conclusions

We are all unique, with a certain propensity for sexual arousal. Some of us have low thresholds, some high. Some of us respond to many stimuli, some to fewer. Our inherent biases are partly genetic and endocrine but they are only biases, not inescapable orders. Our emotion-sensitive nervous system, with all its inborn predispositions, is modified by

social and cultural learning, and the trial and error of experience.

I can accept that nature has prepared me to prefer a rounded buttock to a flat one, a more to a less ample breast, and a firm body to a flabby one. It is also easy for me to believe it is nature's way that the majority of men prefer sex with women and vice versa. But why I am attracted to a woman with a sense of humour, an independent, sensitive and curious mind, is not so apparent. And why I find the twin on the right much more erotic than her sister on the left is a bewitching mystery. The differences are almost too subtle to put into words.

In fact it makes good sense that perpetuation of our species should depend on highly individual and varied reasons for arousal. Sex drive, however construed, does not have to be demonstrated by everyone but it does need to be demonstrated by a sufficient number of people to maintain a rich gene pool. If men and women did not find each other attractive for

In the end it is never a single thing – dress, physique, voice, personality – that brings two people together but a subtle mix of biology, experience and expectations, a mix unique to every relationship.

such a variety of reasons the gene pool of our species would become impoverished and the rearing of viable offspring would be in jeopardy. Perhaps the same evolutionary imperative that has me looking for certain physical features also instructs me to look for certain personality traits. Where the human species is concerned evolution occurs through learning and acculturation as well as the random mixing of genes. Accumulated wisdom and the teaching of elders complement and influence our biological heritage.

From another perspective, it would be sad and frustrating if we all responded only to specific stimuli in specific circumstances – that is the fate of the fetishist. Given the choice I would rather opt for a system in which arousal was more variably obtained and more variably satisfied. I would also choose a world in which the total process of sexual enjoyment was more important than orgasm. I would also like everyone to possess the instruments necessary to achieve sexual satisfaction. This would ensure that everyone, not only those with stereotyped beauty, had the maximum possible chance of finding a partner. This is the kind of world that evolution has already created for us.

So, for now, do not be surprised if a turn of the head, a certain smile, a way of walking, the twist of a wrist, ankle or lip, the movement of a breast or thigh or crotch seems to evoke your desire to know its originator sexually. And do not be surprised if others feel quite differently about the matter. That is how sexual attraction works. You yourself have probably aroused lots of other people without ever having been aware of it □.

When I consider, pro and con,
What things my love is built upon –
A curly mouth; a sinewed wrist;
A questioning brow; a pretty twist
Of words as old and tired as sin;
A pointed ear; a cloven chin;
Long, tapered limbs; and slanted eyes
Not cold, nor kind nor darkly wise –
When so I ponder, here apart,
What shallow boons suffice my heart,
What dust-bound trivia capture me,
I marvel at my normalcy.

DOROTHY PARKER, *The Searched Soul*

3

The body you love with

At one time or another all of us look in the mirror and evaluate our appearance, comparing what we see with an imagined ideal constructed from watching other people and learning the values of our particular society. Many of us come away from the mirror wishing we were prettier or more handsome, taller or shorter, slimmer or heavier, or that certain parts of our body were a different shape.

Living with Miss World and Mr Universe

Each society has its own ideals which are publicized and praised in popular culture. In contemporary Western society these are represented by movie stars and sports personalities, fashion models and pin-ups. A review of those images most popular or currently in fashion shows that the ideal is not always constant.

Everyday life quickly reveals the enormous variety of physiques and facial types; the fact is that very few of us fit the stereotypes. Generally we manage to accept and live with our shortcomings even if we are unhappy about them. Discontent with facial features, height,

or body weight and its distribution is extremely common. Advertisements, magazine features and the stars of stage and screen aggravate our insecurities and sharpen our desire to be considered attractive, sexy, likeable. But even if we are accepted as being all those things self-doubts can still lurk. Even fashion models and actresses, at the top of their profession because they apparently embody the ideal of the moment, can suffer from self-doubt. Dorothy Lamour, famous Hollywood sex symbol of the 1940s, confessed that she always felt her image a burden; it was unwarranted, something she felt she could never measure up to.

First meetings

There is no denying that physical attractiveness is a major factor in how one is evaluated as a potential sex partner. A study led by American researcher Elaine Walster among students at a college dance showed that physical attractiveness was the only factor directly related to whether students wanted to see their dancing partners again. Other attributes such as intelligence, personality, sociability, masculinity–femininity, introversion–

Standards of display, 1901 and 1984. In 1901 it was risqué to reveal breasts; today the centrefolds of magazines such as Playboy *show pubic hair and more.*

49

extraversion and self-acceptance had no such direct effect. The students concerned were assigned their partners for the evening on a random basis. Later they were asked how much they liked their partners and whether they wanted to pursue the relationship. The more physically attractive the partner, the more affirmative the answer. Interest in personality, intelligence or social confidence seemed far less significant. All efforts to find additional factors that might have a bearing on attraction failed. Evidence from other studies has shown that, logically or not, strangers who are considered physically attractive are thought of as being sexually warm, responsive, sensitive, supportive, sociable, outgoing and exciting.

Particularly when a relationship is beginning, most people unconsciously base their assessment of their partner on his or her looks. And yet many studies of adolescents and college students, from the work of the 1920s and 1950s and 1960s to the most recent, show that looks are invariably placed *after* characteristics such as personality, sincerity and dependability when respondents are asked to list desirable qualitites in a potential mate. And intelligence usually comes lower on the list than looks. This is the 'disparity in KAP' phenomenon at work. Why, then, are looks so powerful during first encounters?

Five main theories have been suggested. Each, in varying degrees, is probably influential in all of us. The first theory is biological and evolutionary: our attentiveness to looks ensures that mating behaviour occurs primarily in response to simple physical signals. The other theories are social or psychological. One is that our upbringing teaches us that erotic relationships are most appropriate with physically attractive partners. Our heroes and heroines are routinely handsome and beautiful, seldom average or plain. Ogres and witches, representing undesirable character traits, are ugly or deformed. In advertisements, television shows and films successful and happy people are almost always sexy and stylish, and it is rare to see a match in which the partners are not equally attractive. In fact we suspect the motives, even the mechanics, of Beauty-and-the-Beast type relationships.

A third theory is that being associated with an attractive person is a way of gaining prestige. Willard Waller, the American sociologist who put forward this theory in the

1930s, believed that people interact with others more for what they receive in external rewards from onlookers than for the intrinsic rewards of the relationship. There is some truth in this theory, cynical as it may seem. A man paired with a woman made to appear unattractive is viewed negatively, but when the same woman is made to appear attractive, he goes up several notches in the impression he gives.

The counterpart experiment of an attractive or unattractive man with a woman has also been done. University students were shown slides of various couples (all were presented as married) and asked to comment on their status or attributes. The ratings given to the men were again influenced by their partner's appearance, particularly so if the man was unattractive. Where the man was markedly unattractive in comparison to the woman, he was seen as rich, professionally successful and high up the social ladder. Ratings of the

Actor Tom Selleck kicks against being labelled America's hottest sex symbol. 'All this attention has turned me into a very slow worker with women,' he says. 'I don't want to be Magnum in bed, I really don't.'

Left *The man in the Soloflex bodybuilding ads. Would he collect the kids from school, help old ladies across the road, leap into the canal to rescue a stranger? Does anyone care?*

woman's attractiveness were independent of her spouse's physical appearance. Because of her good looks it was assumed she possessed many more desirable social characteristics than her unattractive partner.

The fourth theory is the antithesis of the notion that beauty is only skin deep. Inner beauty has never been satisfactorily defined, nevertheless the idealist in us would like to see it associated with outer beauty. We therefore want to believe that physical beauty reflects inner beauty. In one study men and women were presented with photographs of attractive and unattractive people and asked to say what their personality characteristics were. Surprisingly, both sexes gave similar responses when rating either sex. Attractive people were expected to possess almost every personality trait considered socially desirable, from modesty to extraversion, from sensitivity to strength and supportiveness. Those rated as average or unattractive were less often given the benefit of these generous assumptions.

Lastly, there is the theory that says that we respond positively to attractive people because we hope they will give us something of value, sexual satisfaction if nothing else. Perhaps we also believe that in some mystical way the association will confer attractiveness on us.

The desire to be sexually attractive develops in adolescence. Teenagers universally entertain feelings of insecurity matched by a strong desire to belong and to be accepted by their

Above *Strong is beautiful, or is it?*

Left *In the early 1900s, when Elinor Glyn invited a scandalised public to sin with her on a tiger skin, soft curves were in.*

Right *Triumphant shrinkage from 40-34-43 to 34-26-36! For many women fat follows motherhood.*

peers. Disappointment with physical growth and development may be a significant obstacle to socializing and establishing sexual relationships. Skin and hair, because they are constantly on display, are often a cause for deep self-criticism.

The muscular ideal for men has been pursued from Grecian times, if not earlier, and is now an international competitive sport. Ideals for women, as mentioned earlier, are more variable, cross-culturally, and remain so even in Western culture, as we shall see. Having beaten a path into most traditionally male sports, women now have body building contests of their own. In typical female beauty contests there is as much emphasis on a beautiful face as on an ideal body, but in body building as a male sport the focus has always been on the size, proportion and muscular definition of the limbs and torso, ignoring the attractiveness or otherwise of the face. Should female body building lay more emphasis on the development of curves and beautiful proportions? Some aficionados of the sport think so. I for one am highly doubtful that female body building marks a move towards a more muscular ideal for women.

The slimming obsession

In countries where hunger is endemic and occasionally devastating, the fleshier female ideal is possibly related to the concept that fatter equals healthier. Meanwhile, in affluent Western countries, many women and girls accept the heavily promoted view that slimmer equals healthier, and more attractive. In extreme cases slimming is excessive and obsessive. Anorexia nervosa is an illness of excessive dieting in which eating, and even the idea of eating, becomes repugnant. Every year there are deaths from anorexic malnutrition. A related problem is bulimia, heavy food bingeing followed by enforced vomiting and abuse of laxatives. The anorexic individual becomes so thin that she (rarely he since female anorexics outnumber male by thirty or forty to one) is not particularly attractive, but there is little doubt that such extreme tactics are tied up with the search for a feminine ideal.

Feminist psychotherapist Marlene Bosking Lodahl believes that anorexic females are far from rejecting their femininity. 'These young women' she comments 'have never questioned their assumption that wifehood, motherhood and intimacy with men are the

fundamental components of femininity ...their obsessive pursuit of thinness constitutes ... an exaggerated striving to achieve it.' With anorexic males the problem seems to be low self-esteem, general despondency and passivity, a fear of women, and an inability to sustain relationships.

When girls and women become concerned with their bodies, their preferred methods of improving on nature are diet and dress rather than sport or exercise. That is why dietary problems are far more common among women than men, especially in professions where slimness is *de rigueur*, among dancers and fashion models for example. Exercise tends to be a resort mainly for middle and upper class women. But among women of all social strata dietary issues are a continual distraction and the prognosis is that this preoccupation will increase. Psychologist David Garner, psychiatrist Paul Garfinkel and their associates found a significant and steady increase in articles on diet in women's magazines over the past twenty years, which correlates well with an increasing preoccupation with

Work out and shape up. Aerobics, slimnastics, dancercise and weight training are usually more than narcissism. The long-term goal is to stay healthier longer.

slimness. Winners of the Miss America Pageant and also the beauties of *Playboy's* centrefold – all reflections of stereotyped ideals – have been getting slimmer over the past twenty years. Ironically the average American female under thirty years of age has become heavier over the same period. Men too have been getting heavier but seem less obsessed with the consequences. Margaret Mackenzie, an anthropologist studying obesity and diet, comments: 'Upwardly mobile women in this era are competing with men, yet most of them are still conditioned to thinking of success personally and professionally in terms of sex and beauty, which are equated with thinness.'

Western and Japanese fashion generally promote the slim ideal, though present Indian and African preferences are typically more weighty. This is displayed in fashion models who, in the West, would be considered heavy. In arranged marriages, one of the selling features of the prospective bride is her full-bodiedness.

Surgical improvements

Where none of the usual solutions works, some people resort to surgery. Facelifts, belly tucks, rump and thigh reduction, breast reconstruction, hair transplants and nose surgery are all means of achieving a physical reality more in keeping with one's fantasy. In the United States an eight-fold rise in elective cosmetic surgery is predicted by the year 2000.

As elective surgical procedures become more popular practitioners and clients are opting for the term aesthetic surgery rather than cosmetic surgery. 'Aesthetic' seems to carry with it a more positive aura: everyone approves of aesthetic reasons; cosmetic reasons are somehow suspect. The distinction is not a semantic superficiality if it eases a conscience or bolsters feelings of self-worth. The desire to be attractive, or at least better looking, is not solely narcissistic. It carries with it the intuitive knowledge that good looks smooth the way for many everyday relationships, whether they involve strangers, friends or lovers. But no amount of muscle building, slimming or surgery will compensate – or at least not for long – for an insecure personality or a lack of social graces.

Biologists readily accept that the force of appearance is very strong. They see it as part of a consistent evolutionary trend in which mating behaviour is primarily triggered by simple

physical signals. But the phenomenon deeply worries social scientists. Indeed most of us would prefer social interaction to be based on something less aleatory and more substantial than mere looks. It is rotten luck as well as fundamentally undemocratic to be handicapped by physical characteristics one can do little about.

Fortunately for most of us our self-doubts and discontents are made bearable by the positive experience of being accepted as

A Lebanese movie poster showing the heavier ideal of womanhood favoured in the Near and Middle East.

worthwhile, attractive and socially desirable by our family, peers and lovers. Although we acknowledge the ideals and stereotypes, most of us also accept that they are just that and get on with the practical realities of life. If our appearance is not ideal we tend to develop social skills, traits and personality characteristics to compensate.

Am I normal?

Confidence about one's body, and a sense of comfort and ease, are prerequisites for making the most of one's heritage to sexual pleasure. Am I normal? Am I an acceptable sexual partner? Such anxieties are common, but since the variety in size and shape is great and the diversity of taste extensive, the answer is almost always 'yes' to both questions. Becoming familiar with the function and appearance of one's body and genitals, and acquiring an awareness of the myths and unnecessary anxieties related to sex, are important steps towards confidence as well as comfort.

Many men wish for a longer penis and many women wish for larger breasts – they believe bigger is better. But size has little to do with erotic ability, sexual attraction or satisfaction, or emotional and personal confidence, nor is the desire for bigger breasts absolutely

comparable with anxiety over penis size. Though most people are familiar with a number of physical stereotypes for clothed and unclothed bodies, few have detailed knowledge of the appearance of a variety of genitals, so no real standards exist. Therefore, in both sexes personal fears and fantasies thrive on ignorance. Here, I can present some basic factual material and put to rest a number of associated myths.

Profile portrait, a preparatory phase for corrective surgery on nose and chin. 'Nose jobs' are the commonest form of cosmetic surgery; not too far behind are facelifts. The effects of a facelift are not indefinite – up to seven years claim certain clinics.

Below *Is body contact between mother and baby the foundation of our ability to give and receive love?*

Nothing between him, the sun and the wind but skin . . .

Sensual versus reproductive

Biology and medicine divide body structures into systems according to their functions – digestive, excretory, reproductive, and so on. Some organs obviously serve several functions. The breast, for example, is a sexual and a secretory organ. Traditionally, biology or human sexuality texts described the genitals, or genitalia, as structures involved in both sexual activity and reproduction, dividing them into male and female, internal and external. This ignores two important facts. First, most sexual expression takes place without reproduction. And second, modern technology allows reproduction without sexual expression. It therefore seems logical, philosophically and biologically, to distinguish the *sensual system*, those body parts primarily associated with sex play, from the *reproductive system*. In fact the sensual system evokes more complex responses physically and psychologically. Some parts of the body belong to both the sensual and the reproductive system, some to one only.

Skin and the pleasures of touch

In my opinion the skin might, in general, be considered the most important organ of sexual response for both males and females. The genitals and, particularly for women, the breasts are typically considered most important. Indeed they are highly sensitive and most people are very specifically aware of their demands for stimulation during sexual arousal, petting and coitus. Before, during or after sex play the whole skin acts as an organ responsive to sexual communication.

The skin is like a huge antenna with a sensitive surface area of approximately two square yards, ever alert. Touching and being touched, holding and being held, and other stimuli such as blowing, licking and nibbling are among life's greatest delights. Skin contact is a vital source of human pleasure from birth and throughout life. Touching can create and transmit feelings of love, warmth, security, contentment and sexual desire, all depending upon context. Anthropologist Ashley Montagu speaks of the development of 'skin

57

hunger', an innate need or desire for body contact. Indeed the absence of sufficient body contact and stimulation has been implicated in infant illness and death. No scientific proof is required that physical isolation contributes to feelings of loneliness in adults.

Lack of body contact and relaxed touching is often a problem between sexual partners. Common complaints are: 'She never holds me in public, only when we're in bed', or 'He grabs for my pelvis as if that's all I am.'

It is a myth that women require more physical contact than men. Both sexes appreciate being stroked and touched. A lack of physical intimacy can mirror other problems in a sexual relationship, or it may reflect social teaching that discourages touching unless sexual intent is present. Japanese, North American and Scandinavian societies are relatively non-physical compared with

An Indian Tantric diagram of a woman's erogenous zones. According to Tantric belief a woman's sensitivity varies with the phases of the moon and with her menstrual cycle. To reach the peak of sexual ecstasy, the Tantra devotee must pay special attention to these cycle-variable trigger points.

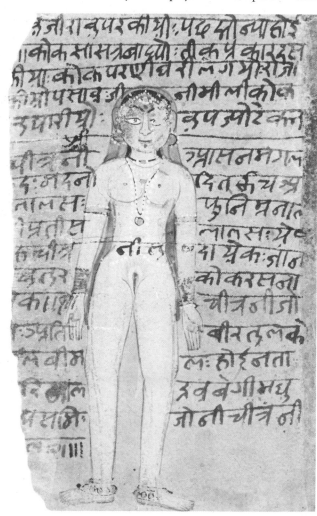

Mediterranean, Slav, Latin and many Polynesian and African societies where touching, even among new acquaintances, is common. The infant desire to be held, groomed and stroked is strong and springs from roots deep in our primate heritage, but it is often frustrated by cultural traditions.

An erogenous zone is any part of the skin that is particularly sensitive to stimuli that are experienced as sexually exciting. The skin of the genitals, breasts, face (particularly the mouth), ears, neck and thighs are most sensitive in most people but, depending on the individual, any part of the body may be specially sensitive. The degree of variation in sensitivity is truly enormous and the only real way to know what kind of stimulation your partner enjoys is to experiment or ask. Women tend to have a greater number of erogenous zones than men. According to Kinsey some women can be brought to orgasm solely by having their eyebrows stroked or from gentle blowing on body hair – no men have been found to respond to such indirect stimulation.

Taboo zones – areas of the body that cannot be freely touched – are not necessarily the same as erogenous zones. Usually they are taboo in anything other than an acknowledged sexual relationship. Full social and sexual development involves learning who, how, when and where to touch and how to allow oneself to be touched. Only lovers and parents with small children have free access to all parts of each other's bodies. Even so, personal preferences determine individual taboos. In industrial societies it is generally acceptable to touch babies and toddlers anywhere except the genitals in affectionate contact, but as puberty approaches – as girls develop breasts for example – the boundaries are redefined and licence to touch is taken away from parents and awarded to boyfriends and girlfriends.

One can pick up many clues about relationships by observing the physical access that people give each other. Any physical contact involves a certain invasion of body space and to touch another person without direct or implied permission violates rules of conduct in all societies. Of course taboos can be social or religious, as well as sexual. In present day Thailand, as in traditional Hawaiian culture, it is improper to touch the top of another person's head, as this is regarded both literally and metaphorically as the highest part of the body.

The external male genitals

The male organ most capable of erotic sensation is the penis. The biological sexual function of the penis is to penetrate the female and deposit sperm; it is also the urinary outlet. Typically it is soft (flaccid) and in response to erotic stimuli (urinary or other reflexes are also occasionally effective) it becomes erect and engorged with blood. Erection increases its length and girth. Softening (detumescence) is the process of returning to flaccidity. The erection and detumescence of a penis are fascinating to watch. Both can be brought on by various physical or mental stimuli, but neither is routinely under voluntary control.

PENIS SIZE

Penises vary greatly in shape and it is a myth that a bigger penis is necessarily better. Just as some men are attracted to large-breasted or long-legged women, some women find a large penis erotic and exciting. In any case, variations in penis size become less marked when the penis is hard. In other words a penis that is small when flaccid tends to enlarge more during erection than a large one.

The majority of women have no physical or psychological difficulty in accommodating a long penis and may even enjoy the deep pressure it applies to the cervix. On the other hand, many women are disturbed by the generally unrealistic fear that they might not be able to accommodate a large penis, and some do find the actual sensation painful not pleasurable. Considering that the vagina is most sensitive at its entrance rather than in depth, some women say that girth is more desirable than length. But, as one might expect, most men have an average-size penis to match an average-sized vagina. For most women it is how the penis is used (and the man behind it) that matters more than simple dimensions.

Few men are unaware of the size of their penis and it is safe to say that, at some time or another, most feel somewhat inadequate. This is partly because evaluations are often made while the penis is flaccid. This is how men generally see other penises, for example in sports changing rooms or public toilets. Also, the penis is difficult to see properly if one

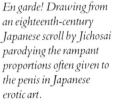

En garde! Drawing from an eighteenth-century Japanese scroll by Jichosai parodying the rampant proportions often given to the penis in Japanese erotic art.

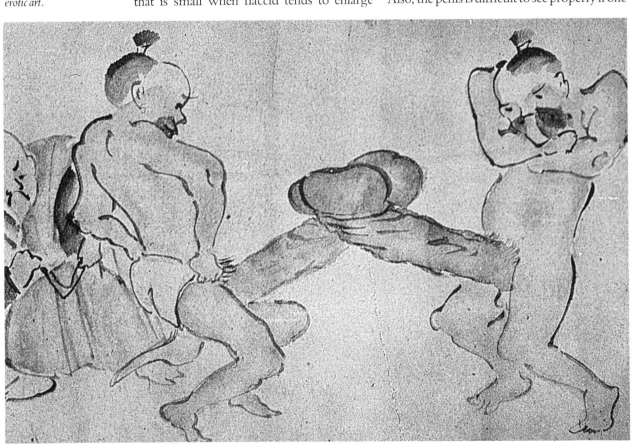

is looking down over an abdominal bulge – this is particularly true of prepubescent boys with so-called puppy fat or middle-aged men with pot bellies, who may, for many reasons, be feeling sexually insecure.

Concern with penis size and shape is not unique to modern or Western man, as is indicated by evidence from many cultures, ancient and modern. In Japanese erotic art a thick, large penis is almost always on display; ceramic figures from Central and South America and statues from ancient Rome, Etruria and Crete are commonly endowed with prominent genitals; traditional and modern African and Hindu art often focuses strongly on the genitals. New Guinea tribesmen and natives of New Hebrides wear penis covers that exaggerate the size of the organ.

While every study of heterosexual males

Leather penis covers worn by tribesmen from the highlands of New Guinea.

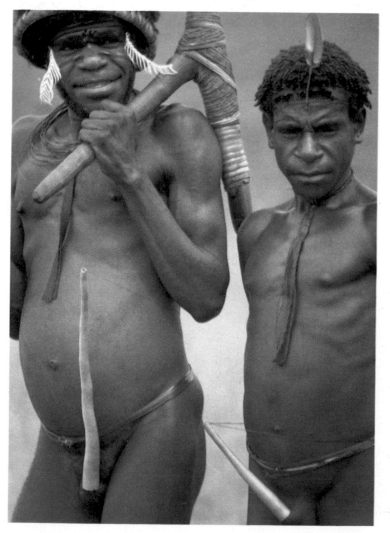

confirms that penis size is highly important and that almost all heterosexual men wish they were better endowed, concern about penis size is not limited to heterosexual relationships or necessarily associated with wanting to impress a woman. A 1979 study of 1000 gay men, carried out by James Spada in the United States, revealed that about 37 per cent thought that the penis size of a partner was very important and 42 per cent thought it unimportant; the other 21 per cent thought it somewhat important. Almost all, however, expressed apprehension that their own penis was too small; even those with penises of six to eight inches in length wished they were larger. In the gay community individuals excessively concerned with size are common enough to be identified as 'size queens'.

It is probably safe to say that most men identify so strongly with their penis that the rule becomes 'love me, love my penis', and any slight on size or shape, or avoidance of the penis in sex play, is taken as a personal rebuke. Praising and paying attention to the penis is equally taken as an important personal compliment. Since so much of a man's satisfaction is derived from his penis, he tends to assume that his partner also derives supreme satisfaction from penetration. Certainly most women do enjoy stimulation from the penis, but they are also capable of being more diffusely aroused and satisfied, and by more varied stimuli. This is something men are commonly unaware of. One student of mine admitted: 'It really bothers me that because it always feels so good to him to have his penis in my vagina he expects me to feel similarly. I just don't always enjoy it. I finally told him it's like when he asks me to scratch his back. His back may feel good, but my fingers don't. I'm not sure he really understood the depth of my feeling but at least he was more understanding after that.'

For all the concern about penis size and shape, and whether or not it will prove satisfying to a sexual partner, it is worth making the point that few men bother to consider whether they would derive more or less satisfaction from masturbation or coitus if they were differently equipped.

No consistent relationship exists between penis size and the ability to give sexual satisfaction. Unless there is marked disparity between the genitals of the partners and coitus is the only activity undertaken, such concern is unwarranted. But when a man who feels anxiety about his penis reluctantly or hesitantly engages in sexual play the result is often fulfilment of a self-fulfilling prophesy, lack of satisfaction for himself or his partner. The problem is less anatomical than psychological.

Nor is there any consistent relationship between penis size and body size. There are slight racial differences – Orientals on average have smaller penises than Caucasians, and Negroes have larger. To some extent penis size is commensurate with vaginal size of the race concerned, but as mentioned above, the ability of the vagina to accommodate is great. It is certainly a myth, although believed in Japan, Thailand, Europe and elsewhere, that the size of a man's nose indicates the size of his penis; in Japan it is believed a woman's lips and mouth represent her vaginal size.

Lastly, no pill, potion, exercise, masturbatory technique or external device will affect penis size. Charlatans gladly separate fools from their money for 'medically approved' apparatus or techniques that promise to enlarge a penis. At best, these are ineffective. At worst, they can be harmful; some vacuum-like devices can rupture blood vessels in the penis. A less harmful but no less bizarre practice among the *yakuza*, members of the underworld in modern Japan, is that of inserting a pearl under the skin of the penis. This is supposed to give superior sexual satisfaction to the woman and so enable the *yakuza* to maintain a hold on the prostitutes they pimp for; supposedly the pearl-penis provides more sexual gratification than that of any customer.

But there is no physical necessity for making any modifications to natural shape and size. Used with pride and concern for the partner, any penis can be satisfying.

SOME ANOMALIES

Individuals have consulted me not only on the size of their penis, but also wondering if they were misshapen, the penis curving to the right, left, sharply up or down. Except for a rare few, all were within normal variation and perfectly capable of satisfactory sexual encounters. The exceptions were able to engage in satisfactory relations by changing coital position or using a pillow to alter the angle at which the penis enters the vagina.

About one male in a thousand has a penis which is unusually small due to a chromosomal anomaly, XXY rather than the typical male XY chromosome set. This is Klinefelter's syndrome. The extra chromosome means that such individuals usually develop feminine breasts (gynecomastia), and have a low sperm count; they also tend to be obese and display a low level of sexual interest.

Even more rare are males medically diagnosed as having a micropenis. Any astute physician will detect this at birth; it is not a condition that develops as a boy grows. A micropenis is too small even to effect insertion. Medical treatment with hormones may be useful and a prosthesis can help. Counselling is always recommended in cases where the child is reared as a boy, since the psychological impact on the affected individual is great.

Penis ornaments. Studs and rings through the glans (top left), corona (top right and bottom left) and perineum (bottom right) are said to increase the pleasure of arousal and coitus both for the wearer and his partner. In the West body piercing is partly done for masochistic reasons, but also for the satisfaction of knowing that one is intimately adorned. Many find even the idea painful!

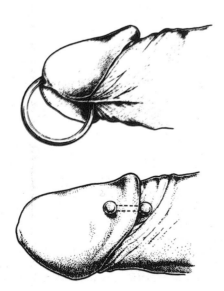

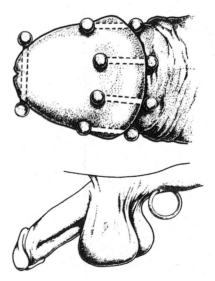

Some pediatricians recommend rearing such individuals from birth as girls, with appropriate surgical reconstruction of the genitals to fashion a vulva. The debate hinges on whether satisfactory male sexual identity can be achieved without a functioning penis. Those who believe that social forces outweigh chromosomal ones recommend surgical intervention. But since it now seems that biological factors are difficult to override many physicians regard psychological support (with prosthesis) as the most appropriate treat-ment. The degree of success in establishing either a male or female identity is highly variable and much remains to be understood about this condition.

In one out of every several hundred Caucasian males the urinary outlet, the meatus, opens not at the head of the glans but on the underside of the penis. (There are no statistics on the occurrence of this condition among other racial groups.) This is known as hypospadias and is typically quite embarrassing to a growing boy and his parents despite the fact that the physical evidence is hidden and the problem itself is relatively common. Corrective surgery is usually carried out before a boy reaches school age to minimize psychological distress. Long-term studies show that after surgery physical, sexual and social development generally proceed along normal lines. A small percentage of males born with hypospadias, however, remain reluctant to engage in sexual activity despite reconstructive surgery. They may require, and often benefit from, psychological counselling.

Epispadias is a condition similar to hypospadias in some ways, but more serious and, fortunately, extremely rare. Here the meatus is on the top surface of the penis and appears to split the penis. In dealing with this problem, psychological counselling is always recommended.

SCROTUM AND TESTES

The scrotum, a wrinkled sac of skin that hangs behind and below the root of the penis, is also highly sensitive in sexual arousal. It contains two egg-shaped testicles (testes) to which are appended the epididymides in which sperm mature and are temporarily stored. Attached spermatic cords carry the sperm to the penis.

The scrotum is quite flexible and distend-able. Sensitive to touch, temperature and sexual stimulation, it can hang loosely or retract close to the body. Typically, ejaculation is preceded by the testes and scrotum contracting tight against the body. This contraction is only slightly susceptible to voluntary control. The scrotum and testes in fact perform a visible alternating contraction and relaxation cycle – a more or less continuous, slow, wave-like movement. In response to threat or painful stimulation the scrotum pulls toward the body. This is the cremasteric reflex.

The testicles are the male gonads. They

True hermaphrodites, possessing both testicular and ovarian tissue, are extremely rare. In Greek and Roman times such individuals were looked on as favoured by the gods.

provide sperm and the hormones, mostly androgens, crucial for male development and functioning. The testes normally hang at different heights, the left usually being lower than the right, but the reverse is not uncommon. This is probably to reduce the pressure of one against the other as the body moves. Even slight pressure can produce sharp and lasting pain.

Cryptorchidism, or hidden testicle, is a common condition affecting some 2 to 5 per cent of males at birth. During gestation the testes develop inside the body near the kidneys. Normally they migrate to the scrotum prior to birth, but sometimes, and for unknown reasons, one or both may fail to descend properly. The scrotum of a male infant is routinely examined to check for this. If descent is delayed beyond several months, hormonal or surgical treatment will be used to induce descent into the scrotum. If the testes remain too long within the abdominal cavity the body's internal heat can kill the sperm-producing tissues and cause subsequent infertility. The scrotal environment is about 3°C cooler than the internal body temperature and more hospitable to sperm production.

Recent findings have complicated decisions in such a situation. It is now known that a significant percentage (estimates vary widely) of cryptorchid testes, even if surgically drawn down, will become tumorous, but as yet there is no way of predicting in which individuals this will occur. So the decision has to be made whether to leave the testes in place for developmental, endocrine, fertility and psychological reasons or remove them to prevent a potential cancer. The tendency among physicians is to leave them in place but keep regular surveillance. Either way, this is no easy decision.

Why nature has evolved this relationship between temperature and reproduction in the male is an intriguing matter. It probably has something to do with the fact that our pre-mammalian ancestors were cold-blooded animals with body temperatures lower than our own.

External female genitals

The general region of the external female genitals is referred to as the vulva. Most girls, as well as boys, grow to adulthood quite ignorant of the fact that vulvas vary greatly in appearance. Considering that the medical term for the crotch region is *pudendum*, Latin for shameful, this is not difficult to understand. Having been taught that it is not nice to attend to one's genitals, many women have never even looked at themselves, let alone others. Many men, experienced or not, are similarly unaware. If you have not yet looked closely at your own body or at that of a partner, do so. It's a fascinating exercise in sexwatching.

VULVA

Typically, the view of a mature woman's vulva mainly reveals the *mons pubis* or *mons veneris*, a hair-covered mound formed by a soft fat pad over a bony prominence. On further inspection, with the legs apart, an inner and outer set of lips can be seen. The outer lips (*labia majora*) are elongated rolls of fat tissue that pass just below the skin from pubis to anus and are covered with hair. The inner set of lips (*labia minora*) remain hairless throughout life. They cover the vaginal entrance, so that typically the vagina is not seen. These inner lips vary greatly in shape and size from woman to woman. They may have any colour from pale pink to dark purple, and the colour intensity deepens during sexual excitement. Betty Dodson, a woman artist, classifies vulva styles as Baroque, Danish modern, Gothic, Classical and so forth, the names reflecting the symmetry or asymmetry, size and shape of the labia. Dodson says she was inspired to

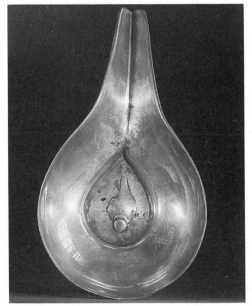

An Indian ritual vessel made of copper and shaped like a vulva. Yoni *(vulva and* lingam *(phallus) images abound in Hindu art. Vulvic figurines and amulets were once common in Europe, the Aegean and the Near East. Even the proverbially 'lucky' horseshoe is a degraded vulva symbol.*

paint and classify women's genitals in order to liberate women from negative feelings about their appearance 'down there'. She considered herself ugly and deformed until a new lover convinced her that her vulva was beautiful and of common shape.

The vestibule, which leads directly into the vagina, is a basin-shaped area bounded by the *labia minora*. Like the latter it is a highly sensitive and erotic area for most women. Above the vagina, also opening into the vestibule, is the urethral meatus, the urine outlet. Anxiety that urine may get into the vagina or be released during coitus is rarely warranted. Sphincter muscles normally prevent urine release unless it is deliberate. If some urine is passed it is sterile and of no hygienic significance. A woman may be embarrassed if this happens during coitus but most men are unaware of it unless it is particularly copious. It just appears to be added lubrication. Urination prior to sex play usually solves this problem.

The vagina opens in the floor of the vestibule. While the opening is more or less round, the vagina itself is not, as so often pictured, an inflexible tube-shaped receptacle but rather a flexible glove-like space whose walls part to accept and conform to any shape, fingers or penis, that enters.

Most women know even less about their internal sex organs than their external. Ellen Frankfort in a recent article entitled 'Vaginal Politics' describes her first real look at another woman's sexual organs.

Carol ... placed herself on top [of a long table] and, with her legs bent at the knees, inserted a speculum into herself. Once the speculum was in place, her cervix was completely visible and each of the fifty women present took a flashlight and looked inside ... I hesitate to use the word 'revolutionary' but no other word seems accurate to describe the effects of the first part of the evening. It was a little like having a blind person see for the first time – for what woman is not blind to her own insides?

This illustrates the very different attitudes accepted by and for men and women. Every man has the opportunity to examine his own penis and see that of other men, to become familiar with the form and make comparisons. Women have had no such physical or psychological familiarity with their own sexual organs until quite recently.

HYMEN

This is located at the opening to the vagina. In fact it marks the boundary between the external part of the genitals, which develop from the skin, and the internal structures of the sexual-reproductive system. In some women the hymen may be more or less retained as a perforated, soft sheet of thin skin. In some girls this tissue, present during infancy, seems to dissolve with growth, so that only slight remnants survive at puberty. Hymenal remnants are seen as soft tags around the vaginal entrance. First coitus may or may not result in bloody separation of tissue. In some sexually experienced women a goodly portion of the hymen remains, depending upon the relative size of the vaginal opening, the hymen's ability to stretch, and the size and activity of the penis it accommodates. This great variety makes it impossible to say with certainty, on the evidence of the hymen alone, whether a woman is a virgin, whether she has masturbated, or indeed anything else about her sexual activity.

In some cases the hymen is unusually thick or strong. Usually reasonably forceful entry of a penis will overcome the obstruction, though the woman may feel some discomfort. In rare cases, it may be necessary to consult a physician, who can snip open the hymen to allow access.

Various cultures foster the myth that all first instances of hymenal penetration are painful

Black Iris *by Georgia O'Keefe, a modern interpretation of the vulva – velvet-soft, sensual, flowering ...*

and show bleeding. To accommodate these expectations, women often feign pain and discomfort, and to ensure the presence of blood stains a woman or her mother may see to it that there is some blood available, perhaps from a freshly killed chicken. Among the Kurd people of Mesopotamia proof of chastity and bloody penetration is given by displaying stained sheets from the marriage bed for all the village to see. In both the West and the East where vestiges of such myths remain (in many communities in China and Japan, for example, or Italy, Greece, Spain and Turkey), cultural demands are still such that a midwife or physician may be called upon to place a suture in the entrance of the vagina so that a penis feels some obstruction and its giving way offers some superficial blood. This is no more than a sacrifice to ignorance and tradition.

In some women the pain caused by hymen rupture interferes with the enjoyment of first coitus; in others the pleasure of sex more than compensates for any pain. But there is not always pain, or even discomfort, where coitus is a natural development of sexual play.

Buyer beware! A brothel client inspects a 'virgin'. Eighteenth-century French engraving.

A classical study of 475 French and Belgian women by Marc Lanval in 1935 revealed that half felt their first coital experience was 'good' and half felt it was 'bad' – the only two choices he offered. Using a five-choice scale, the 1980 *Cosmopolitan* magazine survey of some 100 000 readers found that 18 per cent of respondents described their first experience of

A village wedding feast, the work of the Flemish painter Brueghel the Younger, a contemporary of Shakespeare. The bloodstained sheet from the nuptial bed is displayed on the wall behind the diners.

sex as 'thrilling' (top of the scale), while an equal 18 per cent found it 'painful and upsetting' (bottom of the scale). The majority of *Cosmopolitan*'s respondents had generally favourable recollections of their first coital experience, even though it did not include orgasm. It satisfied their need for companionship, and gave them a sense of belonging, of having been initiated into the sisterhood of non-virgins. It seemed to fulfil many needs.

CLITORIS

The clitoris (from the Greek word meaning hidden) is a relatively concealed structure. It is covered by a foreskin formed by the forward ends of the minor vaginal lips and can usually be exposed by moving these aside. What is then seen is an organ that varies greatly in size and shape from woman to woman.

The clitoris is unique in that its primary function seems to be to receive erotic stimulation. This can be direct, or indirect from movement of the labia, vagina or mons region. For many women the sensitivity of the glans clitoris, particularly after arousal, is such that they prefer indirect stimulation. Nevertheless, the majority of women in several studies reported that they found stimulation of the shaft of the clitoris very enjoyable, both in masturbation and partner contact. Unfortunately, as Hite and others have noted, most women find it difficult to ask their partner to stimulate them in this way and also feel guilty about masturbation, particularly when they are with a partner. Typically, women like clitoral stimulation to be part of a total involvement and not to seem like an obligation. It should be soft and slow at first, gradually building more pressure and speed. A technique frequently preferred is that stimulation should start with whole hand massage and then evolve to the use of only one or two fingers. As with other erotic techniques individual nuances in preference are great; experimentation and communication, asking and telling what is wanted and found exciting, are the key to satisfaction.

THE G-SPOT

The G-spot is described as an area 1-1½ inches across and located about two finger joints deep to the vaginal entrance. Its sensitivity to stimulation was first noted by the physician Ernst Grafenberg. In 1950 Grafenberg wrote:

An erotic zone always could be demonstrated on the anterior wall of the vagina along the course of the urethra . . . Occasionally the production of fluids [due to its stimulation] *is so profuse that a large towel has to be spread under the woman . . . This convulsive expulsion of fluids occurs always at the acme of the orgasm and simultaneously with it . . . expelled not from the vulva but out of the urethra in gushes . . . it had no urinary character . . . no lubricating significance.*

American researchers Beverley Whipple and John D. Perry dubbed this region the 'G-spot' in Grafenberg's honour. In 1982, with a colleague Alice Ladas, they created a publishing sensation with their book *The G-Spot and Other Recent Discoveries about Human Sexuality* written for a popular readership. However, few women seem able to locate their G-spot.

From the data currently available it is impossible to say what percentage of women have a G-spot, what percentage have a gush of fluid at orgasm and how frequently and under what conditions. The origin and nature of any expelled fluids still have to be determined.

Some researchers claim that a G-spot is present and easy to locate in all women; others doubt its universal existence. William Hartman and Marilyn Fithian, two highly respected investigators following the research of Arnold Kegel, well noted for his work on vaginal exercises, claim that the most sensitive areas of the vagina are located not at the '12 o'clock' position as reported for the G-spot, but at the '4 o'clock' and '8 o'clock' positions.

On balance – on the basis of my own findings, but more importantly on the basis of my review of the literature and conversations with many of the scientists involved – I am convinced that the G-spot exists, but that it is not responsive in all women, certainly not readily self-palpable. I also accept, on similar grounds, that some women 'ejaculate' at orgasm, that the fluid emitted is distinct from urine and that emission may be followed, as in males, by a refractory period.

But what I find almost as interesting as the quest for biological fact is the avid interest that greeted the findings of researchers such as Whipple and Perry. It is understandable that most sexually active people want to give and receive the erotic pleasure they believe others enjoy. However, it would be a pity if the G-spot and female ejaculation became yet another source of anxiety. To envy what happens or to feel inadequate because of what you think happens in another person's bed to the extent of devaluing the pleasures of your own is a waste and a shame.

BREASTS

The message that comes across from magazines such as *Playboy* and *Penthouse* is that, for sex appeal, women with small breasts need not apply. As we shall see in the next chapter, most men prefer, as an ideal, fairly generous bust proportions. What do women themselves prefer? As we shall see, a breast size that is pleasing to both men and women cannot be defined.

Breast development is one of the first signs of puberty in both boys and girls. Embarrassment about budding breasts is often one of the reasons why many pubertal boys and girls are shy about showing their bodies in public, for example in showers or locker rooms at school. The teasing that such embarrassment often

An operation to reduce breast size. More commonly it is dissatisfaction with small breasts that leads to surgery.

attracts can become so hurtful that the individual may play truant to avoid it.

In girls, breast development may be evident a year or so before menarche, the onset of menstruation. Depending upon the culture, girls who develop more slowly than their age mates often feel embarrassed or humiliated. The pubertal growth period occurs at just the age when young people are most anxious to be accepted by their peers. In boys, breast development also causes embarrassment and anxiety, but it is the body's way of building-up an extra store of fat in preparation for the growth ahead. Breast development can occur in males at times other than puberty, or persist long after its completion, but such conditions, called gynecomastia, are usually associated with certain drug treatments, medical problems, or alcoholism. These have the effect of increasing oestrogen levels in the body either directly or by altering normal hormone metabolism.

Hypnosis and prayer, pills and potions,

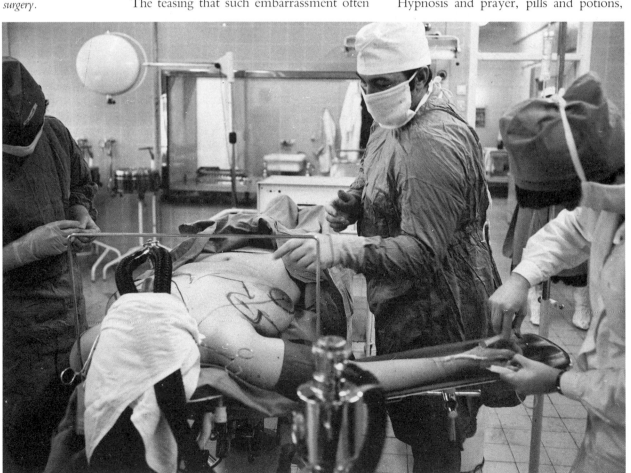

exercises and diets – women have tried almost everything to increase breast size. Exercises can build up the back muscles and so increase overall bust measurement, and they may tighten the muscular support of the breasts, but they cannot significantly increase breast size. Since the breast is mostly filled with fat it is only by gaining weight that size will materially increase. But distribution of that extra fat cannot be controlled – it could equally well deposit itself around the hips, thighs or waist. The other main constituent of breasts, apart from fat, is glandular tissue, the special tissue that secretes milk. Pregnancy is therefore a stimulus to increased breast size. Hormone preparations may be helpful in those rare cases where small breasts are due to hormone deficiency; a deficiency of this kind typically shows itself in other ways and is therefore relatively easy to spot and treat. Like most other aspects of growth and body development, breast size and shape is genetically determined. All of us have at least some physical characteristics which we recognize in our parents or grandparents.

Large breasts are not desirable *per se*. They can be a source of social or physical discomfort. The kind of attention they provoke is sometimes less than flattering. Very large breasts may be too heavy for the muscles that support them; the result is stress and pain in the neck and shoulders. In the United States breast reducing surgery is the third most common elective procedure after rhinoplasty (nose jobs) and breast augmentation.

There is no ideal breast size or shape that simultaneously pleases men and women any more than there is an ideal and universally satisfying penis size or shape. Few women want breasts so large that they are out of proportion with the rest of their body or steal attention from their total appearance and personality. Each woman's shape has its own appeal and many men find small breasts attractive, erotic and stimulating. As one small-breast fan put it: 'Anything over mouth size is wasted.' For some men it is not the shape but rather the natural hang and swing of the breasts or the projection of nipples behind a soft blouse that is erotic. For others it is the artificial accentuation offered by an uplift bra.

Most men assume that most women appreciate having their breasts and nipples stroked and kissed and are surprised to find that there are women who take little or no pleasure from such stimulation. Men themselves seem to be fairly equally divided as to whether they find occasional stimulation of their breasts and nipples pleasurable and arousing – some men do but an almost equal number find it distracting and unappealing. Some women can be brought to orgasm by breast and nipple stimulation alone, but this is almost unknown among men. For both sexes it is usually the nipple and its surrounding areola that are more sensitive than the breast itself. Blowing, sucking and licking produce sensations that each have their own appeal.

Anxieties about the appearance of breasts and nipples are not uncommon. Areolae, the pigmented areas around the nipples, vary greatly in size and not uncommonly sprout hairs, more so than the rest of the breast. If they are a cause of concern, these hairs can be plucked as any other. Some women are con-

An Mbuti pygmy woman and child. Older Mbuti women sometimes sling their breasts over their shoulders to keep them out of the way.

The many-breasted statue of the fertility goddess Artemis of Asia Minor at Efes, Turkey. Some women do have more than two breasts.

Circumcision, male and female

Despite their great disparity in size, both the penis and the clitoris have a root, shaft and an expanded head called the glans; the rim of the glans is called the corona (crown). Covering the glans in the uncircumcised male is a loose hood of skin called the foreskin, or prepuce. In the female the prepuce is also called the clitoral hood. The prepuce, glans and skin on the underside of the penis and clitoris is attached by a thin strand of skin called the frenulum. The glans, prepuce, corona and frenulum are the most sensitive areas of both the penis and the clitoris and their stimulation during sex play gives pleasure to most people.

Male circumcision is the removal of the foreskin covering the glans. Much debate and mythology revolves around the medical necessity for circumcision and the relative sensitivity of the penis after the procedure. For most males, child or adult, circumcision is not medically necessary, nevertheless it is often recommended for reasons of hygiene and preventive medicine. This is particularly so in the United States where circumcision is routinely done in hospital soon after the birth of a male child. In Great Britain and Europe the practice is less frequent and much more dependent on the preferences of individual physicians. Those in favour of circumcision are generally urologists or paediatricians who have seen the problems that can develop with a retained foreskin. The most common is smegma, a cheesy accumulation of dead skin, dirt and fluids under the prepuce, which if not regularly cleaned away, can become a source of irritation, and conducive to infection. Secondly, a prepuce that is too tight (phimosis) hinders normal erection of the penis, making coitus painful or impossible. Without circumcision, penile infection and phimosis are not uncommon. On either count, circumcision seems a worthwhile measure.

There is no definite evidence that circumcision affects penis sensitivity one way or the other. Studies of men who have been circumcised as adults or as infants have not revealed anything consistent. Some men report that after foreskin removal in adulthood, exposure of the glans did provide a different sensitivity for some months but that this decreased with time. A few men complain that after arousal the glans of the circumcised penis is too sensitive for direct stimulation.

One argument against circumcision is that

cerned that one breast is a different shape or size from the other or that one nipple or both may not protrude. These are common occurrences and not abnormal. Like most other individual features they are usually of little or no concern to a loving partner. They do not in any way interfere with nursing or sexual pleasure. In any case during sexual arousal inverted nipples become erect and respond in the same way as protruding nipples.

Less common is the presence of supernumerary nipples or breasts. These are extra breasts or nipples that develop in the armpit or along the so-called milk-line from armpit to normal nipple. They can easily be removed if they cause embarrassment. A modern Japanese love story, *Gobancho yugiri row* (Fifth District Shop) by Minakami Stomu, has as part of its theme the love and adoration of a woman with a supernumerary breast. It has become so popular it has been made into several movies and plays, with aspiring and accomplished actresses queuing up to play the part of the heroine!

And lastly no woman need be apprehensive that her breasts are not adequate for nursing. It is a myth that women with small breasts produce insufficient milk.

the foreskin is nature's way of protecting the glans from undesirable and extraneous stimuli. It is supposed that without a foreskin, the glans will develop a harder surface, rendering it less sensitive and thus increasing the individual's ability to prolong coitus. Conversely it is argued that without a foreskin the glans will be increasingly sensitive, thus decreasing the individual's capacity for prolonged coitus! Actually there is no evidence of any greater or lesser duration of coitus or of a marked tendency to quick ejaculation. Nor is there any evidence that circumcision facilitates or hinders masturbation.

An additional argument against circumcision is that it can cause unnecessary trauma and perhaps subconscious psychological damage. Some people also point to the risk of faulty surgery, which may result in a disfigured or dysfunctional penis. There is no evidence whatsoever for the first argument, and cases of faulty surgery are extremely rare.

Interestingly one major study revealed that a large percentage of women did not know whether their husbands were circumcised or not. Among those women who had experience of both states and could recognize the difference, no consensus as to preference was found. Some voiced a liking for the cleaner or neater appearance of the circumcised penis, but others found erotic appeal in the glans emerging from the intact foreskin.

In the female, two different but related procedures are worth mentioning. One is comparable to male circumcision and, depending on the culture in which it is practised, involves removing various amounts of prepuce, clitoris or even parts of the labia. This is the custom in some Arab and African cultures where males are also routinely circumcised. In some societies it is believed that circumcision will lessen a woman's sex drive, deterring her from masturbating or straying from her husband; in other cultures it is a sign of religious or group affiliation. Female circumcision has become an issue in Western sexual politics, where it is interpreted as representing the view that a woman's body and desires should be subject to controls imposed by the dominant male culture. The practice is uncommon in the West on either cultural or hygienic grounds, but in Middle Eastern and African countries it is widespread. The fact that it is often done by laypersons without the proper skills adds fuel to the controversy.

As with many other issues the matter is not

Excision or mutilation of the genitals is perhaps one of the most questionable of all rites of passage. In remote African villages the operation is likely to be carried out with an old razor blade, a safety pin or even the sharpened lid off a tuna can, sometimes with fatal results.

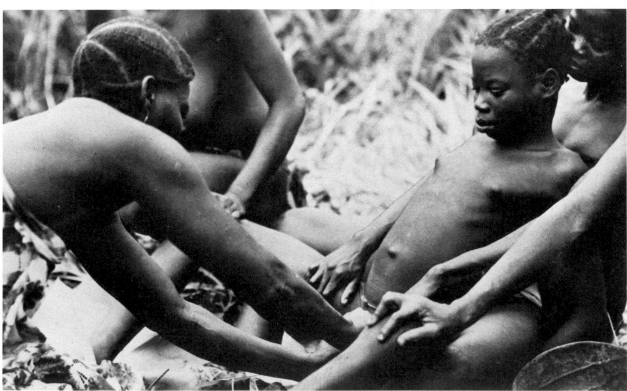

simple. There are reports of enhanced sexual response following at least one type of female circumcision. One clinical researcher, Leo Wollman, an obstetrician–gynecologist and psychiatrist, reported:

> My opinion, based on clinical experience, is that the sensuality of the clitoris is greater when there is no tissue covering the clitoral head... Of 100 consecutive patients referred by psychoanalysts and clinical psychologists to the author for treatment of frigidity, 68 benefited by surgical female circumcision; of the remaining 32, 28 showed no need for this procedure; 4 refused to be treated by this technique.
>
> The technique of surgical circumcision in the female involves a small dorsal slit of the membrane covering the clitoral body... The ideal result from a female circumcision, where it is indicated, is an increase in quality of the orgasm, as well as an increased rapidity in achieving this sensual result in love-making.

The second procedure, technically called clitoridopexy, was initially promoted by various feminists and professional sex therapists in the 1950s following the work of Robert L. Dickinson, a pioneer sex researcher. Dickinson reported that freeing the clitoris, enhancing its mobility by separating any adhesions tying the clitoris to its hood, would increase sensitivity and the probability of female orgasm. Another American researcher, Thomas P. Lowry, editor of two books, *The Classic Clitoris* and *The Clitoris*, has been quoted as saying that this procedure may be 'tremendously helpful' when clitoral adhesions exist. Masters and Johnson have claimed that clitoridopexy has doubtful value, but Kinsey supported the practice.

As with male circumcision, there is no controlled study which has proved that either female circumcision or clitoridopexy affects erotic sensation for better or worse.

The preponderance of opinion in the West now is that female circumcision is an unwarranted mutilation and a cultural anachronism even in those societies where it is still widely practised. It is outlawed in Norway, Sweden and Denmark but most legislators do not concern themselves with the issue, leaving the matter to personal discretion. While Britain's Royal College of Obstetricians has called the practice 'barbaric, futile and illogical' there are

A young aborigine boy solemnly awaits initiation by circumcision. Elcho Island, northern Australia.

private physicians in London who perform clitoral surgery for immigrant women.

The debate is complicated, because it is not argued on similar grounds by both sides. It is an argument that attracts irrational gusto. For example, where female circumcision is part of religious tradition, it is seen as the fulfilment of a covenant with God; the opposite view is that it may cause unnecessary pain, is of questionable hygienic value and affirms the subordinate status of women.

In some cultures male circumcision is required by religious custom and may even be made deliberately traumatic, as part of a pubertal rite to mark a boy's admission to adulthood. In the pubertal rite of Australian aborigines the glans penis is split to resemble that of a kangaroo. Other societies practise subincision (slitting the underside of the penis) and the Ponapeans of the Caroline Islands remove a testicle as well. Youngsters are proud to admit having undergone such traumas. Like risking death to slay a lion or a whale, they are ways of testing and asserting their manhood and their ties with a particular group. Such practices are so entwined with traditional and personal beliefs that rational argument for or against is difficult, and when pressure for change comes from outside the culture in question, it has a presumptive aspect that is seldom welcome. In 1980 at the World Conference that marked the United Nations Decade for Women, the issue of female circumcision and clitoridectomy was discussed. Delegations from various African countries either left the conference or advised their sisters to mind their own business in regard to these practices.

There is enough clinical data, personal feeling and social pressure to keep the debate on circumcision, male or female, in currency for some time to come.

Buttocks

I mentioned the erotic attraction of buttocks in Chapter 2. They may be more than an arbitrary stimulus. Kinsey said the contractions of the buttocks 'reflect, more than any one factor, the development of the...tensions involved in erotic arousal'. The buttock muscles are among the strongest in the body and they come into play during intercourse and masturbation; a small percentage of women masturbate simply by tensing and relaxing these muscles.

Fondling the rump is considered pleasurable by both men and women. But involvement of the anus and rectum in sex play is highly individualistic, culture-related, and linked to sexual preference. More than half the heterosexual respondents to Kinsey's surveys in the United States indicated that, while it was not a common part of their sexual practices,

In both sexes the buttock muscles powerfully increase sexual tension. Michelangelo's statue of David in Florence.

they had had experience of anal stimulation or anal intercourse. Recent indications in the United States are that some 10 per cent of couples regularly have anal intercourse. And among homosexual males recent surveys show that 50 to 75 per cent regularly engage in anal intercourse and manual stimulation of the anus. In some cultures such practices are part of male initiation but in others they are severely condemned; indeed Judaeo-Christian teachings ban them altogether.

The anus and rectum are the terminal parts of the digestive system. The anus is highly pigmented and surrounded by ring-like sphincter muscles that are normally tightly closed. The anal region, vagina and penis share the same nerve roots. This partly explains why males and females can find anal stimulation erotic. Like the vagina, the anal region is most sensitive close to its opening. Deeper inside, pressure and stretching are easily felt but are more painful than pleasurable, and problems can quite easily develop without warning. This is why routine rectal examination is a wise measure whether or not one engages in erotic anal activities.

Anal intercourse is sometimes thought of in terms of dominance and submission. Some individuals refuse to allow penetration while perfectly willing to play the role of penetrator; others feel psychologically uncomfortable with a role they think of as dominant. More often anal intercourse is regarded as an extension of natural sexual curiosity, of the desire to know a partner's body as fully as possible and to find as many ways of giving and receiving pleasure as possible. A client of mine told me: 'My husband had often wanted to but I wasn't interested. In fact I was repelled by the idea. After the divorce I let my lover try it and I've come to like it. In fact I even ask for it now.' As Morton Hunt recorded in a Playboy Foundation report and Linda Wolfe wrote in her *Cosmopolitan* study, some people are repelled by the idea, some are indifferent, and others find it very appealing. Both writers emphasize that it is an increasing practice among couples not because sadistic, dominant individuals want to impose themselves on submissive love objects but because it is now frequently acknowledged as another option in the cause of mutual sexual pleasure.

However, since the rectal sphincter is tight and lubrication in this area is minimal, anal intercourse should be slow and gentle, with the penetrating partner applying plenty of lubrication, either saliva or any water soluble gel, to avoid the possibility of damaging the rectum or causing pain. As a simple matter of hygiene, fingers or penis that have been inserted into the rectum should be washed before oral or vaginal play.

Pubic hair

Hair growth in the pubic region is one of the first signs of puberty. Distribution may be sparse and localized or widespread and luxuriant, and the growth pattern differs in men and women. While in both sexes pubic hair grows in the shape of a shield (escutcheon), in men the upper border tapers centrally toward the navel and in women the line is relatively straight.

Even the sight of pubic hair is exciting to most men and to some women. Stroking it or gently pulling it can be quite erotic. Several centuries ago false pubic hair-pieces, merkins, were used. At the other extreme some cultures and certain groups within cultures prefer a shaved pubic area.

The removal of body hair from the pubic region, armpits, legs and other parts of the body has become a feminist issue. Many women feel that shaving, electrolysis, depilation and waxing are done only to please and stimulate men; they find the whole process inconvenient, sordid, sometimes painful, and degrading; why should they be made to feel critical and embarrassed about their own bodies? Other women feel they do it for themselves, for their own aesthetic reasons.

The debate on this issue, as with circumcision, is tied to cultural and social expectations. In most of Western Europe it is usually women of the middle and upper classes who remove body hair; working class women and those living in rural areas tend not to bother. In Spain and Latin America, a woman's moustache or body hair may be considered sexy but not necessarily in good taste.

The mouth

Lips and tongue together are an extremely sensual organ, ranking highly with men and women alike. *The Perfumed Garden*, the classical Persian love manual, states 'A humid kiss is better than hurried coitus.' The mouth is sensitive to tenderness and passion and a kiss can suggest or accompany genital penetration.

Most erotic play in Western societies includes oral activity. For some people the mouth rivals the genitals in erotic significance and some women can come to orgasm through kissing alone. But kissing as we know it, like many other sexual practices, is not universal. Among some cultures it is unknown or rare. Some Eskimo and Truk Islander groups rub noses rather than kiss. Other techniques involve sucking the lips and tongue of the partner, as among the Kwakiutl Indians, and among the Trobriand and Truk Islanders.

Erotic mouth-to-mouth kissing includes movements of the tongue and lips to simulate the action of penis and vagina in intercourse. Tongue, lips and teeth can be used with amazing versatility to stimulate, press, tickle, caress, lick, suck, pull, blow, nibble or nip any part of the body. Kissing the breasts and genitals is a common part of sexual play, although the idea and the act of using the mouth to directly stimulate the penis or the clitoris and vagina are still distasteful to many people. Like the skin, the mouth has enormous sensual potential. If one partner feels the other is too quick in moving to coitus and orgasm, oral activities have a broad potential well worth exploring both as an hors d'oeuvre and as a dessert! □

Mouths are highly sensitive. Mouth and tongue have more nerve endings than any other part of the body.

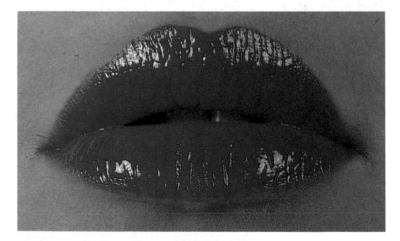

4

Aphrodisiacs and anaphrodisiacs

Aphrodisiacs are named after Aphrodite, the Greek goddess of love who was formed from sea foam when the god Chronos killed and castrated his father and threw his genitals into the sea. They are substances purported to excite love or sexual desire. Anaphrodisiacs do the opposite. Folklore, medicine and modern therapy have all attempted to solve the problems of unrequited love, unmatched or unsynchronized desire, too much or too little passion. The search for aphrodisiacs and anaphrodisiacs – charms, spells, rituals, potions, philtres, diets – is age-old and universal.

The ideal aphrodisiac would have to be all things to all people. It would have to be 'partner specific'; it is the love or desire of a particular person, not of the world at large or of a complete stranger, that is desired. It would also have to be 'time specific'; a woman may want to prolong her partner's erection but not delay his orgasm indefinitely. Despite the need, and despite an accumulation of literature and folklore, no potion, powder or drug exists that can selectively and safely manipulate both sexual desire and performance. No charm or magic has such power either. Nevertheless hope springs eternal.

Like helping like

Many folk preparations from around the world come under the heading 'sympathetic' medicine. Their 'efficacy' comes from their similarity to the body organ or process in question. The horn of a rhinoceros or deer represents a firm, erect penis. Olives represent testes and oysters vaginal labia. Peppers create a sensation of heat and cooked okra represent vaginal lubrication.

Belief in such sympathetic potential is a

Left *The unicorn myth interpreted in a fifteenth-century manuscript and in a Paris nightclub. The unicorn symbolizes male potency. According to legend a unicorn could not be captured until it had laid its head in the lap of a naked virgin.*

Below *Scourging scene from a fresco in the Villa of Mysteries in Pompeii. Erotic art is the most universal of all aphrodisiacs.*

feature of various homeopathic therapies and magical procedures. The 'success' of such remedies is usually quite coincidental, or the result of the extra care and sensitivity that accompany the situation in which they are given or taken. If they do not work, it can always be said that they were not prepared or used properly. In fifth century Rome Caelius Aurelianus warned:

> *To distil the true essence of Satyricon* [sexual desire] *is no light task; many fail to render the liquor efficacious through ignorance of the root's idiosyncrasy. For it is to be noted that of the twin testicles of this plant* [probably mandrake] *the one is ever flaccid, soft and wrinkled and shall therefore be discarded, since its virtue is of a nature called Saturnine by Celsus, which has the contrary effect of repressing and extinguishing desire.*

The Roman historian Martial thought that 'bulbs' (probably onions) were effective for whatever ailed one sexually. The success of the remedy depended simply on taking enough:

> *He who is unable to show himself a man in the Cyprian joustings* [natives of Cyprus were once held to be extremely licentious in their behaviour] *let him eat of bulbs and he will be doughty enough. In the same way, should your anus languish, do not cease eating of bulbs, and charming Venus will once more smile on your frays.*

In modern parlance, if one teaspoon doesn't help, try two!

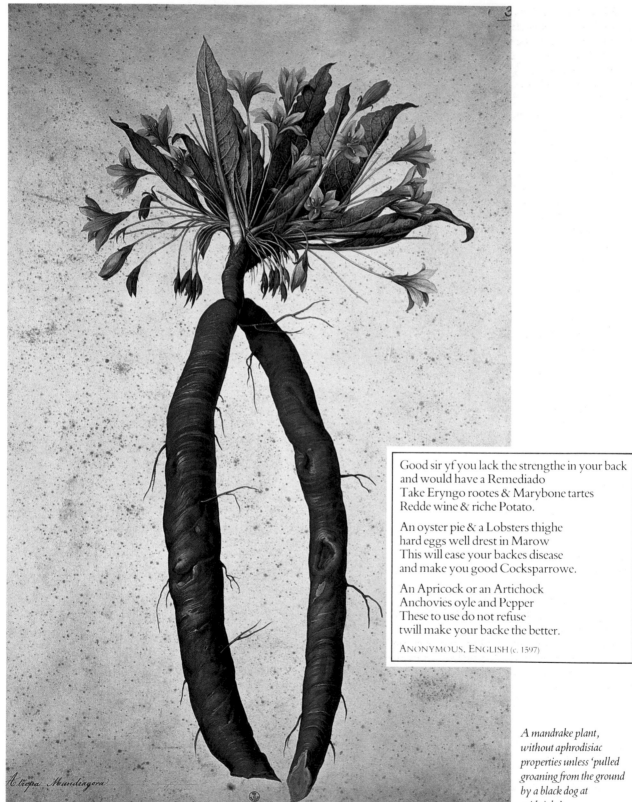

Atropa Mandragora

Good sir yf you lack the strengthe in your back
and would have a Remediado
Take Eryngo rootes & Marybone tartes
Redde wine & riche Potato.

An oyster pie & a Lobsters thighe
hard eggs well drest in Marow
This will ease your backes disease
and make you good Cocksparrowe.

An Apricock or an Artichock
Anchovies oyle and Pepper
These to use do not refuse
twill make your backe the better.

ANONYMOUS, ENGLISH (c. 1597)

*A mandrake plant,
without aphrodisiac
properties unless 'pulled
groaning from the ground
by a black dog at
midnight'.*

When partners conspire to use a 'love potion', the result is often a self-fulfilling prophecy. Whatever the effect of the potion, love-making may be enhanced by the relief from responsibility that the introduction of such an outside element affords: 'I was under the influence...' On the other hand, someone who sticks pins in a doll is likely to behave aggressively to the person represented by the effigy; in consequence he or she may well abandon any effort to be sexually pleasing.

At one time potatoes and tomatoes were looked on as 'love foods'; eating them conferred sexual and reproductive bliss. As long as they were exotic and difficult to come by they kept their mystique; but once in common use their love-enhancing powers became discredited. The rarity of truffles today allows them to keep their reputation (undeserved) as aphrodisiacs.

Spanish fly, mandrake and yohimbine

Three substances often cited in the Western world as aphrodisiacs are Spanish Fly, mandrake root and yohimbiné. Spanish Fly is the common name for a powder made from ground *Cantharis* beetles. The powder is a powerful irritant which can inflame the skin as well as the lining of the digestive and excretory tract. The substance may have earned its reputation from farmers seeing cattle eating the beetles and noting that they then behaved as if they were in heat. In men Spanish Fly can cause erection but there is a price to pay. The erection is usually painful, not pleasurable, a reflex reaction due to pelvic irritation. Women given Spanish Fly may begin to moan, but this is a moan of pain, not arousal. In both men and women, ulceration may be induced in the digestive and urinary tract. Therefore Spanish Fly is not only ineffective as a love potion but also highly dangerous.

Mandrake root, somewhat like ginseng root in the Orient, is reputed to be efficacious because of its resemblance to the human form or, more specifically, to a penis. It was recommended as an aphrodisiac in Ancient Egypt and Greece and there is mention of it in the book of Genesis: when Leah went out to meet Jacob she said to him 'Thou must come in unto me; for surely I have hired thee with my son's mandrakes.'

In fact the active principles in mandrake root are atropine and scopolamine, both of

The beetle from which Spanish Fly is prepared.

which are sleep inducing. Jacob and Leah may have slept together, but perhaps that was all they did! In large doses mandrake causes mental confusion and hampers respiration. So, like Spanish Fly, it is to be avoided.

Yohimbiné is a drug prepared from bark of the yohimbé tree, an African species mainly restricted to the Cameroons. Its reputation is based on more than travellers' tales; there are now several drug companies that maintain that it increases sexual performance. The drug has been mixed with testosterone and other ingredients (strychnine, for example) to help induce erection. Its efficacy, however, remains in doubt. Controlled animal and human studies by myself and others have failed to confirm that it is an aphrodisiac *per se*.

To conjure up desire modern English witchcraft favours symbolic magic rather than drugs. These love charms, an effigy and a sheep's heart pierced with thorns, were found quite recently at Castle Rising, Norfolk, England.

Slivers of deer horn on sale in Hong Kong.

Over the limit, for everything!

organs can be used to improve the sex lives of those who believe in their efficacy. The wilder and rarer the animal and the more difficult it is to catch, the greater the potency of its organs and appendages. Technologically advanced societies put their faith in other kinds of aphrodisiacs; cola and aspirin, for example, were considered a good bet about thirty years ago, and more lately marijuana or cannabis.

Alcohol and marijuana

Perhaps the most widely used sexual stimulant is alcohol. In moderation alcohol does seem to lessen inhibitions and interpersonal tension. Since these often hamper sexual interest, ardour may indeed be increased by reducing them. Alcohol also reduces discrimination, so fewer restraints exist. But there is no evidence that alcohol by itself stimulates sexual activity. As Shakespeare observed, drink 'provokes the desire, but it takes away the performance'. Neither does marijuana directly stimulate sexual behaviour or induce amorous desire in an unwilling person, although, like alcohol, it certainly reduces inhibitions.

Many substances, including alcohol and marijuana, appear to be effective because the persons using them expect a specific result and act in such a way that their expectation becomes reality. This is the famous placebo effect at work. Also the situations in which such drugs are used often reflect a tacit understanding that sexual activity will follow.

Controlled studies of the effect of alcohol and marijuana have met with mixed results.

Organs from animals

Testes or testes extracts are quite commonly used as male aphrodisiacs and rejuvenators. Sheep testes sold as 'mountain oysters' or beef testes sold as 'prairie oysters' may be enjoyed as gourmet delicacies but are without special powers. Injectables from these and other animal tissues are considered unethical in the United States but are permitted in Europe and elsewhere.

Every culture has its special aphrodisiacs. To this day many rhinos, elephants, deer, sheep and other animals lose their lives so that their penises, testes, horns, tusks or other

The sex-conducive effects of marijuana or cannabis include relaxation, gentle feelings and an apparent slowing down of time.

Left *'Anything with it, Miss Bronston?'* Punch *cartoon.*

Pharmaceuticals

Cocaine is increasingly used, although illegally, as a recreational drug and has some reputation as an aphrodisiac. When it is inhaled like snuff or taken intravenously, the resulting 'high' often gives a feeling of power, and with it a feeling of potency and desirability. Indeed erections are often prolonged and orgasm delayed. For those who think longer is better, this is viewed as a plus, as is the drug-induced sense of accomplishment. Sexual drawbacks exist, however. Extended cocaine use can lead to priapism, a prolonged, painful erection in men and prolonged vaginal dryness in women. In both sexes cocaine use can lead to an extension of copulation time but an inability to reach orgasm.

Other drugs have been reputed to enhance sexual experiences. Amyl nitrite and isobutyl nitrite induce physiological changes – increased heart rate and blood flow – which may be personally interpreted as signs of sexual excitement. These drugs, sold as volatile liquids, are usually inhaled at the start of sex play or at impending orgasm. They are not necessarily innocuous, since increased blood flow can be detrimental if one happens to suffer from heart, cerebrovascular or eye disease.

Ubiquitously available drugs such as amphetamines, antidepressants, tranquillizers, stimulants and anti-psychotic preparations account for more than 60 per cent of all prescriptions in the United States. Since these drugs are given to people who are not functioning normally, their sexual effects are hard to define. When depression or anxiety are relieved, libido and potency tend to increase. In many people amphetamines and stimulants seem to energize sexual response. The relaxant drugs tend to reduce potency and orgasm, but they also reduce inhibitions. The general picture with prescription drugs is that at the prescribed dosage little sexual effect is detectable, although effects vary from person to person. This is even more true when such drugs or street drugs are used recreationally, for then neither dosage nor content is properly controlled.

Anaphrodisiacs

Are there any substances that reliably decrease arousal or ardour? Zealous parents and guardians have been known to seek anaphrodisiacs to inhibit the sexual development of those in their care, as have legal authorities in the

Large amounts of alcohol depress emotional expression, including sexual desire. In men impotence due to alcohol is common. To be sure, the amount of alcohol which constitutes a large dose varies from person to person, but as a rule of thumb two shots of whisky, wine or beer per hour are enough to induce a feeling of expansiveness, warmth and comfort. This would be enough to reduce inhibitions about initiating or accepting sexual advances and, simultaneously, about vocally and forcefully rejecting them.

At twice this level of alcohol in the blood – at around 100 mg of alcohol per 100 ml of blood (0.1%) – decision-making and discriminating abilities diminish markedly. At this level one would be at or above the legal driving limits in the United States, Great Britain, Scandinavia, Australia, Austria and many other countries. Sexual advances, or the rejection of such advances, may be quite forceful. Erection is still possible, but orgasm in both sexes is generally retarded. At higher blood alcohol levels, erection may be difficult to achieve or maintain; orgasm is also unlikely, if not impossible, whether one is a man or a woman.

Prolonged marijuana use (i.e. daily for more than two months) severely reduces both sexual activity and sperm production in men because it depresses the production of androgen. But in women it seems to correlate with a higher probability of coital orgasm. However, both men and women commonly report that 'grass' seems to make sex more pleasurable and last longer. Since marijuana is known to influence perception of time, it is difficult to test whether such reports reflect reality or altered perception. For many the difference is immaterial since it is the perceived effect which provokes the response.

treatment of various sex offenders. Common among soldiers, sailors and prisoners is the myth at their food is routinely doctored with various ingredients to dampen sexual interest. People not easily aroused themselves have looked for such methods of cooling the enthusiasm of others. As with aphrodisiacs, the list of drugs reported to do the trick is long while the list of efficacious drugs is short.

Saltpetre (potassium nitrate) is probably the most often mentioned of all anaphrodisiacs. There is no evidence, however, that it has the power to inhibit sexual interest or performance. It can increase urine flow and in large doses can be fatal – an unnecessarily drastic solution! Its reputation may be due to the fact that it was once used medicinally to reduce fevers, with the faulty reasoning that it would similarly lower the 'heat' of sexual ardour. Its main use, prior to modern refrigeration, was to cure and store meat, so the idea may have arisen, among those forced to subsist on cured meat, that their food was drugged.

While certainly not taken as such, heroin, opium and other opiates are effective anaphrodisiacs. Along with their sedative and anaesthetic effects, these drugs diminish libido, potency and orgasm. Sexual interest is replaced by passivity and a craving for the drug itself. Male or female opiate users may prostitute themselves, but it is for drug money, not for sexual pleasure.

Barbiturates are indeed 'downers' when it comes to sex. Initially, like alcohol, they take away inhibition but with increased use they also take away sexual interest and potency. In women who abuse barbiturates menstrual and ovulatory abnormalities are common.

Pharmaceutical companies have been successful in developing several antisexual drugs. One is cyproterone acetate (CA), which acts by competing with testosterone so that the hormone cannot do its work. Effective in men, the drug reduces libido, erectile potential and orgastic capacity. Although it is still considered experimental in the United States, in several European countries CA is given to rapists, child molesters and other male sex offenders.

The ethics of using sex-active substances

If sexual expression is so natural, why try to tinker with it? Does interference lessen its significance or value? As a couple may wish to

experience different gastronomic pleasures by becoming gourmets or vegetarians, or by adding or ignoring salt or wine, I see a similar case to be made for people mutually wanting to experience different sexual pleasures. Surely when two people conspire to spice up, figuratively and literally, or tone down their amorous or erotic adventures, it is presumptuous to approve or disapprove. As an informed sexwatcher, one would wish them to be aware of possible negative side effects but, issues of legality aside, there is no moral problem involved. The motivation to tinker with nature, especially if what is natural is unsatisfying or frustrating, seems to me wholly legitimate.

Many couples find that the sexual bliss held out by the media, hinted at by friends, gloriously fulfilled in their private fantasies, or recalled from past experiences, is unmatched by reality. On the other side of the coin there are individuals who regard chastity as a gift from God or simply as a right way to live. Whether it is more or less sex that is needed, the desire for a remedy that is a few swallows away is very understandable.

Nor is the motive for change always selfish. A sympathetic lover may recognize reluctance and inhibition in a partner and genuinely want him or her to enjoy erotic experiences more

Oh, the tease of all those buttons and laces! Turn off or turn on?

Right *Eating for lovers, Lesson 1: it's not* what *you eat that matters, but* how *you eat it. Take grapes . . .*

fully. It would be ego enhancing to realize that someone desired you strongly enough to offer an aphrodisiac.

Very broad ethical issues are involved in using drugs or any other means to rectify disparity in sexual interest or performance. Should such disparities be regarded as a purely personal matter, in which case aphrodisiacs become recreational choices, options in sex play? Or are they medical problems requiring pharmaceutical treatment, psychiatric disturbances requiring therapy, or symptoms of an insecure, sex-obsessed society that needs to reassess its values? And in cases of rape and other sexual offences, should we use drugs, physical punishment, or imprisonment, or all three simultaneously?

Moral and legal issues aside, aphrodisiacs are a fascinating field of study, with a literature that is arcane and fabulous. Here is a good example of the genre, prefaced by a piece of advice with which I unequivocally agree:

> To lovers we therefore say: devour partridge and oyster and asparagus for their pleasurable taste, rather than in the hope of performing prodigies with the beloved.
>
> And put not your trust in Arabian skink, in Roman goose-fat or Roman

'See anything you fancy?' Punch cartoon.

goose-tongues, in the arplan of China that 'maketh a man renew his youth and astonish his household', in spicy culinary dishes, eringoe root, or the brains of love-loving sparrows . . . in pine nuts, the blood of bats mingled with asses' milk, root of valerian, dried salamander, cyclamen, menstrual fluid of man or beast, tulip bulbs, fat of camel's hump . . . the pounded tooth of a corpse, wings of bees . . . garlic, the genitals of hedgehogs, Siberian iris, rhinoceros-horn . . . the blood of slaughtered criminals . . . or stag's horn crushed to powder: aphrodisiacs all, and all impostures.

Paneros, NORMAN DOUGLAS (1932)

5

Body language

Most of us, as part of our sexual delight, enjoy observing the sexual pleasure and response of a partner. His or her facial expressions – smiles, frowns, grimaces – sounds, body movements and skin texture are in themselves erotic. In many ways they are also the most private of all responses, usually seen only by a cherished and privileged partner. In most Western societies it is considered a gross invasion of privacy, indeed illegal, to wilfully observe others in sexual activities without their permission, or oblige others to watch such activities.

Sexual activities are considered so private that Kinsey and his colleagues in the 1940s and 1950s were criticized and ridiculed for expecting the public, or at least the American public, to believe that people could be encouraged to talk candidly about sex and answer questions honestly. Less than a generation later William Masters and Virginia Johnson shocked the public again by announcing that, with the permission of those involved, they had not only interviewed scores of men and women but had observed them in sexual encounters. More than that, they had filmed many of the intimate details and measured them with scientific instruments. By such means they had detected things that millions of lovers over thousands of years had failed to notice. Surprising? Not really when one considers that most sex takes place in the dark and in circumstances where the participants are less than concerned with scientific accuracy.

Intimate signals

The questions men and women ask each other often reveal that intimate signals are not always recognized or understood. Such questions may not be asked easily or in so many words. 'Do you want to make love?' may be a kiss or a touch which is sensitive to similar or different feelings in return. Asking 'Are you ready to go to sleep?' may really mean 'Let's make love.' 'Are you ready?' is a question between partners who care about pacing their movements so that both reach a satisfying climax. 'Did you come?' and 'Couldn't you tell?' also reflect a common reality: orgasm is often unrecognized by those closest and most willing to observe. And if that peak sensation goes unrecognized, how many other less intense moments of sexual intimacy remain unappreciated?

Words are not always the most loving or effective way to signal desire or a particular sexual response, and even non-verbal signals are not always consciously given. Being sensitive to tiny clues that another person is unaware of giving adds a richness to any encounter. Dress, facial expression, body movements and tone of voice can all be clues to sexual interest.

Signals such as a thumping heart and heavy breathing are unambiguous in a sexual context – they signify physical and emotional excitement – but the smaller tell-tale signs of sexual arousal are less easily perceived or correctly interpreted, even by people of considerable sexual experience. One of the problems is that behaviour does not always match thoughts and feelings. A man can have an erection that is neither pleasurable nor desired. In very rare cases this may be due to disease, but usually it is a reflex action – a full bladder or nervous anxiety can cause an erection. Desire for coitus, however strong, is not always accompanied by an erection. This is a common experience and the causes are many; anxiety, fatigue and preoccupation head the list. Similarly a woman can exhibit contradictory signs. The vagina can wet copiously independently of sexual arousal, or remain dry even when coitus is much desired. Orgasm may be desperately willed but remain elusive.

The sexual response cycle

One of the major discoveries of Masters and Johnson was that sexual arousal is accompanied by a very distinctive set of physiological changes : the sexual response cycle. There are five stages in the cycle – rest, excitement or arousal, plateau, orgasm and resolution.

This discussion of sexual response attempts to deal with the subject as part of a total picture of mind and body. The descriptions I am about to give are not models to be lived up to. Variation is great and these generalities are intended to give the reader a better understanding of how male and female bodies work during sex play and coitus. This may sound

mechanistic, but my aim is to provide firm ground on which to base an appreciation and indeed a questioning of sex in wider context. I should also point out that the responses involved are the same whether in the context of homosexual or heterosexual activity.

Most of the time we are sexually at rest, in neutral as it were, busy doing non-sexual things. Consciously or unconsciously these things may be related to sexual pursuits but they are not accompanied by any of the physiological events that signify sexual arousal. Thoughts or fantasies about a real or imag - ined lover can intrude on everyday activities but leave one sexually at rest. A man at rest has a flaccid penis; a woman at rest has a relatively dry and relaxed vagina.

Tension and worry are the enemies of sexual delight. Anxiety levels can be monitored by recording changes in the electrical conductivity of the skin. Free from the 'inner noise' created by anxiety one is often more receptive to sexual suggestion and stimulation.

AROUSAL PHASE

As sexual interest increases, in response to some psychological or physical stimulus, the excitement or arousal phase begins (some sexologists claim that between rest and arousal there is a 'desire' stage). In both men and women arousal is marked by an increase in blood flow to the pelvis (vasocongestion) and an increase in muscular tension (myotonia). In women this combination produces vaginal sweating (I use this term because physiologically the process is akin to sweating and serves functions other than lubrication) and in the man erection of the penis. Almost all men are aware of their own erections, but many women are unaware of their vaginal sweating. If one must look for equivalent processes in male and female, then it is vaginal sweating, not erection of the clitoris, that is the counterpart of erection of the penis. The clitoris becomes engorged with blood and may also enlarge, but in most women it does not become erect. These are not processes that are usually under voluntary control. Wishing

A pottery Priapus lamp found at Pompeii. In Greek mythology Hera, goddess of marriage and motherhood, gave Priapus his permanent and deformed state of arousal to spite Aphrodite, goddess of love.

In the game of 'ten toes up and ten toes down', proximity, kissing and fondling set a complex train of physiological events in motion.

does not necessarily bring them about or cause them to go away.

Sometimes the cause of sexual arousal seems obvious – reading an erotic novel, seeing or being with an attractive or sexually provocative person, viewing a sexually explicit film. But often the upsurge of desire cannot be pinned down to any obvious stimulus. It is as likely to happen during periods of boredom and inactivity as during passionate involvement with another person. But whatever the psychological or physical stimulus, desire and excitement persist only as long as the stimulus persists. Many a sexual episode falters at this initial stage, but if excitement continues to mount, the plateau phase of sexual response is reached.

PLATEAU PHASE

During this phase the penis becomes more rigid and deepens in colour, the scrotal muscles tighten, drawing the testicles closer to the body, and the testicles themselves increase to two or even three times their usual size.

Sometimes a few drops of fluid (called 'love drops' by some) appear at the meatus or opening of the penis. This fluid is produced by the bulbourethral glands at the base of the penis and it cleanses and lubricates the urethra (the duct inside the penis) in readiness for ejaculation.

In women excitement first causes the labia to swell. The inner lips double or triple in thickness, become reddish-purple and sometimes draw apart. The vagina, in addition to sweating more copiously, flushes deep pink or red. Its inner two-thirds balloons while its outer third narrows and tightens (Masters and Johnson coined the term 'orgasmic platform' to describe this region of narrowing and tightening). The clitoris also becomes extra sensitive and, in a seemingly protective reflex, withdraws under its hood.

In almost all women and about one in two men nipple erection occurs during the plateau phase. The pigmented areas around each nipple, the areolae, become larger as the breasts themselves become engorged with blood – this is especially marked in women who have never given birth. As sexual tension increases from excitement to plateau stage the nipples appear to retract. They do not actually retract but become less prominent as the breasts swell slightly around them. Also about

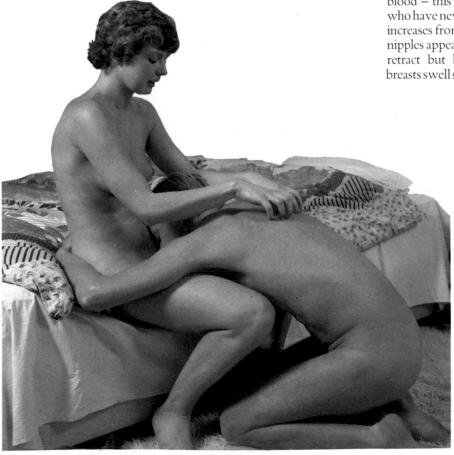

If both partners enjoy it, rhythmic mouth-to-genital movements can contribute to arousal.

There are many ways for genitals to touch and meet.

seven in ten women and one in four men develop a transient rash-like flush across the chest, breasts, back and neck. This event was one of the striking discoveries of Masters and Johnson. Although easily seen under good lighting conditions, it is not difficult to understand why generations of lovers should have failed to notice it.

Many other body movements – a general increase in muscle tension, a pounding heart, and faster, deeper breathing – also accompany the advancing plateau phase. Tension becomes particularly noticeable in the thighs and buttocks, around the mouth and in the strap muscles on either side of the neck. These signs of apparent stress, disconcerting sometimes to an inexperienced partner, mark a build up of sexual tension and a reaching for release. Taken together they usually signify 'yes' in answer to the question 'Are you ready?'

ORGASM

If sexual activity continues, a point of no return is reached and orgasm – also referred to as climaxing or 'coming' – follows. Orgasm is, in simple terms, the rapid reaching of peak sexual tension closely followed by its rapid release. Orgasm may be subjectively experienced as many different things (as a 'symphony', as an 'explosion', as a 'tidal wave') but the physical events that constitute it are much more down to earth.

Orgasm in a man is typically accompanied by ejaculation, the spasm-like release of sperm and semen. Ejaculation is not the same as orgasm. Usually they occur together but either can be experienced without the other necessarily occurring. Just before ejaculation a man usually passes the point of no return: he knows he will climax and can no longer prevent it. He tends to thrust vigorously and deeply, and tightens the muscles in his thighs and buttocks; other muscles may also contract spasmodically. His breathing becomes laboured and irregular. With orgasm and ejaculation he will probably reflexly withdraw his pelvis and halt his thrusting movements. Ejaculation may or may not be accompanied by sounds, but it usually involves a brief loss of awareness.

Orgasm in women is more variable both in frequency and in its physical manifestations. Most men regularly experience orgasm during coitus and tend to worry if they do not. But for women things are not so reliable. Only about half the women interviewed in various studies report regularly experiencing orgasm during coitus; between 10 and 25 per cent of adult women have orgasm rarely or never, and the remaining percentage experience it irregularly. During orgasm the orgasmic platform contracts, the contractions being few or many, weak or strong, and tailing off in frequency and intensity. In both men and

Above *Penetration and still the tension builds, reaching for release.*

Right *The point of no return as signals from breasts, genitals and body blend into orgasm.*

women orgasm also involves contractions of the anal sphincter, the ring of muscle around the anus.

The signs of orgasm in women are richly varied. Some women have a response similar to that of the typical male described above – vigorous pelvis movements, muscular tension in the thighs and buttocks, laboured breathing. Others may show a more explosive response, with a great deal of involuntary movement and noise. They may laugh or cry uncontrollably, or look and sound as if they are in pain (a very small number of men do this too). This can be frightening, even embarrassing, when it is first encountered, but it is quite normal.

Recent controversy has focused on the question of whether female ejaculation occurs. Some women have reported a heavy loss of fluid from the vagina or urethra at orgasm. Research has so far failed to identify its character. There are conflicting theories suggesting it may be extra lubrication, an involuntary release of urine, or an expulsion similar to the fluid released in male ejaculation. Female ejaculation is linked to the existence of a sensitive G-spot, described on page 66.

For perhaps a majority of women the plateau phase is prolonged and orgasm is not explosive or obvious, not so much a distinct climax as a crossing over into a more relaxed state. For those men and women who show it,

the skin flush is most developed at orgasm. In some women climax occurs with little noticeable movement or noise. But in neither sex is a great expenditure of energy – scratching, writhing, loud cries – any measure or guarantee of satisfaction. An orgasm with little noise may be just as satisfying as one with a lot. Again, the best way to be sure that a partner feels satisfied is to ask.

Right *For many men orgasm is an explosive sensation. In three or four major bursts of seminal fluid up to 350 million sperm are propelled deep into the vagina and towards the cervix.*

While both sexes usually feel very positive about the experience of orgasm, the answer to the question 'Did you come?' is not always physically obvious, even to the most attentive and loving partner. That is why it is helpful to establish a convention whereby each tells the other, verbally or otherwise, whether climax has occurred and whether to continue. A gentle kiss on the ear or eyelid is one way.

Orgasm, like other phases of the sexual response cycle, is a highly individual expression. Almost all men masturbate from early adolescence and therefore recognize the sensation of orgasm, or at least the fluid that accompanies ejaculation. They, and also those women who have quite dramatic orgasms, may find it difficult to accept that some women do not easily reach climax or even know when they have.

RESOLUTION PHASE

In general the time immediately following orgasm is experienced differently by men and women. Men tend to become passive and refractory, that is unresponsive to further sexual stimuli, and the penis becomes limp as blood flows away from the pelvis and muscle tension decreases. This is the resolution phase of the cycle, a more or less rapid return to physical and emotional rest, expressed most directly in the urge to sleep. Some women also return quickly to rest and sleep, but few go through the refractory period that is typically part of the male experience. Most women remain sexually responsive during the resolution phase. Some are still sexually excited, invite more stimulation and climax again before returning to a state of rest. It is this phenomenon – a second orgasm reached without returning to a pre-plateau level of arousal – that is somewhat sensationally labelled 'multiple orgasm'. It is a feature of the sexual response cycle of between 10 and 15 per cent of women investigated, but of fewer than 1 per cent of men. The reason for this disparity is not understood.

Occasionally resolution may be delayed due to retention of the inflow of blood to the genitals and pelvis and prolonged tension in these areas. This is known as 'blue balls' in men and 'pelvic congestion' in women, and can cause discomfort and sometimes pain. Re-engaging in sexual activity, masturbation or coitus, may achieve the desired release, but the problem does resolve itself in time.

Differences in response

If the duration, intensity and psychological significance of each phase of the sexual response cycle were the same for both sexes, and for people of different temperaments, there would probably be very little sexual frustration. But they are not the same. Not being able to engage a partner in willing erotic

After orgasm is a time for tenderness, especially if one partner takes longer to 'come down' than the other. If he simply turns over and goes to sleep she can feel very alone and used.

arousal is as frustrating as a plateau phase that is too short or too long, or an orgasm that never materializes. Some people prefer to prolong the arousal phase, others the plateau. Some find the afterglow or end of resolution more satisfying than the tension of plateau or the brevity of orgasm.

Even for those who regularly experience it, orgasm occasionally fails to occur. More men than women express frustration about not climaxing but then, for many women, physical and emotional satisfaction does not seem to be as closely linked with orgasm. Coitus can be deeply satisfying even if orgasm does not occur; the pleasure comes from the warmth, the trust and the sharing, from the knowledge of being sexually desirable and adept at pleasing another. If one never experiences orgasm, so what? It is unhelpful to focus on orgasm to the exclusion of all else. Nevertheless the absence of it can undermine a relationship and become a source of serious worry and low self-esteem.

Orgasm has, rightly or wrongly, great significance for most people. If orgasm rarely or never occurs, for whatever reason, sexual activities are frequently accompanied by feelings of sin or guilt, particularly when the individual concerned has had a strict religious upbringing. For some the failure to experience orgasm is not the result of inhibition but of physiological ignorance; not knowing their potential for orgasm, they cannot aim for the sensation. For others orgasm is within reach but they forbid themselves to reach it; they see it as an unacceptable loss of control. There are also those who want to climax and get quite close but somehow never reach the final release; in such situations a trained therapist can usually help.

Because climax is not a totally reliable response and because its desirability is greatly stressed, orgasm is often faked. With women less likely to climax than men, more faking is done by women, often with the most loving and altruistic of motives but occasionally to terminate an encounter that has lost interest.

Faking orgasm raises various emotional and ethical questions. Both partners' egos are involved. Lack of orgasm can be interpreted as sexual incompetence, fatigue, lack of interest or lack of responsiveness. Faking salvages the feelings of one or both partners but it also sweeps important issues under the mattress; if you think about it, one of the partners is not

given the chance of adapting to the other, of helping him or her to reach orgasm. If partners cannot be honest in this most intimate of moments, how firmly grounded is the rest of the relationship? According to some therapists, faking may further block the orgasm response of the faker, making orgasm less likely on future occasions.

On the other hand total honesty in sex is rare and not always the kindest course. Disparity in the sexual response cycles of men and women means that compromise – mixing honesty and candour with tact and practicality – is often necessary. Faking once in a while is a compromise. Perhaps it should be thought of as good manners rather than as betrayal of self or partner.

Synchronizing responses

In a casual encounter, when partners find the pace and enthusiasm of their sexual responses mismatched, neither may feel a sense of failure: 'It's just one of those things' or 'It never works out the first time.' But for a young married couple who find the same mismatches occurring night after night, the stresses may spread, with bitterness, blame and frustration ultimately shadowing their love and commitment. In the West we like to think we live in a sexually sophisticated era. Nevertheless sexual topics are still surrounded with a great deal of uncertainty, prejudice and

Orgasm – his or hers – is not totally necessary to a happy sex life. But the fact that orgasm is not a totally reliable response often means that it is striven for all the more. Occasional rewards can drive us harder than regular ones.

mythology. This is what I hear every day from students and others who come to see me. The interesting point is that they are not new problems, but to every couple or individual seeking help they seem unique and insoluble.

One stumbling block to couples trying to solve their own sexual problems is that while there may be sympathy between partners, there may not be empathy, the ability to stand in the other's shoes.

A dramatic change in sexual response is usually temporary. Commonly, it is closely tied to other demanding or unexpected experiences – a new job, a problem with a relative, financial trouble, a change in the fundamental relationship between the people involved. There may be a downward slide with accompanying depression or an acceleration of interest with manic overtones. There may be a medical problem that is itself hidden, or a fear that is repressed.

One or both partners can take steps to make sure the culprit is not medical. If the reason is psychological, it can often be solved by communication, however difficult this may be initially. For some people the advice of a counsellor, as a concerned but not emotionally involved mediator, may point to new avenues of mutual exploration. The deeper the bond between partners, the easier it is to restore or create satisfactory sexual dialogue.

The significance of orgasm
There is no universally accepted pace for sexual activity, any more than there is a standard frequency. Simultaneous orgasm is only one way to shared and equal pleasure, but it is an ambition that preys on people's minds if it does not occur. In fact the chances are quite high that simultaneous orgasm will not occur. For example, most women require deep forceful penetration and sustained clitoral stimulation to reach orgasm, but when men reach orgasm they usually stop thrusting and withdraw pelvic pressure. After orgasm many women are still mentally and physically ready for more sex play, but their male partners may not wish to be touched, at least for a while, and may want to go to sleep.

At the turn of the century dominant medical opinion was that female orgasm was unhealthy and improper and that women were physically and psychologically incapable of enjoying coitus. As long as sex remained something that men 'did' to women, the con-

cept of premature ejaculation was unknown. Indeed from the woman's point of view, the sooner ejaculation occurred the better, since coitus was something to be endured rather than enjoyed.

But as the sexual status of women changed, it began to be accepted that women could and did enjoy coitus. Even so, they were not credited with having an independent capacity for orgasm. This was something a man did for a woman; her pleasure was within his gift.

Western society has now arrived at the concept that sex is something men and women do together and that both are responsible for their own and each other's pleasure. Today a man must restrain his own orgasm until he can be sure of satisfying his partner as well. But it is just as logical to ask a women to speed up as to ask a man to slow down. The perceived importance of simultaneous orgasm is the direct result of social pressures towards equality of the sexes.

This new mutual responsibility is not universally accepted or welcome. It has created higher expectations, a felt obligation to be sexually adept, a demoralizing perception of 'failure' on the part of one or both partners if sex is not a delightful experience. The issues are those of symbolism and egotism. For some partners there is a shared sense of pride and pleasure, for those less lucky a feeling of inadequacy or disappointment: 'Am I doing something wrong or is he/she?'

If a couple reaches the stage where coitus becomes a prolonged struggle for the impossible, it may be better to abandon the goal of orgasm together in favour of orgasm separately. Oral sex or mutual masturbation may bring the long awaited reward, even though the symbolism of coitus is lost. The very fact

At the moment of climax virtually all bodily processes cease, except for the convulsions of orgasm itself. Loss of awareness at this time the French call la petit mort*, the little death.*

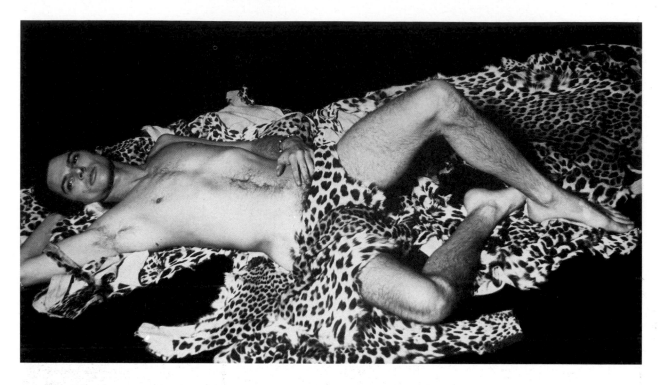

The fantasy Tarzan of a would-be Jane? For both sexes fantasy can give a powerful push towards orgasm.

of knowing that there are various stages in the sexual response cycle and that each individual may variably prefer any phase opens up the possibility of more leisurely, less perform-ance-oriented sex play. When a sufficient level of excitement has been built up through oral sex or mutual masturbation, coitus can be resumed, or if desired bypassed altogether. The enjoyment of travelling can surpass the pleasure of arrival.

Different kinds of orgasm?

Is there a difference between so-called vaginal, clitoral and total orgasm? The answer to this very much depends on whom you ask. One seldom hears the question: is there a difference between a penile and a scrotal orgasm? What this reflects is a greater variety in the climax responses of women. What really matters is that sexual partners should communicate their desires and pleasures so that peak moments, however achieved, should not remain elusive.

The original distinction between clitoral and vaginal orgasm came from Freud. He thought that as a woman matures psychosex-ually she shifts her attention from the clitoris, typically stimulated by masturbation, to the vagina, stimulated by coitus. There is little support today for the idea that one type of orgasm is more 'mature' than another.

However, many experts argue that, yes, there are differences in the source and quality of orgasms in women. Others say, no, the phy-siological response is the same no matter how the orgasm comes about, by clitoral or vaginal stimulation, or from more subtle personal preferences based on other erogenous zones. Lately there has been discussion of a total, or blended, orgasm, involving sensation not only in the clitoris and the vagina but in the uterus as well.

Shere Hite reported that 70 per cent of the 3000 women she surveyed did not regularly reach orgasm as a result of intercourse. A large majority of these women said that they reached orgasm much more reliably through masturbation than through coitus. Hite's comment was:

An unrealistic expectation has placed a great burden on women (and men) . . . Women are not dependent on men to have orgasms, yet in sex they are taught to act as if they are. Why is there such a stigma on masturbation? . . . Why shouldn't women give themselves orgasms while their partners are cooperating by kissing them, etc? I am advocating that women take power over their own bodies and their own sexual lives.

Obviously the psychological component of

orgasm is important because it influences how physiological events are felt and valued. For example, if a woman knows that masturbation is a more reliable means of reaching orgasm she may find difficulty climaxing during coitus. There may well be different kinds of orgasm available to women, but if a woman believes that one is more significant or satisfying than another, her subjective assessment of the physical experience will be different. Many people, men as well as women, do indeed say that orgasms brought on by coitus, masturbation, or oral–genital activities feel different. But one can feel great psychological satisfaction whether orgasm occurs or not. Vice versa, physical satisfaction is no guarantee of emotional satisfaction.

Orgasms during sleep are much more common in males than females, typically starting in puberty and most frequent during adolescence. They may continue for many years into adulthood. Generally 'wet dreams' – ejaculation occurring, with orgasm, during dreaming sleep – are more common in single men; that is they seem to be related to a man's general level of sexual activity. Even so, about one in two married men say they have wet dreams. Usually these cease when a man reached his fifties. Women can also have nocturnal orgasms, with profuse sweating of the vagina.

Periods of arousal in sleep usually occur during rapid eye movement or REM sleep, which coincides with periods of dreaming. Even if arousal does not end in orgasm, which it often does not, erection and vaginal wetting take place. The content of the dreams that accompany nocturnal arousal is usually erotic.

A futuristic version of the macho caveman/ cavewoman fantasy?

Growing older

What happens to sexual response as people age? Almost every mental and physical aspect of each phase of the sexual response cycle changes with age. The changes are slow and subtle, and vary according to the constitution, health and mental outlook of the person concerned. With a receptive and active sexual partner the changes will probably be slower. If sexual opportunities are infrequent they may be quicker.

Until quite recently it was 'common knowledge' that women past the menopause and men over 50 lost interest in sex. This reflected the convention that tied sex to child-bearing capacity. Until the 1960s sex in later life was a subject for ridicule, carrying the image of the dirty old man and the frustrated old woman. Somehow the idea of senior citizens indulging in sex damaged the dignity that the elderly are supposed to have. Also the young are often reluctant to see their parents or grandparents as sexual beings: 'My mother wouldn't do that! And certainly not my grandma.'

Fortunately, as discussion of sexual topics became freer during the 1960s, the assumption that old age is non-sexual or neuter was found to be a myth. Many researchers reported that while ageing was accompanied by a general decline in frequency of sexual activities, much depended on previous experience, present attitudes and aspirations for the future. One group of researchers found that 15 per cent of those in their study actually increased their sexual activity as they aged. It seems, in general, that those who arrive early at the party stay late, and those who come late leave early!

Age-related changes seem mainly to affect the timing and strength of physical responses. In men, as the years advance, erection is slower, coitus less urgent, and orgasm delayed. This more leisurely pace is sometimes seen as an advantage. Each phase and mechanism in the sexual response changes at its own rate. The intensity of orgasm is first to weaken and if one lives long enough it will fade completely. Erectile ability is next to decline. In some men all physical responses cease for days at a time, as if in an extended refractory period. The ability to be mentally aroused lasts longest.

Unfortunately, women have to contend with more physical changes as they age than men. This is largely due to the rapid decrease in female hormones at the menopause, between the ages of 45 and 55. This can cause loss of the firm fat pads on the pubis, hips and breasts, thinning and loss of suppleness of the walls of the vagina, and less copious vaginal lubrication. The latter does not necessarily reflect lack of sexual interest. The discomfort of dryness can always be solved by using a lubricating gel. Vaginal wetting can also decrease as the result of infection or certain drugs. Arousal

In how many older men is there a younger man who still longs to get out?

*'Trade's good this year'.
Marriage seems to be good
for most people. In the
West married individuals
live eight to ten years
longer than single
individuals.*

and orgasm develop more slowly and occur less often. Again, this is not a sign of indifference or inadequacy. On the plus side, relief from the burdens of work, family and home-keeping can even stimulate renewed sexual interest in late middle age.

Partners who face ageing realistically and adjust accordingly find no diminished pleasure in sex. They are free of the fear of pregnancy, have more time and more privacy than when they were young, and do not expect grand prix performance, all of which make for greater relaxation, tenderness, considerateness and pleasure in all forms of sex play and close body contact.

There are many ways to enjoy a partner's body, pleasure oneself and bring both to peak sensation. As both heterosexual and homosexual couples prove, a penis fits in places other than the vagina and is not needed for stimulation of the clitoris. For many couples non-coital techniques – oral–genital sex, simultaneous or not, for example – become those most preferred. It is also true that sexual pleasures are heavily dependent on past experiences and fantasies, that is on the organ that lies between our ears, not between our legs. It is the total person, and not the genitals alone, that makes sexual response meaningful and special □.

6

Growing up

The declaration 'It's a boy!' or 'It's a girl!' is the first public acknowledgement of a process of sexual development that starts at conception and affects the individual for the rest of his or her life.

From birth every child progresses through cultural and sexual training to a maturation at once predictable and unique. It is predictable to the extent that every child is a product of the forces of family, peers, culture and biology, yet unique in that these forces are variable in their strength and sometimes conflicting. In open societies many different sex and gender roles, and many modes of erotic expression, are possible. With love, support and guidance most boys and girls grow up to be self-accepting adults able to meet the demands of a complex society. Yet many families, societies or institutions do not allow free choice and stifle individual expression. 'Deviance' may be severely repressed rather than understood and accepted as 'variation'.

As adults we can look back through old photographs, remember childhood friends and games, and see the gradual development of our physical selves. It may be more difficult to recall childhood feelings or the many questions that occurred to us as we grew up. And perhaps we never were aware of some of the vital factors that gave us our sexual identity.

After all sexual development begins long before birth, and it is during gestation that some of the most critical forces make their play.

Inside the womb

Sex is determined at fertilization. The union of sperm and egg not only stamps the future individual as male (one Y and one X chromosome) or female (two X chromosomes), but endows him or her with twenty-two other pairs of chromosomes containing half a million genes that will, like a computer program, influence the unfolding, maturation and even the ageing of that individual.

Both male and female embryos appear similar until about the seventh intra-uterine week. Then a series of dramatic events takes place. Between the seventh and twelfth weeks the embryo becomes a foetus, with visible and increasingly distinctive male or female characteristics. Internally a set of testes and male organs, or ovaries, uterus and associated female organs, develop; externally these are matched by a penis and scrotum or a clitoris and labia.

These changes are brought about by the organizing influence of hormones released from the gonads of the foetus. If the foetus is male, the gonads release androgens, male-fostering substances. An absence of

Right *The behaviour of boys and girls begins to be different at quite an early age. Girls' play is nearly always cooperative and other-centred, whereas boys' is nearly always combative and self-centred. As one psychologist put it: 'When boys and girls build make-believe castles, girls build them to entertain their friends in, boys build them to keep their enemies out.'*

androgens, rather than the presence of female hormones, at this critical period will set the foetus on the road to development as a female. The female gonads do not produce oestrogens at this stage so are not comparably involved in the differentiation process. This implies that the foetus is basically female unless the presence of androgens determines otherwise. Regardless of chromosomal sex, a foetus will develop as a female if gonads are absent or if they do not produce adequate androgens, or if, by some biological quirk, it does not respond properly to androgens. In real life it seems that Adam is created from Eve, rather than vice versa.

Sex hormones are known to have a dual ability. They bring about the foetal changes I have just described and later the changes that mark puberty. But they also sensitize the individual to future sex-linked influences, organizing his or her body so that it is receptive to them. Sensitization occurs most notably in the womb. During gestation androgens make the foetus responsive to adult beard growth and muscle development, and their absence makes the foetus responsive to breast enlargement by oestrogens; at the same time females are given the pattern of the later reproductive cycle (males do not develop such a cycle).

Hormone influences during gestation also affect future responses to erotic stimuli and bias the way the individual will interact with social experience and the way in which sexual behaviour will manifest itself. That is not to say that behaviour is preordained, merely that certain avenues of development are made less or more likely at this time. The opening or closing of these avenues is closely related to future measures of masculinity or femininity.

Experiments with monkeys have shown that females given androgens at critical periods in their gestation show more masculine behaviour as juveniles and adults than their untreated sisters. They more often engage in rough and tumble and mounting displays. Among rat embryos, females nestled like peas in a pod between male embryos and therefore exposed to higher than normal androgen levels behave more like males than females when they reach adulthood. Females surrounded in the womb by other females show more female-like traits and fewer male-like traits when mature.

In humans, females exposed prenatally to

male hormones (this can happen if their own or their mother's adrenal glands produce too much androgen, and for other reasons) are usually tomboyish. No matter how they are brought up they show marked preferences for typical male careers and aspirations. They, more than the average female, enjoy working outdoors or at physically demanding jobs, and rarely look forward to having many children. Human males, if deprived of a normal prenatal androgen supply, are also significantly different from their peers in adolescence and adulthood; they tend to be less physically and sexually aggressive and are likely to be assessed as effeminate.

In humans all major visible changes in the genitals have occurred by the fourth foetal month. The remainder of gestation is essentially taken up with overall growth.

The roots of sexuality

Photographs and sound 'pictures' taken within the uterus show that male foetuses have regular and repeated erections; it is assumed that females have the capacity for vaginal lubrication. Certainly both erection and lubrication are known capabilities from birth on, and frequently occur spontaneously. This does not imply that infants are erotic in the same ways that adults are, only that the physiological mechanisms that are part of adult sexual expression can exist at birth.

How these capacities are influenced and how sexual behaviour is shaped is a matter of passionate scientific and political debate. Many people think that sexual behaviour can

or should be carefully shaped and controlled; others believe it is already subject to too many controls, many of them imposed for no better reason than that they are traditional or just socially convenient.

Each individual, as he or she grows up, responds to a myriad of interacting biological, cultural and social factors. This interaction leads to immense variety, in attitudes and behaviour. However, the individual will always be biased towards a particular sex because of the genetic and hormonal influences that operate before birth and continue operating until death; and the individual's sexuality will also be biased by the sexual mores of the environment he or she grows up in. In Western society, for example, a boy who shows traits generally regarded as feminine is likely to be the target of more criticism and ridicule than a girl who acts like a tomboy. Yet in some societies, among certain American Indian tribes for example, effeminacy in a man is taken to be a sign of extraordinary powers.

Growing up sexually involves more than physical development. In the fullest sense it means evolving as a socially functioning man or woman. The fact that identical twins have much in common physically and mentally even when brought up separately is often cited as evidence that maturation proceeds largely in accordance with biology. Others believe that sexual development proceeds largely in accordance with social forces, with children naturally assimilating the characteristics and attitudes of their elders and peers. Both points of view are correct up to a point, but it is not

Left I'm having a tantrum so give me what I want! Growing up is an emotion-filled process. Children of both sexes seek attention through tantrums but society expects girls to display emotion, boys to conceal it.

Developing sharing skills?

really a question of nature or nurture. To look most meaningfully at physical, socio-sexual and erotic development, and the development of sexual identity, we must recognize that innate factors and learned factors operate simultaneously and interdependently.

Imagine for a moment that you are a pediatric surgeon and you are presented with a newborn baby in whom the genitals are quite ambiguous – no vagina or penis, or apparently both. How would you decide which sex to assign to the child? Should the child be brought up as a boy or as a girl? Or suppose a 4-year-old boy came into the emergency ward with his penis completely cut off because of an attack by a deranged adult or an accident in play. Would you decide that growing up without a penis would be so difficult that it would be better to bring him up as a girl and give him appropriate surgical and hormone

treatment? Or would you consider his four years of life as a boy the most crucial factor, in which case it might be better to help him adjust to the loss of his penis? Such cases are not exactly common but they represent the kind of problem a surgeon in a large hospital might have to deal with several times a year, and they force one to carefully consider what the major influences on sexual development are. Of course a newborn child is not the same as a 4-year-old with several years of training, habit and social acceptance as a boy behind him. But in both cases the surgeon or physician, in consultation with the parents, would have to decide how crucial the appearance and functional ability of the genitals are for satisfactory sexual development, and what further internal and external developments are likely to occur with puberty.

In surgical terms, it is easier to fashion a functional vagina and female genitals than to structure a functional penis. So to some extent anatomy is used to determine whether the infant is assigned as a boy or a girl. This is the simplest, but not always the best course. However there have been cases of infants having female internal organs but externally appearing more male than female. If these children are reared as boys, physiological and psychological problems appear at puberty when secondary female characteristics – periods for example – declare themselves. The reverse situation, where the internal organs are male and the infant is raised as a girl because the genitals are ambiguous or female-like also has its problems.

The male and female brain

Some thirty years ago most American psychologists believed that infants were sexually neutral at birth and could be conditioned to behave as male or female, if necessary in conflict with biology and anatomy. It was also thought that the experience of the first three or four years of life set an ineradicable pattern. This view, proposed in the 1950s, has now been modified to incorporate a substantial degree of biological predisposition.

No human being is neutral and without sexual direction at birth. There is no evidence that one can take an individual who is unequivocally male at birth, bring him up as a female and produce someone who as an adult behaves like a woman. Nor is there any evidence for the converse, bringing up a female to

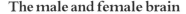

Sexual curiosity is as natural among children as any other sort of curiosity.

behave like a man. I would hypothesize that there are, from conception onwards, chromosomal and endocrine influences on the nervous system that will manifest themselves however the individual is reared. I suspect it has something to do with the differential development of the two hemispheres of the brain, and the critical timing of this development.

Each of us has a left side of the brain which is verbal, rational and concerned with imposing order on experiences, and a right side which is more concerned with emotions and impressions. In most of us both sides work in synchrony, but there is also clinical evidence that male and female use different parts of the brain for various functions. On the grounds that most males in most societies show be-

haviour rather more obviously associated with the left side of the brain than the right, one can hypothesize that in XY individuals (males) the left side is imbued with an essential 'maleness', albeit in primitive form. The lessons learned in childhood resonate with this basic predisposition and the individual develops as male. Similarly in a female the right side of the brain may carry a primitive 'femaleness'; this too would be developed by upbringing. Most of us develop comfortably using both sides of our brain, utilizing or ignoring parts of our sexual inheritance according to our life experiences.

The conflict that occurs in transsexuals – who are convinced that they are trapped inside a body of the wrong sex – may be due to a conflict between the left and right sides of the brain, one side agreeing with genital anatomy, the other with that part of the nervous system responsible for sexual identity. This mismatch might occur if the timing of biological, neurological or endocrine development was out of phase at a crucial early stage.

Sexuality in infants and children

It is conventional wisdom, but wrong, that infants and children are asexual unless given encouragement by adults. They have a sexuality that is quite independent of adults. Only recently have researchers begun to explore the subject, and a lot of embarrassment still attaches to it. It is significant, for example, that Freud was castigated more for his courageous attempts to understand childhood sexuality than for any other facet of his work.

Genital and erotic behaviour on the part of infants and children is not allowed in most Western homes, and so it becomes private, secret, hidden and undiscussed. By word and deed children learn that such activities, going to the toilet for example, are to be concealed. Discussion of them is limited, evasive and privileged. Games like 'Mummies and Daddies' or 'You show me yours, I'll show you mine' are played in secret. Like the bulk of the iceberg, direct sexual expression exists with great strength and substance beneath the surface of accepted behaviours.

In the United States, Alfred Kinsey and his colleagues recorded what is widely accepted as the most complete set of data prior to 1950 concerning normal sexual behaviour. These records, and some more recent reports from the United States and from Norwegian, English and Israeli scientists, show that sexual expression by pre-pubertal children in modern industrial societies is common, despite sanctions against such behaviour. From early childhood to puberty, sexual activity is largely clandestine.

Pre-school children spontaneously show interest in their own genitals. They study, fondle and exhibit them and seem to get pleasure from playing with themselves. Among both sexes the penis seems to attract more attention than the vulva, perhaps because it is more visible. Playing tricks with a penis, such as getting it to erect, or urinating at targets, is seen as good fun. The penis is usually named ('wee-wee', 'willy', 'peter') but the vulva or vagina is simply referred to as 'down there'; nevertheless the vagina is a

Top *Maternal instincts at the bottom of the garden?*

Left *Catching up on vital reading. A near perfect imitation of adult bathroom habits.*

source of wonder as a place to stick things in and the area of the vulva is marvelled at as the magic fount of a flow of urine.

Despite the obvious physicality of a boy's penis, it is girls more often than boys who first investigate their genitals and spontaneously learn to masturbate. As children grow older the frequency and duration of such activity increases. At puberty boys learn about masturbation from their peers and more than nine out of ten have started to masturbate as they enter adolescence. No group of females in Western studies has shown such a high occurrence of masturbation.

Masturbation to orgasm is rarely reported in the first years of life but genital play, obviously pleasurable, starts between 6 and 12 months of age in both boys and girls. By kindergarten age masturbation for its own pleasure is not uncommon and is occasionally taken to orgasm.

One observant mother who frequently noticed her 3-year-old masturbating recorded:

> *Lying face down on the bed, with her knees drawn up, she started rhythmic pelvic thrusts, about one second or less apart. The thrusts were primarily pelvic, with the legs tensed . . . in a smooth and perfect rhythm which was unbroken except for momentary pauses during which the genitalia were readjusted against the doll on which they were pressed . . . There were 44 thrusts in unbroken rhythm, a slight momentary pause . . . then 10 thrusts, and then a cessation of all movement. There was marked concentration and intense breathing with abrupt jerks as orgasm approached. She was completely oblivious to everything . . . There was noticeable relief and relaxation after orgasm.*

Pelvic thrusting accompanies many instances of infant play and affection. Mutual kissing, cuddling and stroking is common. Individual involvement is of course highly variable. Some children are quite active sexually, others much less so, depending on the interacting forces of natural bias, genital sensitivity and parental attitudes.

In the industrial societies of the West there are marked class differences in the way parents seem to deal with masturbation, working class or blue-collar parents being the most conservative. In general, in North America, Scandinavia and Western Europe, it is becoming less common for middle or upper class parents to be upset by the fact that their child masturbates. Perhaps with some ambivalence, they are most likely to direct the child not to play with himself or herself in public.

A wealth of data reveals that romantic attachments occur before the age of six. Coitus is rare but coital play and mutual masturbation occur as part of many children's games, whether among children of the same or opposite sex. The scope and likelihood of all these behaviours increase as children approach puberty. Whether these activities are spontaneous experiments or attempts to copy adult models is not clear. Nor is it known to what degree children's erotic sensations and experiences are comparable with adults'!

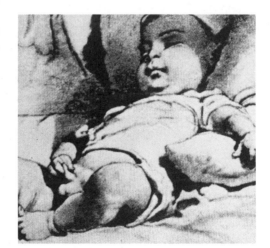

Fingers, toes and ears get played with, and so do genitals, by both boys and girls. Drawing by Mihaly Zichy.

Below *Spontaneous nuzzling or imitation of adult behaviour?*

Encouraging and discouraging sex play in children

In some cultures social traditions have evolved that explicitly encourage the capacity of young children for sexual expression. The Muria, a non-Hindu tribal people of Central India, build *ghotuls*, sacred compounds in which toddlers and young children can become accustomed to social interaction. Sexual expression is not only allowed, it is expected. Boys and girls usually lose their virginity by the age of six, and certainly by eight. In some *ghotuls* children are arbitrarily paired off with many different partners to widen their sexual experience. Sexual involvement is not forced as part of an initiation rite, as it is in some other societies; rather it is seen as a natural unfolding of curiosity and learning.

The *ghotul* is not a form of marriage bureau. In fact marriage to a preferred *ghotul* partner is quite rare. As is common practice in India, marriages are arranged to suit parental and family considerations. Among the Muria the concept of promiscuity does not exist and premarital pregnancy is rare, probably due to adolescent infertility (see page 108) and to early marriage. The Muria simply recognize that children are sexual beings and, in common with the large majority of non-industrial cultures, put sexual expression in its place as a natural and integral part of childhood. Nevertheless it is thought socially desirable that sexual experience and proficiency should be encouraged. It is not known to what extent these practices survive among the Muria.

However, the Muria are not unique in their permissiveness. Indeed cultures more permissive than our own are in the majority around the world, although their practices differ. Among the Chewa of Africa, children build huts outside the village where they play house. This includes the exchange of sexual partners, and all such activities have parental approval. The Ila-speaking people of Zimbabwe give their young daughters small houses where they are encouraged and expected to entertain boys. The Ifugoro of the Philippines have dormitories for the unmarried, and frequent swapping of sex partners is encouraged.

Perhaps the sharpest contrast to present-day customs in industrial societies is that provided by cultures such as the Lepcha of the Himalayas and the pre-missionary Polynesian cultures of the Trobiand Islands, Mangai and Hawaii, in which adults instructed children in erotic and genital play and occasionally took part as well. This was done openly and with the full approval of all concerned and did not appear to have any negative effects. Educating children even in most intimate details of sex was considered a responsibility and a duty, not something to be left to chance, and sexual training was given to both boys and girls at all social levels.

Since the early part of this century, and the restrictive influences of missionaries and of white men's laws, some of these naturally permissive cultures have moderated their sexual practices, though remnants of former attitudes still persist.

Western societies, with the possible exception of Scandinavia, are among the world's more restrictive cultures. Eroticism and sexual expression among children are not sup-

In the southern highlands of Papua New Guinea girls and women – and pigs – live apart from men and boys in special meri *houses. There is no deliberate mixing of boys and girls as there is among the Murias.*

posed to exist, though everyone knows that they do. Any display of junior sexuality is looked on as deviant, shameful, even sinful. In the West our fear of social disapproval, and perhaps of punishment in a life hereafter, has been manipulated to prevent undesirable sexual behaviours. This repression is still dramatically apparent in some countries, in Ireland for example, where the injunctions of the Roman

The modern dilemma: how to help a child acquire a strong sense of being female or male without holding up undesirable stereotype models of what it is to be a woman or a man. By the age of four most American children have watched 3000 hours of television and imbibed the message that men are tough guys and women need lots of shampoo to look pretty. Is it good for all girls to look forward to pregnancy?

Catholic Church maintain a great deal of force. Only a decade ago an anthropologist studying an Irish island community he called Inis Baeg reported that the island's priests threatened to put a curse on sexual wrong-doers and encouraged their parishioners to inform on each other.

In some societies corporal and even capital punishment is used to keep sexual behaviour under control. In Islamic countries such as Saudi Arabia flogging is not uncommon for even minor infringements of sexual conventions. Marriage without a father's permission may merit decapitation. Even kissing in public between husband and wife may be considered offensive; foreign television programmes are 'cleaned up' accordingly. Let us remember, however, that even in Europe sexual be-

haviour was once controlled by capital punishment. In the Middle Ages adultery and prostitution were occasionally punished by burning at the stake. Even today, in some European countries, one can be imprisoned for foul language, indecency and soliciting.

Sexual activities between adults and children are considered particularly repellent among most restrictive societies. In the United States anyone convicted of sexual activities involving children, whether they were enjoyed by both parties or instigated by the child, is almost automatically labelled a 'child molester'. Not only are such people given long prison sentences; they also spend most of their time in prison fearful of reprisals from other inmates and extra harassment from prison officials.

Some identification with the same-sex parent is inevitable, but perhaps familiarity with the birth process is more important, for boys as well as girls, than picking up tips about pipe-smoking.

Male and female: inner conviction and outward expression

Depending upon the circumstances and the attitude of parents, a child's emerging sexuality may be seen as cute and appropriate or disgusting and threatening. Certain behaviours will be reinforced, others ignored or punished. Certain aspects of sexuality may become dormant or increasingly expressed, again depending upon the extent to which they are encouraged or discouraged. Children whose sexual explorations are severely censored are more likely to become emotionally impoverished adults, handicapped in their general as well as their sexual relationships.

As outward sexual behaviour develops, private and personal aspects of sexuality also form. Between the age of two and six a child begins to express an inner awareness of being male or female: 'I'm a boy and I'm going to be like Daddy', or 'I'm a girl and I want to be like Mummy.' With or without parental encouragement, most children become very interested in exploring adult roles and activities. Games such as dressing up or playing Mummies and Daddies are routine. So is question-asking unless positively discouraged. Parents and society recognize that children need to ask questions, even if some are awkward to answer. Competing with or reinforcing these influences are children's personal experiences, their observations of the behaviour of peers, parents and others.

As the individual matures he or she gradually becomes aware of how well or poorly he or she measures up to social expectations. But a child's sense of discomfort with the gender role imposed by society has to be most acute before it is expressed openly. As far as possible he or she tries hard to please, and strives to reconcile his or her feelings with the actual situation. This is the time of life when 'modelling' is particularly noticeable. Boys want to do what their fathers do; girls want to be like their mothers. Parents tend to keep their children close to them and are fairly direct in their instruction.

While not necessarily expressed in behaviour until after puberty, a general sexual preference, an orientation towards males or females, also emerges around the age of five, six or seven. Adult male gays often recall being strongly attracted to other boys at around this age. And it is often during these early years that many people become aware of other types of sexual urge that fit or do not fit in with cultural expectations. Expression of these urges depends on whether society permits or represses them.

Many forces are involved in the development of sexual identity and orientation. While genital activity is usually private, even if it is controlled by explicit or implied influences, sexual identity and orientation are definitely publicly fostered. Our sex and our sexual identity are biologically biased. But our gender identity – how well we see ourselves fitting in with society's expectations – is not. These derive from our interactions with our social environment.

Not everybody develops in the way parents and society expect. This engenders argument as to whose 'fault' it is. Charges of right and wrong contaminate activities that might, in other societies, merely be seen as acceptable variations. In the West parents and society are never neutral in regard to the sexual development of children, and most of this anxiety focuses on homosexual activity in boys and heterosexual activity in girls. Our value system says that boys should not grow up desiring sexual relations with men and that girls should not desire men too early.

By the age of three, most children express a conviction of sexual identity which coincides with biological reality. The social pressures reinforcing such convictions are immense. Every language has separate male and female grammatical conventions and many have separate vocabularies. For example, a Japanese man would use the word *boku* for 'I' but a woman would use *watakushi*; other words a man would use would also be more assertive and direct than a woman's. In many Thai expressions women and men use different suffixes, the women's always more polite. This convention of feminine politeness and masculine directness is almost, if not completely, universal, and is of course fostered where there is also segregation at school, at work and in other areas of everyday life.

In most cultures, the clothing worn by boys and girls differs from infancy onwards. The pink and blue colour convention in the West is well known, as is the rigid distinction that only girls wear skirts. Codes of dress at school and work, and uniforms of all kinds, reinforce these stereotypes.

In almost all cultures expectations for boys and girls are different. Boys are expected to be

rough and tough, girls to be gentle and sweet. Traditionally boys are expected to be seekers and doers while girls are expected to be sought and have things done for them. Males are supposed to be aggressive and assertive, females passive and pacific. While there are cultural variations, these are the expectations that reign in the majority of societies studied probably because they are biologically biased.

As children grow up they learn which behaviours are appropriate and inappropriate for their sex. The term appropriate here does not mean desirable or best, but socially anticipated. Although one hears a lot about social expectations and gender roles changing, the changes may be more wished for than real. To quote just one study carried out in California in 1982: 'Despite current presumptions of equality, boys and girls at sixth grade levels still live in totally different worlds, with the classroom and television their only common experience.'

Very élite, very grown up, but still at school. Lengthy education and delayed responsibility do not guarantee happiness or sexual competence.

However the divergent development of boys and girls comes about, it is a fact that by puberty individuals of both sexes are strongly aware of their sexual identity, aware of the behaviours expected of them, and aware of their preferences for relationships with the opposite or same sex. The experiences of puberty and adolescence will strongly influence how these feelings are expressed.

Puberty and adolescence

Both puberty and adolescence refer to extended periods of time rather than to abrupt changes. Puberty is a three- to five-year span between the ages of 9 and 13 in girls and 10 and 15 in boys. During this period the mechanisms created during gestation are activated towards adult functioning. This is most notable in the workings of the genitals and in sexual behaviour. During these years a constellation of biological processes occurs, usually culminating in reproductive capacity, symbolized by menstruation in girls and ejaculation in boys. While the biological events of puberty are more or less the same for youngsters all over the world, the cultural events that mark puberty vary enormously. Some societies go

in for dramatic initiation rites for one or both sexes. Others, at least on the surface, make very little fuss. For some youngsters puberty may come as a traumatic shock; among the Haviks of India or the Irish of 'Inis Beag', for example, girls do not learn of menstruation until they start to bleed.

Adolescence is the transition phase between childhood and adulthood. In some societies, in the United States and Europe for example, the transition is protracted. Typically it extends over five years or so, during which the individual acquires the kind of education, training and social experiences that will equip him or her for economic and social independence. In other societies the transition is early and abrupt and the demands of adulthood immediate. In many marriage at puberty is the custom – Mahatma Gandhi was married at twelve. The rigours and hardships of living north of the Arctic Circle or in the Amazonian jungle or the Sahara desert make it necessary for children to assume adult roles and tasks as quickly as possible. Even so, it is only during the last century or so that the luxury of a long adolescence has become the norm in the industrialized West.

Below *For these African children adolescence is short. The little girl is Masai; at four years old she is already responsible for a baby brother. The boys are Samburu; they start herding cows and goats at the age of six or seven.*

Physical signs of puberty

Puberty first declares itself as disproportionate growth in various parts of the body. Feet usually start to grow before legs, for instance. About two years later – around the age of 12 in girls and 14 in boys – there is a very noticeable gain in height. Temporarily girls may be taller than their male age mates. This gangling and uneven growth is transitory, but it can lead to lasting sensitivity about looks.

In girls the earliest signs of puberty are changes in body shape. These occur between the ages of eight and ten. The hips begin to widen and fat deposits soften the skin and round out the body. These events are mainly the result of increased oestrogen secreted by the adrenal glands and maturing ovaries. Oestrogen catalyses the growth of other secondary characteristics such as breasts and pubic hair. The onset of breast development is termed telarche. A year or two later, when the breasts are well shaped and pubic hair is more plentiful, menarche or the onset of the menstrual cycle occurs. Menarche is brought on by the interplay of several different hormones – hormones from the hypothalamus and pituitary in the brain interact with those produced by the ovaries and these in turn interact with the lining of the uterus (endometrium). Ovulation does not occur regularly until all these hormones and organs have orchestrated themselves properly. Until they have, conception and pregnancy are unlikely. The onset of menstruation does not necessarily indicate readiness for childbearing, as is sometimes believed.

Among some groups, adolescent sterility lasts for a year or longer. Early menstrual patterns may be highly irregular and there is no sure, simple way of telling whether a girl is ovulating. Adolescent sterility accounts for the low pregnancy rate among young girls in many sexually permissive societies. Thus one study in Mangai found that only 3 out of 29 women between the ages of 14 and 20 had conceived, despite frequent coitus from prepuberty onwards. In the West adolescent sterility appears to be a relatively brief phenomenon lasting only several months to a year. It cannot

This gorgeous head-dress, from Bali, is worn as part of purification rites after a girl's first menstruation.

Left *Bedboard from a hut in which girls of the Bajokwe tribe (Zaire) are kept in isolation during puberty rites.*

be relied on as an alternative to effective contraception.

Growth of the testes, scrotum and penis is one of the first physical signs of sexual development in boys. Growth begins at around the age of 10 or 11 and the genitals reach nearly full size by about the age of 15 but a great deal of individual variation exists. As the testes grow the production of male hormones, mainly testosterone, increases. As in the female, hormones activate and fuel most of the changes associated with development of male secondary characteristics – increase in penis size, growth of pubic and underarm (axillary) hair and, later, growth of hair on the chest and other body parts, enlargement of the larynx and deepening of the voice.

Spermarche, the first appearance of sperm in ejaculated fluid, is analogous with menarche. The ability to ejaculate does not mean that a boy is fertile. Unlike ovulation, sperm production is continuous until the seventh decade of life and beyond. A brief period of adolescent sterility is also apparent in males. In the Mangaian study, for example, none of the boys among the thirty sexually active adolescent males was a father.

At puberty masturbating behaviour and wet dreams become increasingly common. Girls also have orgastic dreams, with more vaginal sweating than usual, but apparently less frequently than boys.

These obvious physical charges in both sexes are accompanied by a prodigious increase in physical activity, energy, appetite and social interactions. This is most noticeable in boys where there is a clear match between physical and social changes; the correlation of testosterone production with erotic activities is dramatic and well established. In girls the transition is more gradual.

Wish I was really as big as I look!

Growing towards self-reliance

Socially and sexually, puberty and adolescence are periods of uncertainty, introspection, experimentation and testing limits. There is a subtle but marked shift away from reliance on the family for support and encouragement. Peer pressures are more strongly felt; it becomes highly important to be 'one of the gang', to be accepted and desired as a friend and sexual companion. Charismatic age mates and other admired figures attract more attention and loyalty than parents or family. The goal of all these behaviours is the development of individual competence and self-reliance.

Adolescence is a transition, often stormy and emotionally trying, from insecurity to self-assuredness. Unfortunately, for many people, the insecurities that develop during puberty persist into adulthood, even though the causes may no longer exist and may have been forgotten. It is not uncommon, for example, for boys who are slow growers or girls who sprout like beanpoles to remain self-conscious of their size even when they are adult and quite within normal adult ranges.

Ritual tests

Puberty is also a time of social testing. The individual is formally or informally put on trial to show that he or she is ready to meet the obligations expected of adults. In societies that have very formal trials – such as circumcision (male or female), certain rituals of dress and behaviour, or tests of skill or daring – the individual emerges from them with his or her merit and self-worth publicly affirmed. Certainly any boy who for any reason land dives from an 80 ft tower bound only by the ankles to overhanging liana vines, as is the custom in the New Hebrides, gains my admiration for courage, as does any girl who undergoes scarification or ritual marking of the skin.

In Western societies the trial may take the form of passing crucial school exams, completing a *bar* or *bat mitzvah*, earning merit badges or other symbols of accomplishment such as a driving licence, reaching voting or drinking age, or being drafted into military service. Even without such outward and visible signs of maturity, many adolescents feel driven to prove their worth to themselves and to a circle of intimates. The result may be some extraordinarily positive accomplishment, or utterly destructive and disruptive. Sexual experimentation leading to pregnancy and various kinds of criminal or antisocial behaviour may, at a deeper level, be a bid for autonomy, a cry for recognition. And whether they realize it or not most prospective sons- and daughters-in-law are put through a probationary period, often beginning with the traditional and sometimes awesome invitation to dinner 'to meet the family'.

Stepping up sexual activity

During puberty and adolescence, all prepubertal sexual activities increase in frequency and scope, often with a lot of boasting and encouragement from friends. For about six in ten boys masturbation becomes a fact of life by the age of 15; by the age of 20 the ratio is more like nine in ten. Initially masturbation may be done in private or in groups but eventually it becomes a solitary practice. Girls also increase their masturbatory activity but rarely to the extent of their male peers. By the age of 15 about one in three girls masturbates and, by the age of 20, six or seven in ten. It seems that masturbation in girls today is a commoner habit than it was thirty years ago but the current figures for boys are very much the same as they were thirty years ago.

Homosexual experimentation is also a feature of puberty, but more so for boys than for girls. For the large majority of teenagers homosexual experiences are transitory and never repeated. For the minority of adolescents who prefer same sex relationships the stage is set for future orientation.

Sex teaching

Sex education for children in most industrial societies consists, at best, of being told about reproduction and menstruation. This is changing but the pace is slow and the forces of conservative tradition remain strong. Sex education classes are not notable for their lucidity and they seldom teach young adults what to do in bed, how to cope with mental and physical responses to sexual activity, or how to manage sexual problems. Scandinavian countries are the exception here. The teaching of sex behaviours is part of their school curricula, and starts in kindergarten. Outside the West, in restrictive countries, sex education is even more limited, often lumped in with morality teaching, the stated or implied message being 'not until you are married' and then 'only in an approved manner'.

Right *Death-defying leaps like this divide the men from the boys in the Solomon Islands.*

Far right *The monstrous lip ornament worn by this Soya Indian boy from Brazil is less sinister than the scars on his stomach and chest. These mean that he has recently killed an enemy.*

Do-it-yourself sex education.

Early sex and late marriage

In the last few decades there has been a marked rise in sexual activity among teenagers in the West, marked that is in comparison with teenage sexual behaviour at the beginning of the nineteenth century. But that does not necessarily mean that parents and responsible adults condone such behaviour. They are more likely to resign themselves uneasily to the 'climate of the times', and accept the life-style of their children as long as it is not too far out of line with that of their peers and does not, as with pregnancy in an unmarried girl, bring disgrace on the family. Teenagers themselves are much more liberal and accepting of sexual freedom in their own behaviour and that of their peers.

Restrictive controls on children began to be relaxed during World War II. The tension of the times, the absence of strong discipline at home, changing needs and expectations all changed social habits. It became more common for both parents to work to meet economic demands. Movement away from grand-parents and the family home in order to attend school or find a job further reduced adult supervision. Religious dicta lost their restrictive power. There also began to exist the distant but ever present foreboding of a nuclear Armageddon, and of other brands of man-made eco-doom. This foreboding has replaced belief in a future Utopia, shaken faith in an afterlife. Fewer people are willing to postpone pleasure. Couple these factors with increased awareness of adult sexual behaviours, higher divorce rates, and the greater exposure of sexual topics in the media, and it is hardly surprising that adolescent sexual activity has increased. Cohabitation, with or without parental knowledge or approval, is also more common. The premarital period is also longer because people are marrying much later than in the past.

I suggest, however, that recent 'permissiveness' is not a new pressure on unwilling and unready youngsters but rather a release that enables them to follow their natural predilections with fewer inhibitions. As in so many other matters, one's assessment of the importance of such changes depends on the timeframe in which one sets them. In biblical times adolescence as we know it today did not exist. Adulthood, and with it marriage and sexual activity, arrived very soon after puberty. The time that elapsed between the emergence of sexual drives and the opportunity to satisfy them was relatively short. It remains this way in much of the Third World.

Today in the industrial world marriage, and with it overt genital expression, has been postponed until the individual is capable of making his or her way independently. Our protracted system of education and job training has delayed independence. What we are now seeing is a return to more open postpubertal sexual activities, but no longer accompanied by the custom of early marriage. The advent of modern birth control methods, the automobile, and better and more private housing, have provided the necessary technical assistance.

Unfortunately all these things have not made, nor are likely to make, the transition from adolescence to adulthood any easier for youngsters or their parents. The mores of the past are still with us, and guilt still accompanies a lot of sexual behaviour, particularly for girls and women. Nevertheless adolescent sexual activities are a necessary training ground for sophistication in forming the intimate social and psychological relationships needed in the modern adult world.

Facts and figures on teenage sex

In countries where data are available, the incidence and frequency of adolescent genital petting and coital activities have increased markedly since World War II. Virginity before marriage has lost a good deal of its mystique and value. While most premarital coitus still takes place with an intended spouse, a significant proportion of those marrying have already had a number of coital relationships. Premarital coitus is now the norm rather than the exception in the United States, Scandinavia, and continental Europe, Australia, England, Scotland, Wales and Canada. Among 18- and 19-year-olds sexual experience is more common than virginity. Few persons in Western society seem to be 'saving themselves' for marriage.

Some numbers will help to put this into perspective. One important study of young adults in England, published in 1973, reported: 'premarital sexual intercourse is now the normal pattern both for men (80 per cent) and for women (61 per cent)'. In a majority of

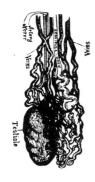

Above *The withering effects of masturbation on the male testes. Sexual misinformation like this – 'masturbation makes your testicles shrivel/makes you go blind/makes you go soft in the head' – appeared in textbooks right up until the end of the nineteenth century.*

Left *Early sexual encounters usually begin with group groping and horseplay.*

Right *More intense one-to-one relationships come later.*

these cases, the first experience was unplanned. In the United States a major survey carried out in 1979 found: 'The proportion of U.S. teenage women residing in metropolitan areas who have had premarital sexual experience rose from 30 per cent in 1971 to 43 per cent in 1976 and to 50 per cent in 1979...' In 1979 two out of every three men and women had had coitus by the age of nineteen. A small study in Stockholm carried out in 1976 reported that by the age of nineteen, 80 per cent of the boys and 89 per cent of the girls had had coital experience. In 1978 another Swedish study, done in Uppsala, found that among first year high school students (average age sixteen) almost half the girls and a third of the boys had experienced coitus. In a Canadian study of university students in 1978 premarital coitus was reported by 58 per cent of the females and 62 per cent of the males, compared with 32 per cent and 40 per cent respectively recorded in 1968.

The specific meanings of such findings depend on many social and cultural factors. For instance a 1979 study of unmarried university students in Nigeria reported that 83 per cent of the males and 56 per cent of the females claimed to have had premarital coitus; amongst married students the figures were 14 and 8 per cent respectively. The majority of those who were unmarried did not start having coitus until they were over twenty-one. Of course, premarital coitus is viewed differently in a 16-year-old and a 36-year-old. Whether in Nigeria or America a 36-year-old virgin, male or female, would be considered 'a bit odd' and parents or friends might take steps to 'remedy' the situation.

What of Eastern European countries and the Soviet Union, where sex studies are rare? It is probably fair to estimate that teenage coitus rates are not too dissimilar to those reported in America and Europe. We do know something about Czechoslovakia though. Unique in Eastern Europe, it has the excellent Sexological Institute of Charles University in Prague. One of their 1980 reports indicated that for one in two married women born in the 1950s first coitus occurred before the age of eighteen; for those born in the 1920s the first experience was after the age of nineteen.

There has definitely been an increase in teenage sex in Japan since World War II. In the seven years from 1974 to 1981, coital experience for male adolescents increased from 26 to

The search for identity, in this case social and political identity rather than sexual identity. Interestingly, punk garb is determinedly unisex though punkers never leave any doubt as to who is what.

37 per cent and for females from 11 to 28 per cent. The majority of teenagers interviewed did not see their behaviour as promiscuous, and most of the girls said they regarded intercourse as a reasonable part of a relationship; fewer boys felt this way – they focused on the sex, rather than the relationship,

Even when youngsters think themselves as devoted and well matched as Romeo and Juliet, the partner is largely a vehicle for self-discovery and exploration. 'Am I attractive?' 'Will she let me feel her breasts?' 'Will he get an erection if I kiss him? If so what do I do then?' 'Does he enjoy kissing more than I do?' 'What does coitus feel like?' For many people these are questions that recur throughout life.

Damned if you do and damned if you don't?

Exploring one's capabilities in sex, social skills, responsibility, and love all at the same time can be a formidable agenda, especially in a society where early heterosexual and homosexual relationships are officially taboo. Nevertheless one is expected to know how to manage adult relationships, including sexual ones. One is expected to acquire enough knowledge and security about one's own anatomy and physiology, and those of others, to be able to turn attention to developing full partnerships. For most people, basic sexual knowledge is not difficult to acquire; but knowing what it is one likes and values in

Right *Would the flawless sophisticates of their dreams fuss and titivate in public?*

others takes longer, and finding out how to please others takes the longest.

The pace of change today has tended to magnify intergenerational differences. Parents, counsellors and teachers are routinely caught in the bind of trying to prepare children for a future which is uncertain, unappealing or incomprehensible. Acutely aware of the procreative capacity of teenagers and the coming pressures of adult life, they often reach for the tried-and-tested recipe of social comformity rather than encourage individual expression or trial-and-error learning. Teaching children about all important feelings is difficult; it is not easy for adults to transfer the emotional wisdom gained from hard and

trying experiences. Also many parents admit that they do not know how to help their children meet the future.

In an ideal environment children would learn to satisfy their needs and expectations without provoking unnecessary hostility and adults would learn to provide support and encouragement without imposing their own prejudices and fears. Learning is necessary on both sides. Respect for one's parents' views is compatible with developing one's own sexual potential; respect for the individuality of one's children is compatible with following a lifestyle one has chosen for oneself. Parents and children, in mutual respect, can grow together □.

7

Sexual patterns

One aspect of sexwatching is so obvious that it seems almost superfluous to mention it, but not to do so would be to pass up a rich opportunity for added perspective. As we look around us we see that to a great degree males and females do different things. This is broadly true at home, at work, at play, east, west, north and south, and despite moves to enforce equality between the sexes. In primitive and developed societies, in sophisticated cities and sparsely populated rural areas men and women behave differently.

He drives the car, she packs the picnic. She washes the dishes, he dries. He plays football, she cheers from the sidelines. These are, to some people, trivial differences. But they are indicative of deeper differences that are highly significant and symbolic.

His job and her job

Men are most numerous in those occupations associated with heavy physical labour, exposure to danger, the distribution of wealth or power, and prolonged absence from home. They run governments, businesses and industries. Women predominate in those occupa-tions associated with child rearing, clerical work, personal service, in the 'caring' professions, social organization and health. In some primitive societies, the men specialize in hunting, fishing, and raiding, while the women look after the land and the livestock, and gather food. In many Third World countries, where women are held in low esteem, these generalities hold as strongly as ever except that women, as well as men, are expected to perform physically demanding and dangerous tasks as a matter of routine.

Well before puberty, in the tradition of our primate cousins, the sexes begin to play apart. Boys tend to roam further from home and form gangs or teams; girls stay closer to home in the company of two or three close friends. Aggression, physical rivalry and rough body contact are for boys; less active, less exploratory and less dangerous pursuits are for girls. There are excellent athletes of both sexes, but mostly they compete separately and with different rules.

Leaders such as Margaret Thatcher, Golda Meir and Indira Gandhi notwithstanding, in every society it is typically men who hold key positions in the political hierarchy and in every

Women's work, a New York mural.

society it is women who have the primary responsibility for domestic chores and the daily necessities of family existence. Men provide for prestigious or major acquisitions, be it a cow or a new car. Men deal with inter-tribal and international disputes and conflicts. Women fight and defend home and family when necessary but it is men who carry arms into enemy territory. Women adjudicate family squabbles and in-house disputes but men enforce state or national laws and mete out punishment. 'Just you wait until daddy comes home...' is a threat used by mothers the world over.

There never has been a race of Amazons, except in mythology, no truly matriarchal society with power and control concentrated in the hands of women. This is a matter of historical fact. That is what has been, not what might or could or should have been. Remember my third sexwatching axiom in Chapter 1?

In fact the very concept of 'roles' creates problems. It suggests that much of life is staged and played out according to the expectations of others rather than as truly felt expressions of self. We should therefore ask ourselves how much role play is intrinsic to this or that activity and how much is unconsciously copied from models. Many specifics of any role have to be learned but it is debatable which and to what degree. In all probability any role is appropriate for any individual, having due regard for his or her biological, social and psychological inheritance and for the fact that people tend to want out from roles that are unfulfilling even though they may be under powerful social and personal pressures to stay in them.

Achieved roles and given roles

Some roles are earned. One can work up from stock clerk to company president, displaying appropriate behaviour on successive rungs of the ladder. The same person acts differently and in turn is treated differently at each level. These *achieved* roles confer class or prestige. Other roles are less easily changed, because they are imposed or accepted, rather than earned, felt or desired. These are *ascribed* roles and the behaviours that constitute them are fairly rigidly stereotyped. Though true of some people in any given category, they are not true of all.

We ascribe roles to race ('Blacks excel in sport', 'Orientals are wise'), to nationality

('Germans are methodical, the French romantic, the British reserved'), to age groups ('young people are reckless', 'old people are crotchety') and most significantly to sex. 'Masculine' and 'feminine' are social and gender roles ascribed on the basis of sex.

Every individual from infancy onwards confronts the stereotype of his or her sex; if he is male he is under pressure to be masculine and boyish; if female to be feminine and girlish. In a classic experiment observers described babies dressed in blue as 'very active', and the same babies dressed in pink as 'gentle'. When the same babies wore yellow the observers were confused; many wanted to know the sex of the babies before making judgements about them! One experiment is not conclusive proof, but it does show the serious implications of conventions which may seem trivial.

If adults need external clues to make judgements (and a whole fabric of assumptions)

A vase painting of 460BC showing Amazons (beardless) fighting Greeks. Amazon means 'without breasts' – one breast was removed to allow freer handling of the bow and the sword. Perhaps the significance of the myth is that upbringing has a lot to do with danger-seeking behaviour, or that all subordinate groups dream of being dominant.

Left *Driven steed and driven rider – mud, speed and adrenaline.*

'Look baby, Daddy's making a personal appearance'.
Punch *cartoon.*

about the sex of an infant, infants themselves apparently do not, judging by a study done at Edinburgh University by T.G.R. Bower and his colleagues. In this study, Bower claims, 13-month old infants were able to tell the sex of other 13-month old infants, despite the removal of all external clues and a great swapping of clothes that had most of the adults involved completely confused as to the sex of the infants. Apparently certain movements allowed the infants to distinguish boy from girl. Male infants were more interested in other males, and females more attentive to other females.

Of course societies enshrine their gender stereotypes in many things other than dress — in different first names, different vocabularies, different education, different occupations, different leisure activities, different intellectual pursuits, different marital rights and duties, different sexual and erotic practices, even different burial rituals. Some of these differences have a strong biological rationale, others less or none at all.

Stereotypes: socially or biologically based?

How have these differences in gender roles come about? Soldiering, mining or tree felling require attributes more often possessed by

Am I a he or a she? You want a closer look? OK, here I am. Now what do you say?

In the Orient, white is worn for mourning. A Korean mother mourns after the airline disaster of September 1983. In many societies open expression of grief is a female prerogative.

men than women. And the care and nurturing of young infants requires attributes more often possessed by women than by men.

But not all behaviours have an obvious physical or biological base. Certainly many occupations, especially in a technological society, cannot be neatly segregated by sex. Any view across different cultures shows how each has various conventions concerning appropriate male and female behaviour; these are gender patterns. In one New Guinea tribe, for example, the women tend sweet potatoes and the men tend yams. It would be difficult to think of a biological reason for a convention like this.

Nowadays many people, especially women, see stereotyped occupational roles as a product of social systems engineered to keep subordinates subordinate and the dominant influential rather than as a product of biological invariants. Some patterns are decreed by civil law – in many countries soldiering is done by men only and midwifery by women only – or by ecclesiastical law – only men are admitted to the priesthood.

Dress conventions

Each culture has its own dress rules, evolved over centuries, but convention almost everywhere dictates that clothing for males and females is somehow different. Only in particular occupations where the needs of the job outweigh considerations of gender, such as in combat, heavy industry or special crafts, will men and women dress alike.

The fashion for unisex clothing in the West

has a particular bias: while women have found jeans to be comfortable and appropriate for many different occasions, men have shown little interest in adopting skirts. Even among punk rockers, where there has been a marked shift towards feminine colours and design, one seldom sees a male wearing a dress. Unisex clothing or not, there is rarely any doubt as to who is what; some aspect of sex-specific appearance is maintained, often in the form of personal decoration.

Some societies not only prescribe different dress for males and females but use clothing to distinguish children from adults and married from unmarried, divorced or widowed.

Sunday best for churchgoers in Samoa. Contemporary convention dictates that men's skirts can show more leg than women's. Before the missionaries arrived, men and women went bare-breasted and wore scant clothing. But even then men were freer to reveal more of themselves.

Italian widows wear black, Korean widows white. Personal ornaments are also used. The wedding ring is one of the most widely understood symbols of sexual status.

As far as dress is concerned, there is no obvious link with biology. Overwhelmingly it is social custom that influences the way people clothe and adorn themselves, even though the origins of a particular convention may have been forgotten. Social invention can also be credited with sex-segregated first names (why else is Bernard a boy and Eve a girl?), forms of address (Sir, Madam), and gender-based vocabulary ('*la table*' feminine, and '*le taxi*', masculine).

When one considers other patterns of sex segregation the element of social invention is still obvious but a biological link begins to intrude. In every society the concept of physical aggression as masculine and gentle nurturance as feminine, patterns that are biologically linked, organizes the broad spectrum of social conventions.

Left *Men – unless they are transvestites or entertainers – are universally reluctant to wear women's clothes. Disguise is another matter. Here, during a street demonstration in Iran, two men and their weapons hide beneath women's robes.*

Right *Men, more so than women, very early learn the knack of making themselves feel better by making others feel worse; by reducing others, especially women, to the status of objects they gain a sense of power, autonomy, invulnerability.*

Left *Will this young woman be trapped by standard definitions of femininity and never explore her own special talents? Psychologists such as Sandra Bem believe that men and women who see themselves as both masculine and feminine are psychologically healthier than those who see themselves as strongly one or the other. They are more adaptable, more socially competent, better able to cope with stress. Other psychologists debate this.*

The pros and cons of stereotypes

In spite of conventional patterns there are individuals who act in ways considered typical of the opposite sex. Does that mean that the behaviour patterns of a great number of men and women will change markedly in the future? I doubt it, but it is impossible to predict. Intuitively I would say that if people are allowed greater opportunity to follow their personal preferences the total sum of human experience will be enriched. Greater freedom ought to lead to more fruitful lives and relationships. Denial of opportunity on the grounds of gender seems not only un-democratic and a great waste of natural resources, but also unwarranted blocking of avenues to general happiness and satisfaction.

Nevertheless our expectations of our own sex and of the opposite sex are not excess

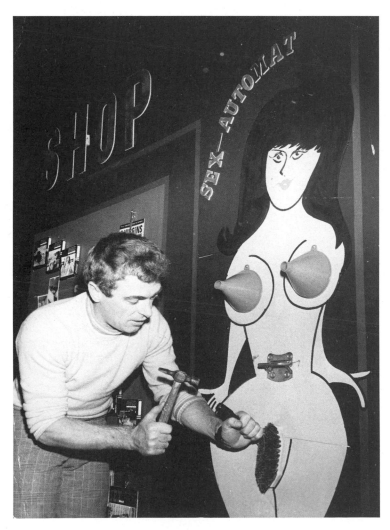

mental baggage but crucial grist from which we form our self-image and solidify sexual identity, and equipped with that image and identity we develop all our sexual and non-sexual relationships.

Gender roles are the lubricants of social interaction; their images facilitate most social activities. Uncertainty is unsettling and un-welcome for most people. Role expectations, even if later found to be misplaced, provide initial guidelines on how to act and what to expect. Just as one expects different be-haviours and reactions from an oil tycoon and a priest, an athlete and a scholar, one has quite different expectations for males and females.

Yet each of us generally prefers and deserves to be judged on his or her own merit rather than on stereotypes. So although sex role and gender role expectations have the advantage of shortcutting communication and, when ful-filled, offer feelings of competence and suc-cess, they can be disadvantageous. They form mental pigeonholes which limit the explora-tion and testing of one's own abilities and those of others. They build barriers against opportunities to change or expand the nature of relationships. And they stifle communica-tion and creativity. Fortunately many people successfully negotiate their way out of role stereotypes. Others explore them, find them unsuitable, and attempt to make changes. Others neither explore alternatives nor feel free to change; unwittingly they remain trapped all their lives.

Erotic stereotypes

Certain erotic behaviours, because of their private nature, are not easily transmitted from person to person, and therefore do not seem to be part of role stereotypes. For instance, even with regular and agreeable sex partners, more males masturbate more frequently than females and men are more often visually aroused than women. These two findings are only part of a more general pattern that appears to have its roots in biology rather than in social learning: men, more than women, are driven to erotic and genital gratification, experimentation, partner variety and multi-formity; men, more than women, are lustful opportunists, geared towards orgasm, a wider range of sexual practices and a variety of sexual companions; men, with all their urges to roam, are more sexually jealous than women; cultures practising polygamy are

123

common, those practising polyandry rare; fetishistic desires are common in males, uncommon in females.

George Bernard Shaw, who had at least two women in his thoughts for most of his adult life, remarked 'A man should have one woman to prevent him from thinking about women in general.' Dorothy Parker, in her poem called *A General Review of the Sex Situation*, wrote 'woman wants monogamy; man delights in novelty . . . count to ten and man is bored.' And consider this reflection by a Kgatla man in South Africa, speaking of his two wives: 'I find them both equally desirable, but when I have slept with one for three days . . . and when I go to the other, I have greater passion, she seems more attractive . . . but it is not really so, for when I go to the former again there is the same renewed passion.'

There are many men who would agree that they are more interested in the chase than the consummation: 'Getting a new women to go to bed with me is more thrilling than being in bed.' In contrast, many women claim the opposite. As one of my students said to me: 'I find the seduction dance and game playing most unsettling. But the comfort and warmth with my partner, once having made the decision to go to bed, I find most rewarding.' For men, it is the challenge that is important, for women the other person.

Characteristically it is males rather than females who push a budding relationship towards genital play. They constantly test the boundaries of sexual contact. This is still true when the relationship is old and established, when the complications of guilt or shyness have been overcome.

Even without a relationship or challenge to the ego, men are more likely to actively seek sexual satisfaction. The ultimate example of this is rape, which is everywhere almost exclusively a male phenomenon. But it is also exemplified in the use of prostitutes, both female and male, who predominantly service males. In all cultures studied, men are more likely to have extramarital affairs, and with a greater number of partners. They are also more likely to form and maintain a relationship primarily to service erotic needs, often at the expense of other factors.

In a survey among American college students, 75 per cent of the men approached by a female stranger agreed to go to bed with her that same night, but none of the women

questioned by male strangers agreed to do so. Only 6 per cent of the women questioned in the same study agreed to go to the male stranger's apartment, but 69 per cent of the men were willing to go to the female stranger's apartment.

Many more males than females go to singles bars purely to seek sexual satisfaction, as reported in Shere Hite's two studies (1976 and 1981). Even among a population of single, urban, sexually liberated women, she found few who thought casual, spontaneous sex desirable, although many thought they might be happier if they did. In contrast the majority of men she surveyed claimed they did, at least occasionally, desire casual sex.

Bull among the Cows, *a famous nineteenth-century Rajasthani painting of a scene from the* Kama Sutra.

Far right *Hong Kong millionaire Teddy Yip with his 50 ex-mistresses, their husbands and their families. This amazing reunion took place in Acapulco, with all expenses paid by the debonair Mr Yip.*

Novelty versus loyalty

In humans, said Kinsey, the male drive for variety is one of the most common sources of conflict between the sexes. He and his colleagues were struck by the fact that most men readily understand the desire for extramarital coitus whereas many women find it difficult to believe that a man who is happily married might want coitus with someone other than his wife. To Kinsey this fact was 'the best sort of evidence that there are basic differences between the sexes.' A woman may want sexual relations with a stranger who has special status or appeal or because she is temporarily fed up sexually or nonsexually, with her current partner. But to a man, the fact that a partner is new may be reason enough and not necessarily a reflection of his current lover's ability to satisfy him.

Kinsey also noted that 'everywhere in the world it is understood that . . . the female has a greater capacity for being faithful to a single partner, that she is more likely to consider that she has greater responsibility than the male has in maintaining a home and caring for the offspring.'

Double standards

One of the difficulties in making male–female role comparisons is that almost invariably the

'It's terrible. I've sinned again.' Cartoon by Sempé.

life, work, activities and even play of males are awarded more status than those of females. Whether this is the cause or effect of status having been largely defined by males is unknown but, as many women writers have pointed out, recorded history has usually ignored 'herstory'. Double standards for men and women are universal and almost everywhere the advantages accrue to men. For example, a sexually adventurous male is typically considered worldly, a sexually adventurous woman promiscuous.

Status is not always synonymous with importance. Among many primitive societies, the food gathering and gardening activities of women are crucially important for subsistence, but they are not awarded high status. Many people, and not only women, cogently argue that caring for and rearing children is the most important duty anyone can undertake, and yet because it is everywhere mainly done by women it enjoys low status. Status resides less in the job or activity itself than in society's view of it as a male or female activity.

Many countries individually, and the United Nations collectively, have made efforts to improve the lot and status of women. The results over the years have been small but they have been noticeable and are slowly growing. This is particularly true in industrial societies where women are increasingly entering the workforce (men's traditional world) and leaving the home environment (women's traditional world). Regrettably, in many countries, when women enter occupations typically considered a male pre-

Above *Cafés throughout the Muslim world are patronized only by men.*

Top *Turkish peasant women start another day's work.*

serve, such as high school teaching or clerical work, the perceived status of these professions suffers. In Russia and China women have been educated more broadly, and for idealistic and economic reasons encouraged to enter previously all-male professions, especially medicine. In both countries the status of women has improved but the prestige of the medical profession has declined.

Male resistance to change

Women choose to engage in typical male pursuits, but fewer men choose to take on women's traditional roles. A female barrister is more likely to return home to a meal cooked by the au pair than by her husband. Men in Western societies will cook outdoors or on special occasions, but leave women to cook in the home on a daily basis. Men will help with housework, but women get it done. A 1980 research survey among married men carried out by an advertising firm in the United States found that while 56 per cent of the men questioned throught women 'likely to be more satisfied with their lives' if employed outside the home, 60 per cent endorsed the view that 'a woman's place is in the home'. Clearly there is an imbalance in willingness to exchange gender roles.

A 1983 United States study of some 2400 cohabiting heterosexuals and homosexuals and 3600 married couples found that no matter how prestigious or remunerative their jobs, the women were almost always responsible for housework; requests for help were often strongly rejected by their partners. However

Women workers in a light engineering cooperative in China. Whereas women's contribution to manufacturing enterprises had increased beyond recognition since World War II, men's contribution to the enterprise of running a home and caring for children has increased hardly at all.

Left *Cartoon by Sempé. In a recent US survey it was found that the average working wife does 26 hours of housework a week; her husband does 26 minutes. In the same study 35 per cent of husbands said they thought vacuum-cleaning an acceptable male chore, but only 27 per cent had ever done any!*

In Finland boys are expected to learn to cook. Men and women are equally talented as cooks, yet 'chef' has connotations of mystique and leadership that 'cook' does not.

Below *Up telegraph poles and down (wo)manholes. Gender moulds are being broken in all walks of life. Could it be that a woman in a man's world maximizes her chances of finding an ideal mate? Would the odds be similar for a man working in a woman's world?*

most of the women did not regard housework as inappropriate for themselves even if they were in the executive bracket at work. The researchers also found that if both partners were equally work-centred or career-orientated, their relationship was in jeopardy. The basic issue seemed to be of power, with the men reluctant to relinquish any. Married couples, regardless of the wife's earnings, still measured their financial success by the husband's income. In other words, it was up to the man to make the couple's mark in the world. Cohabitors, gay or straight, measured their economic worth as individuals, not as a unit. One of the major conclusions of this study was that, despite the economic and social gains won by many women in the United States,

their impact on traditional gender roles has been relatively minor.

It has now become fashionable to argue that there is nothing natural or immutable about gender differences, that they should be seen as anachronistic social inventions, out of place in the modern world. Social inventions, the argument goes, can be changed if institutions and populations work towards such change, and equality of the sexes is worth working for. On the other side of the debate are the sociobiologists who argue that behaviour and status differences between men and women are not merely cultural aberrations but the result of evolutionary forces designed to ensure the survival of the sexually fittest and hence the reproductive success of the species. While sociologists wonder why males do not play a greater part in the rearing of children, biologists wonder why they take as much interest as they do. That human males are often willing to be monogamous and take direct responsibility for the lives of their offspring runs counter to patterns of behaviour common in other species. To sociobiologists, human sexual patterns reflect both society's conventions and nature's way of maximizing the likelihood that men and women will meet, compete and then cooperate for sexual and reproductive success.

Sociobiologists see sex-specific behaviour patterns as the predictable outcome of several things. The first is the Darwinian concept of sexual selection, in which males compete with each other for females and each female chooses the male most attractive to her. Second is the concept of 'parental investment', as proposed

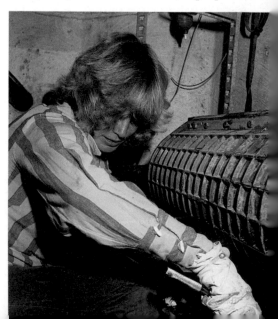

by the theoretical biologist R.L. Trivers. This holds that male and female behaviour patterns have evolved so that parents can maximize the chances of their offspring surviving and at the same time minimize their own personal investment in their offspring. The third concept is that of the 'selfish gene' proposed by Oxford zoologist R. Dawkins. In his words, men and women 'are survival machines...programmed to preserve the selfish molecules known as genes.'

Taking all three concepts together, then, men have evolved to be competitive and will attempt to mate with and impregnate as many females as possible (they can do this because they produce almost unlimited numbers of sperms). They are therefore unlikely to form long-lasting commitments and relationships.

In contrast, females (with relatively few eggs, the development of which requires long investment and commitment) have evolved as though to maximize their attractiveness to males and to be highly selective in their mating. They are likely to take up loyal guardianship of their offspring. While modern society seems a strange and unlikely backdrop for the playing out of such primeval disparities, sociobiologists feel that their thesis is wholly contemporary.

For many the debate cannot be neutral. It is fuelled by conviction or anger, not only at male–female differences themselves, but at their apparent inevitability and the inequity of the double standard associated with them which gives low status to women.

The slow, slow pace of change

Another problem is that many women and perhaps a majority of men feel that, regardless of the origin of the differences, they are basically for the best. They do not see the double standard as necessarily detrimental or reprehensible. The world over, women have never been granted much more than second class citizenship. The defeat of the proposed Equal Rights Amendment in the United States in 1982 and the collapse of the motion in Switzerland to give women full voting rights, shows that even in modern cultures in the 1980s significant changes in gender patterns occur only slowly. Men, and in some cases women themselves, appear to tacitly resist changes of this kind.

Several countries, notably Sweden and Israel, have made great efforts to give both sexes equal status under the law, and in many respects have been successful. But many aspects of everyday male–female interactions seem to have remained the same. Though the new Japanese constitution of 1946 guaranteed equality of the sexes, women are seldom treated as equals at work or at home. Legal decisions do not necessarily alter behaviour, though they may give authority to particular points of view.

An adjustment of values

An aspect of sexual patterns that is less often probed is this: why is work in service or in the caring professions seen as being of secondary value? Why, because they tend to stress relationships more than men do and tend to be less

The male backlash. In many ways men are as much in need of liberation as women.

Left *It is a fact that most people, initially at least, do worse on tasks they think the opposite sex is 'good at'. But when it comes to it, fathers are just as much fun at bathtime as mothers.*

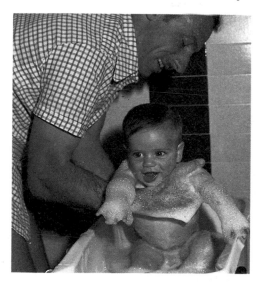

Being depended on and proud of it. Many men, though they exist by virtue of a web of loving relationships, do not feel comfortable admitting as much.

orgastically driven, are women seen as playing only a passive role? The value system that equates maturity with personal autonomy and immaturity with interdependence is only one value system. Many people – I for one – feel that the female tendency to build and protect relationships, rather than gloat on performance and material acquisition, is humanistic and meritorious; that the female tendency to value deep feelings over the selfish urge to succeed is of great worth.

Women, more than men, define them-selves in a context of relationships rather than tasks, or at least they more readily admit it. They also see defence, endurance and the ability to compromise in the face of adversity as strengths, whereas men tend to stay on the offensive and hate 'giving in'. Even if one accepts that such differences are immutable, the relative values societies give them can be adjusted if enough people wish to do so. It is not nature but society that makes judgements on the value of being male or female. Men and women are different but they are not opposites, nor in a fixed relation. They are composites of tendencies that can be maximized for mutual benefit.

Two pluses make a plus

Male tendencies did not evolve in competition with female attributes, but in response to other male tendencies; likewise female tendencies have evolved in response to other female tendencies. Since, for the survival of the human species, males and females must evolve in a way that is mutually beneficial, it is in encouraging the strengths of both sexes that society will gain overall. Some men are naturally tender and nurturant, or learn to be, and some women are aggressive and competitive by nature or when the need arises. Fortunately, there are many gifted, lucky or determined individuals who manage to combine the most valued traits of both sexes. The aim should be harmony without inequality rather than a battle of the sexes, and harmony cannot be achieved without understanding, respect and open communication.

I would like to end this chapter with two quotes. The first is from development psychologist Carol Gilligan, who said:

. . . woman's experience provides a key to understanding central truths of adult life . . . it gives rise to experiences that illuminate a reality common to both of the sexes: the fact in life that there is more than one path to gratification, and that the boundaries between self and others are less than they sometimes seem.

The second is a quote of my own:

The presence of overly rigid forces (parents or others) . . . prevents free choice and thwarts the emergence of . . . natural tendencies.

The healthiest environment for sexual growth is one that provides the widest possible banquet of experiences and models from which the individual can learn without fear of social censure. If each individual is free to act according to his or her sense of sexual identity, preference and role, then men and women will be truly able to express who they are.

Clearly an extreme method of creating new sexual patterns. Another cartoon by Sempé.

CHAPTER 8

On being different

eing unique in a profession is a virtue. Many people yearn to be special – an actor of rare genius, a once-in-a-century pianist, a pioneer surgeon, or more modestly a meticulous craftsman or a conscientious labourer. If we have a particular talent – a foreign language, an appreciation of art or food or music – we like it to be recognized. Yet in sex most people want to be 'normal', or perhaps slightly better than average. To be different in matters of sex is to be suspect. If a woman shows a keen interest in sex she is labelled a nymphomaniac; if she politely refuses a proposition she is sneered at as frigid. A man is dismissed as a 'dud' if he shows scant interest in women or as a 'stud' if he shows a great deal.

The word 'normal' has various implications. In common parlance it means healthy, acceptable, natural. To a scientist 'normal' simply means 'most common', with no connotations of health or sickness, right or wrong. 'Deviant' and 'abnormal', in the scientific sense, simply mean 'unlike the majority'. Used in the popular sense they mean unhealthy, unacceptable and unnatural. Being

different sexually is not easy. Personal habits may be harmless to the rest of the world but nonetheless stigmatized, ridiculed, prosecuted, or seen as evidence of mental illness.

While most of us are normal in most regards, many of us are also sexually deviant in some way. We may have coitus significantly more or less often than others of our age; or at times or in places or in positions different from the majority; or be aroused by stimuli others find neutral or repellent; or indulge in fantasies or practices the neighbours would call perverted. Since most erotic activity takes place in private, it provokes neither comment nor criticism.

For a minority of individuals being different is a way of life. Some keep their difference private because of social pressures. At the other extreme are those people whose preferred sexual behaviours must be imposed on or by others to give them the satisfaction they seek. Between the two extremes are those, the majority of the minority, who simply wish to live as the majority of the majority do, free from curiosity, criticism or condemnation.

Sexual preferences

The terms 'heterosexual', homosexual' and 'bisexual' refer to behaviours, not to people. They merely indicate the sex of the erotic/love/affectional partners a person prefers, whether those partners are of the same or opposite sex, or either. They say very little about the person doing the preferring. A person's choice of sexual partners says almost nothing about his or her style of dress, occupation, recreational habits, behaviour in public (and that include mannerisms and speech patterns), marital status or general happiness. People who prefer homosexual or bisexual relationships are every bit as diverse as those whose preferences are strictly heterosexual – they come in all sizes and shapes and belong to all races, creeds and social conditions.

Whereas the term heterosexual is seldom used as a noun, homosexual frequently is. In fact the label homosexual is too casually used even by those most critically concerned. Often it brackets together those who have regular sexual encounters exclusively with partners of the same sex and those whose tastes are predominantly heterosexual even if they

Sex al fresco and sunbathing in a parking lot – different certainly, but not necessarily harmful to self or others. It is sometimes difficult to accept that others behave very differently from ourselves.

A still from Sunday, Bloody Sunday *(1971), one of the first films to openly portray bisexuality and homosexuality.*

do include fleeting or occasional homosexual experiences or fantasies. Really the term 'homosexual' should be reserved for those whose erotic preference is exclusively, or almost exclusively, for partners of the same sex, 'ambisexual' or bisexual for those who enjoy sexual activity with partners of either sex, and 'heterosexual' for those whose erotic companions are always of the opposite sex. Too often, for statistical or political convenience, people whose sexual tastes are mainly hetero- or usually bisexual are lumped together with those whose tastes are homosexual only. To talk of these groups in the same breath is misleading. One swallow makes neither a summer nor a homosexual.

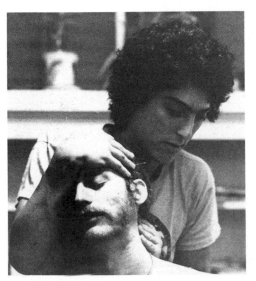

Homosexuality

Although some people who prefer homosexual activity openly flaunt their orientation, the majority take pains to remain covert. Their sexual lives are, like those of their heterosexually- or bisexually-oriented neighbours, private and undisclosed. Their common orientation does not mean that they have any more in common than people of other sexual orientations. A bank manager who is homosexual has more in common with other bankers than with other homosexuals, who might work in the theatre or on a building site.

Recently, homosexuals who want open recognition and respect for their right to a different orientation have come together in social and political groups and the term 'gays' has been adopted as a preferred label. The origin of the term is debated. The practice of referring to heterosexuals as 'straights' has been rejected by many political gays, who point out that the opposite of straight, in everyday parlance, is crooked. In their view the opposition of terms still implies an unwarranted value judgement.

About 1 in 25 Caucasian males in the United States has declared himself exclusively or nearly exclusively homosexual. This is probably a conservative figure. Prevalence is probably similar among most other Caucasian populations, and also among Negroid populations. Appropriate research on Oriental populations is not available, but the figures are probably comparable. A far greater number of men and boys – perhaps 20 per cent – are occasionally

Left *Affectionate touching, a need frequently denied and even more frequently misconstrued, even between members of the opposite sex.*

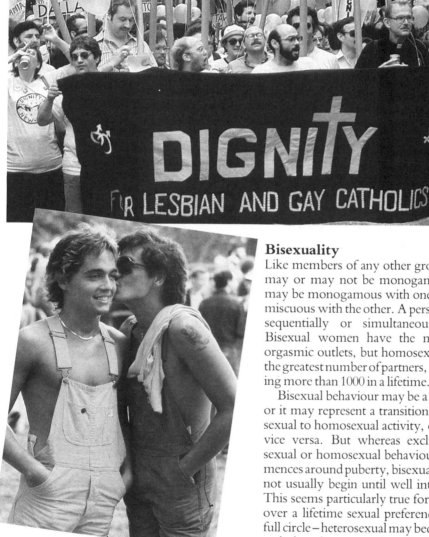

Gay liberation marchers in New York. A major goal of the gay movement is to be accepted in general society and to break out of the ghettos – tea rooms, baths and bars – to which an oppressive 'straight' society has consigned them. 'Dignity' is an organized group of homosexually-oriented Roman Catholics.

attracted sexually to other males and occasionally engage in homosexual activity. It would be more accurate to say that such individuals, most of whom are married, are bisexual or ambisexual.

The visibility and social acceptance of homosexual activity has varied with time and place. Although it is often said that homosexuality is now more prevalent than ever before, there is no real evidence that the ratio of homosexuals/bisexuals to heterosexuals is increasing, though homosexual activity has certainly become more visible in the West.

Bisexuality

Like members of any other group, bisexuals may or may not be monogamous, or they may be monogamous with one sex and promiscuous with the other. A person can also be sequentially or simultaneously bisexual. Bisexual women have the most frequent orgasmic outlets, but homosexual men have the greatest number of partners, many averaging more than 1000 in a lifetime.

Bisexual behaviour may be a passing phase or it may represent a transition from heterosexual to homosexual activity, or less usually vice versa. But whereas exclusive heterosexual or homosexual behaviour often commences around puberty, bisexual activity does not usually begin until well into adulthood. This seems particularly true for women. But over a lifetime sexual preference may come full circle – heterosexual may become bisexual and then homosexual, and then revert to heterosexual.

Woody Allen quipped that being a bisexual immediately doubles one's chances of getting a date for Saturday night. In fact bisexuals have the same chances as anyone else, no more and no less, for happiness and self-fulfilment. Nevertheless in most of the Western world bisexual activities are as much 'in the closet' and suffer from many of the same problems as homosexual activities. Although they are more likely to receive support among homosexuals than among heterosexuals, bisexuals are often seen as 'traitors' or 'fence straddlers' by both groups.

A brief history of homosexuality

Ancient chroniclers such as Juvenal described parts of Athens and Rome where boys cruised the streets and worked in brothels for the pleasure of men. Medieval historians wrote of homosexuality flourishing in France and Norman England, and descriptions of Italian cities of the Renaissance contain accounts of homosexual activities. Gay clubs were quite common in eighteenth century London, and many American cities, notably New York, were revealed as hotbeds of homosexuality at the turn of this century. Today almost any major city in any Western country has a gay community and a gay night life. San Francisco is probably the gay capital of the world, reportedly having the highest proportion of gays of any city anywhere.

Over the centuries, particularly following the rise and spread of Christianity, homosexuality has borne the brunt of many double standards. The Old Testament in the English translation speaks of homosexual activities as 'abomination'. According to the classical historian John Boswell the original Hebrew words meant 'ritually unclean for Jews'; like other prohibitions in the Mosaic code, such as the keeping of dietary laws, the eschewing of homosexual activities was a model way of life and a means of distinguishing Jew from gentile. There was no particular word for homosexual in classical Hebrew or Greek – it was the practice, rather than the person, that was discussed.

For the first 1000 years of the Christian era homosexuality seems to have received a very varied and idiosyncratic reception. There has been much contention over the interpretation of several none too clear New Testament references, and Greek and Roman writers as well as the chroniclers of the early Middle Ages were anything but consistent, lucid or objective in their writings.

Below *An Attic red-figured vase of the fifth century BC. Outside marriage, the ancient Greeks distinguished less between men and women than between men and non-men. Sex between men and boys (non-men) was considered acceptable.*

According to Boswell it was the Roman Emperor Justinian who decreed that homosexuality should be punishable by death, which put it in the same category as adultery. From 533 onwards this legislation was enforced throughout the Empire. Possibly it gave Justinian an excuse to attack politi-

Oscar Wilde, painted by Toulouse-Lautrec in 1895. The tribute of one social outcast to another?

Left *Edward II of England (1284-1327) with his lover Piers Gaveston. His queen, Isabella of France, and courtiers mutter in the background. Piers, never popular, was executed in 1312 by Edward's rebellious barons.*

cal enemies and confiscate their wealth. Thereafter anyone who engaged in homosexual activities – indeed anyone who was obviously different, such as Jews, astrologers and unorthodox Christians – became a ready scapegoat. With or without religious conviction or encouragement from the Church of Rome, rulers after Justinian persecuted homosexuality.

Charlemagne (742–814), who considered himself responsible for keeping the Empire Christian, was apparently disturbed, when he ascended the throne in 771, that there were so few effective anti-homosexual laws and that those which did exist were only half-heartedly enforced. But although he railed against homosexual practices, especially among the clergy, he did not invent any new penalties. In the main, and allowing for a lot of local variation, attitudes towards homosexuality were relatively tolerant in the early Middle Ages.

With time, however, religious and secular leaders became less accepting of sexual 'variations'. Few scholars agree on the forces that brought about this change. Nevertheless the expression 'acting contrary to nature' came to be used for unapproved heterosexual or homosexual acts and punishments ranged from public ridicule, imposed fasting and confiscation of property to torture, castration and even death.

By the time of Richard Lionheart (1157–99), who was not only a Crusade leader and a symbol of chivalry, but also gay, homosexuality was beginning to be regarded as heretical and criminal. The legal description of homosexuality as 'the crime not fit to be named' goes back to the early thirteenth century. The punishments were burning, drowning or being buried alive.

By the time of Edward II (1284–1327), the last openly gay medieval monarch, anti-gay sentiment was widespread. Edward himself was deposed and murdered. The illegal status of homosexual behaviour was retained in English law for another six centuries though punishments grew less severe. English law was of course the model for the laws of many other countries, including the United States.

In 1895 the brilliant author, dramatist and socialite Oscar Wilde was brought to trial in London for 'gross indecency', a legal euphemism for a variety of disapproved of sexual acts. He was eloquent in his defence of 'the love that dare not speak its name', telling the world of the deep feelings, noble sentiments and affectionate companionship he associated with homosexual love. Despite his powerful pleas and his eminence as a public figure he was found guilty and sentenced to two years in Reading Gaol. His personal ordeal not only caused homosexuality to be named in public but also to be brought into open discussion. But it was another 60 years before Britain dropped homosexual acts among consenting adults from its code of punishable offences. To this day the rights of homosexuals under English law do not parallel the rights given to heterosexuals.

The designation homosexual was first used in print in 1851 by the German author Kardy Maria Benkart. Theorizing about the origin of sexual arousal, he used the words 'certain male and female individuals with the homosexual urge'. As we have seen, terminology and recognition have trailed well behind private and public practice.

Homosexuality around the world

Although no society has ever advocated homosexuality as the predominant mode of adult sexual activity, many have never paid much attention to it, and some have condoned or even encouraged it for certain minority groups. In Siwan society in North Africa, for example, all men and boys engage in anal intercourse.

Many cultures have made a distinction not between men and women but between men and non-men. Men are those who have married or passed initiation; non-men, unmarried men, uninitiated boys and unmarried females are seen as possible sex partners. This was true in ancient Greece, and is true of the Aranda aborigines of Australia and the New Guinea Keraki and Kiwai, who consider homosexual activity necessary to ensure healthy development in young boys.

Latin Americans distinguish between *activos* and *passivos*, indicating that the majority of gay males are either penetrators or penetrated, rarely both. Not unexpectedly in cultures where machismo is important, *activos* consider themselves, and are considered, masculine, and *passivos* feminine. These are distinctions which are considered irrelevant or old fashioned among North American and European gays.

Female homosexuality

Anthropologists say that homosexual activity among females is much less common than among males. However, female homosexuality is overt and accepted among cultures as diverse as the nomadic Cukchee reindeer herders of Siberia, the African Azanda, Mbundu, Name, Ojiba and Yuma tribes.

From surveys in the United States, Australia, Japan and elsewhere, same-sex orientation seems to be roughly half as common among females as males. International figures are scarce, but those for Caucasians indicate that about 1 in 50 women is exclusively homosexual and about 1 in 10 occasionally so, or at least in fantasy. The lesbian population is thus even more invisible than the gay male population. For political reasons homosexual women often prefer to be referred to as lesbians, since it gives

This eighteenth-century French engraving shows a typically male fantasy of female homosexuality. Certainly strap-on dildos are used by some lesbians, but most reject artificial penises.

These two Dutch women, Ria Bultema and Harmanna Kalsbeck, received a church blessing when they married in 1983.

them identity as a group. Among the millions of lesbians in the United States, Britain and elsewhere, there is a feeling that their existence as a group deserves acknowledgement, even if not all of them wish to declare themselves.

The invisibility of the lesbian population is reflected in English law. Popular legend has it that Queen Victoria rejected the very idea of lesbianism – it was 'impossible' – when the laws on homosexuality were being revised. Lesbianism was also ignored in the report of the Wolfenden Committee in 1957, which led to long overdue reform of the laws on homosexuality in Britain.

A parallel with the earlier Oscar Wilde case was that of the author Radclyffe Hall. Her novel on lesbianism, *The Well of Loneliness* published in 1928, was branded as obscene by a London court, and all copies of the book

Marguerite Radclyffe Hall, painted in 1918 by Charles Burchell. Fewer lesbians today adopt male dress. Those that do are colloquially described as 'butch'.

were ordered to be destroyed. Radclyffe Hall was not, as Wilde was, prosecuted for her personal behaviour, though she openly dressed as a man and went about London with her companion Una Troubridge.

The culture within a culture

Whereas the term homosexual refers to behaviour, the term gay refers to a sub-culture. Many gay individuals are open about their sexual orientation and can be identified by various mannerisms and activities, sometimes effeminate in the case of males and masculine in the case of females. These may be natural expressions of self or part of highly formalized codes that signal group identity. Many social signals used by homosexuals and heterosexuals are the same, since their purpose is to communicate sexual interest in a way that does not arouse hostility, ridicule or rejection. Nevertheless for homosexuals moving in a primarily heterosexual world certain codes are necessary – subtle uses of tone of voice, stance, code words and eye contact.

Every large city has contact points – bars, clubs, baths, coffee shops – where those seeking homosexual sex or gay companionship can meet. Formality is minimal and there is plenty of opportunity to openly explore sexual possibilities. Places that cater exclusively for the gay sub-culture are secure oases in an often intolerant world. They provide social support and a setting in which to learn the etiquette and values of the group. Bars for gay males are particularly noted for 'cruising', the picking up of partners solely for sex.

In fact the male gay scene deals with overt sexuality with an ease not found in the heterosexual or lesbian worlds. Immediate sexual encounters are available for the asking in public toilets ('tea rooms') and baths; however briefly, 'closet' and open gays can find satisfaction for erotic desires. Most often such pick-ups are purely sexual, with no relationship expected or even wanted.

In many societies, and increasingly so in the West, a gay lifestyle is becoming more openly expressed and less frowned upon. Even so, there are different levels of allowable public behaviour. Some people feel uncomfortable when they see a boy and a girl kissing in public. Many more will feel uncomfortable if the partners are of the same sex. Also, overt sexual behaviour is less remarked in a large capital city than in a small country town.

Children of 'different' parents

To end this discussion of homosexuality I would like to focus on some of the findings of researchers Richard Green, Mary Hotvedt, Jane Barclay Mandel, Brian Miller and others, concerning the sexual orientation of the children of gay or transsexual couples.

Firstly, the children of such parents are no more likely to grow up gay or transsexual than the children of heterosexual parents. Second, gay or transsexual parents do not subject their children to sexual or social harassment or bring them up to be sexually deviant. Their concern for the welfare of their children is quite independent of their own sexual orientation, sexual identity or sexual lifestyle.

As far as single parents are concerned, matched and controlled studies show that there is no difference between children brought up by lesbian single parents or heterosexual single parents. For single mothers, of any stripe, motherhood, not sexual expression, is the focus of their lives. Similar research on single fathers is not available but those cases that have been researched fail to show any difference between the children of gay fathers and the children of heterosexual fathers. Generally it is the absence of a parent – usually the father – as a result of death or divorce, rather than the lifestyle of either or both parents, that seems to have the most impact on a child's social development.

Transvestism

People who habitually dress in the clothing of the opposite sex are broadly termed transvestites (TVs). The vast majority of transvestites are male and heterosexual, although they may also be homosexual. For many heterosexuals cross-dressing has an erotic function; it is sexually arousing, sometimes to the point of orgasm, with the clothes of the opposite sex acting as fetish objects. But among the 10 per cent or so of homosexuals who cross-dress the erotic fetish element is rare or non-existent. In their case cross-dressing is done to appeal to other males, though it may also have an element of showing off in it. Male prostitutes who solicit homosexuals are the most publicly obvious cross-dressers, though by no means all of them wear women's clothes.

People cross-dress for many reasons. Children dress up and put on make-up for the fun of pretending to be someone else or in order to try out a new image. But cross-dressing

The hardest thing the child of a homosexual parent has to cope with is society's attitude towards that parent.

Below *An actor applies traditional Noh make-up. With wig and costume the illusion of delicate femininity is complete.*

140

Below *Most heterosexual cross-dressers are men who lead otherwise conventional sex lives; often they are married and have children. Very few women are compulsive cross-dressers.*

among children is rare; if a child repeatedly cross-dresses it is a strong but not infallible indication of future homosexual tendencies. In adults cross-dressing is more likely to be accompanied by feelings of sexual pleasure, or by the feeling that it satisfies a dimension of personality that cannot be expressed in any other way. For some adults cross-dressing is a compulsion that neither they nor the psy-

chiatric profession fully understand.

Cross-dressing is often referred to as 'going in drag'. Originally the term 'drag' was theatrical, and meant the wearing of women's clothes by men impersonating women. Various male entertainers today capitalize on the novelty value of drag; they cross-dress to shock and mock Establishment stereotypes.

In the history of the West and among many Oriental and primitive cultures, transvestism has been part of artistic or religious expression. It has little or nothing to do with eroticism and is highly regulated in form and style. In Noh and Kabuki theatre, classical art forms in Japan, men play all the parts; on the other hand, the dancers and singers of the Takarazuka theatre, a more recent tradition, are all women. In classical Greek and Roman drama and on the Elizabethan stage all women's roles were played by men.

Cross-dressing was one of the Puritans' main objections to the theatre. They regarded it as a violation of the injunction in Deuteronomy: 'The women shall not wear that which pertaineth unto a man, neither shall a man put on a woman's garment.' In other religions and cultures, the opposite was true. The *berdache* were a special group of men within several American Indian tribes who dressed in women's clothing and engaged in women's activities; homosexuality may or may not have been involved. In Dahomey in Africa cross-dressing was the Sakpota dancers' way of appeasing malign spirits. Among the present-day Yurubas of Brazil transvestism among heterosexuals is well accepted but usually a private matter; the dressing may be quite elaborate but it is not usually displayed outside a circle of trusted friends and relations.

One famous exponent of cross-dressing was Charles d'Eon, a French spy active in the late eighteenth century. Using the pseudonym Madame Lia de Beaumont he was sent as a woman to the court of St Petersburg in Russia and to the Court of St James's in London. His exploits became so well known that 'eonism' became a synonym for transvestism. The British organization for heterosexual transvestites, The Beaumont Society, is named in his honour. He was so convincing both as a man and as a woman that members of the London Stock Exchange made wagers as to his true sex and had his body examined in detail after his death.

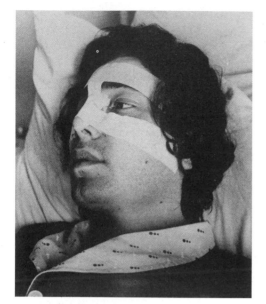

Transsexualism: a mismatch of body and mind

Those rare individuals who believe they have been born in a body of the wrong sex are transsexuals (TSs). Theirs is a frustrating existence, in which sexual identity and the image in the mirror are in conflict. Although their genitals are within the normal range for their biological sex, their mental image of themselves often drives them to seek sex change surgery. Cross-dressing is merely palliative, an inadequate substitute for the body they crave. A male transsexual believes he is really a woman and usually feels that his orientation towards men as sexual partners is properly heterosexual. With a female transsexual the converse would be true. Since sexual identity and sexual orientation are independent, homosexually-oriented transsexuals also exist. Transsexuals very clearly exemplify the distinction between sex and gender: a male transsexual has the sex of a male but the gender of a female; a female transsexual has the sex of a female but the gender of a male.

Transsexuals commonly put themselves through a long period of self-testing to see if they can affirm their bodily sex in spite of their mental doubts. A male transsexual might

Left *Bulent Ersoy, Turkey's most popular singer, shortly after the 'nose job' that marked the beginning of the change from 'him' to 'her'.*

Below left *Ersoy today – glamorous, confident, still idolized. Officially Turkey does not recognize sex changes but when Ersoy was sentenced to a month in prison she was sent to a women's penitentiary.*

Wearing a woman's robe, cosmetics and a tiara, he entered the gates of Rome demanding to be honoured as empress. On another occasion he tried to castrate himself in honour of a Syrian deity.

Transsexualism hit the world headlines in 1952 when it was announced that an American ex-soldier named George Jorgensen had visited Denmark and returned as Christine Jorgensen. She had undergone surgery to remove penis and testicles, had had them replaced with labia and a vagina and had also been given full breasts. Subsequent publicity and open discussion revealed that a surprisingly large number of people felt their true sex was not the sex they were born with. They too wanted sex change surgery. For the first time psychologists and psychiatrists worldwide began to realize that sexual identity does not necessarily reflect genital anatomy or gender upbringing, and that it can override both. Sexual identity is a separate dimension of sexuality. Patterns of dress and occupation are socially appropriate behaviours and secondary to the inner conviction of being male or female and, strange as it may sound, the transsexual is really saying 'change my body, not my mind'.

Left Christine Jorgensen, formerly George Jorgensen, photographed nearly 20 years after her highly publicized sex change operation. Following her lead many males, though fewer females, decided to make the switch.

George Roberts, featured in a BBC television documentary in 1979. His first step towards becoming Julia Roberts was a change of hairstyle. As is usually required, he had to live as a woman for a whole year before he was granted sex change surgery.

volunteer for the commandos, or a female transsexual work as a stripper, and outwardly be well accepted in those gender roles. But they themselves remain unconvinced. They then turn to trying to convince the world that their inner sexual identity is the real one and that the gender imposed by anatomy and society is false. They try all possible means of altering their appearance and behaviour towards that of the opposite sex. In this urgent desire to transform their genitals and their secondary sex characteristics, they resort to hormone treatment, depilatories, hair transplants, and eventually surgery. The results vary from the amazingly convincing to the pathetic and bizarre. At the last, surgery seems to provide an inner peace not available by any other means.

While homosexuality and transvestism have been known since antiquity, transsexualism seems relatively new, perhaps because the hormone treatments and surgical procedures that can turn wishing into reality are new. Several reputed transvestites of the past may have been transsexuals, the Roman emperor Heliogabalus (218–22 AD), for instance.

Pan and Hermaphroditus, from a wall painting in the House of the Dioscuri in Pompeii. The appetite of the frisky, lecherous Pan more usually fastened on young nymphs, but Hermaphroditus became fair game when he acquired the attributes of the nymph Salmacis.

Hermaphroditism

Circus side-shows once advertised half man/ half woman attractions and the mythologies of many ancient cultures celebrate fusions of male and female, but the actual occurrence of hermaphroditic individuals is rare. True hermaphrodites are individuals with gonadal tissue of both sexes. Despite myths to the contrary they could not impregnate themselves even if they wanted to. Pseudohermaphrodites, however, are not rare. They may appear once in every 100 or 200 births. These are individuals who have one or more sexual characteristics – genetic, genital, endocrine, anatomical – out of keeping with the others. Most pseudohermaphroditic conditions are the result of a genetic anomaly; for example, the individual has an XXY chromosome set and the appearance of a feminized male, or an XO chromosome set and the appearance of a female. Most pseudohermaphrodites live comparatively normal lives with relatives and close friends unaware of their uniqueness, and perhaps unaware of it themselves. The word 'hermaphrodite' is a contraction of the Greek names Hermes and Aphrodite; Hermes was the messenger of the gods and Aphrodite the goddess of love.

Incest – the last taboo?

In 1979, in Massachussetts, Victoria Pittorino married her brother David Goddu. They had been separated as young children and adopted into different families. On Victoria's initiative they were reunited after 20 years apart and within a few weeks fell in love and got mar-

ried. Both were brought to court on a charge of incest, instigated by Victoria's adoptive mother. They were found guilty, ordered not to live as man and wife and to seek counselling in order to re-establish the relationship of brother and sister.

A 42-year-old mother in Virginia and her 20-year-old son, reared in a foster home, were not so lucky. Reunited when the son was seventeen, they married and lived together for a year until a social worker discovered their relationship and brought charges. In 1980 they were banned from meeting again for ten years.

These cases, though legally tried and judged as incest, are not typical of the popular idea of incest or the features of incestuous behaviour that are most disturbing to Western society.

Most horrific to Western societies are those cases of incest between father and daughter, where the child is young and unwilling, the age disparity great, and where fear or force is used to maintain the relationship.

In the West incest is defined as sexual activity between individuals prohibited to marry. Among Roman Catholics, incest extends to first cousins – the marriage of President Franklin Delano Roosevelt to his cousin Eleanor was seen by some as incestuous. Among the Navaho Indians incest extends to all the members of the mother's or father's own clan, or 'linked' clans, effectively ruling out hundreds of people as marriage partners. In the Trobriand Islands a girl who marries her mother's brother is committing incest; in Sri Lanka this relationship would be considered an ideal basis for marriage.

Incest has been called 'the last sexual taboo', now that adultery, homosexuality, masturbation and other behaviours previously swept under the carpet have been acknowledged as prevalent.

There is a basic notion that incest is a most ancient taboo, a taboo that is one of the cornerstones of civilization. The French anthropologist Claude Lévi-Strauss described prohibition of sex within the family as 'the fundamental step . . . in which the transition from nature to culture is accomplished.' And yet the Mbuti pygmies have no concept of incest, and incest was not only acceptable but a positive duty among royal families in some ancient and not so ancient civilizations – the Egyptian queen Cleopatra married two of her brothers to secure the succession. Even in the West laws against incest are only a twentieth-

Cleopatra of Egypt and her husband-brother Ptolemy XIII. Deposed by Ptolemy, Cleopatra regained the throne with the help of Julius Caesar, then married her younger brother, who ruled as Ptolemy XIV.

century phenomenon.

One forceful argument against incest is that children born of incestuous relationships are more likely to inherit biological defects if both parents contribute similar defective genes.

But it is an equally forceful argument that incest might enhance genetic assets. Perhaps the strongest argument against incest is that it disrupts standard lines of family authority, puts family members in stressful competition subjects them to secrecy, ridicule and guilt.

Those who want legal sanctions against incest removed say that the law fails as a deterrent and in fact violates personal free-doms of no concern to society at large. They also say that incest by mutual consent may have positive and educative value, and that physical closeness in families is inhibited by fear of the incest taboo.

No very reliable statistics on the prevalence of incest exist. How can they when there is no basic agreement on the definition of incest? It has been crudely estimated that in the United States 5 to 15 per cent of the population have at some time been involved in incest, defined as everything from petting to coitus between immediate family members as well as cousins and step relations.

A scene from Louis Malle's film Le Souffle au Coeur *(1971), a disturbing account of a close mother-son relationship.*

Why be different?

To the ignorant and undiscriminating, homosexuals, transsexuals, transvestites and others who 'break the rules' are all 'queer'. No attempt is made to understand the distinct characteristics of these different manifestations of sexuality. They are seen as deviant, in the derogatory sense, as sick or evil. The opposite view, slowly gaining ground, is that homosexuals, transsexuals and others are 'just different'. Some psychiatrists and sociologists argue that such individuals have poor home backgrounds which predispose them to aberrant sexual development, others that particular family constellations – a weak or absent father or an overbearing mother – are to blame, but their arguments are not very convincing. Children brought up in the same family still go their separate ways – heterosexual, homosexual, bisexual, transsexual.

It seems that nature has provided us with a maximum of sexual drive, a modicum of bias, and a minimum of direction, and so our fertile minds have found a myriad of different ways in which our sexuality can be indulged, expressed and satisfied. There is no evidence that any of the 'different' behaviours we have been discussing are intrinsically harmful either to the individual or to society, except where social and emotional pressures lead to secrecy and private anguish. But being different does not end there. Individual sexual needs and preferences are more numerous still.

Different again

Some sexual practices require a lack of privacy to be effective, exhibitionism and voyeurism for example. On an everyday level and to a certain extent, almost everyone is both an exhibitionist and voyeur. We like to display ourselves and be thought attractive, and we are naturally curious about other people's sex lives. These are minor sexual indulgences. Quite distinct are the rare individuals who achieve their major or only erotic pleasure from seeing or being seen in sexual activity. Such people compulsively risk public outrage and even imprisonment by invading the privacy of others. Usually they are more of a nuisance than a threat, and only when such behaviour is regular and compulsive should the clinical terms 'exhibitionist' or 'voyeur' be used. Exhibitionists, or 'flashers', expose their genitals to unsuspecting women, but shy away from pursuing the encounter, even in

conversation. They hastily leave the scene after witnessing the shock and attention they crave. They are playing out a fantasy in which self-exposure and the shocked response are the triggers to arousal. A voyeur, or 'peeping Tom', may creep up to a bedroom window in the hope of seeing the occupants naked or engaged in sexual activity. The act of flashing or peeping is all that is erotically desired.

Almost all exhibitionists and voyeurs are men and their activity sometimes includes masturbation. Flashing and peeping lie at the elementary extreme of a whole spectrum of sexual expression. For most people, seeing or being seen is part of behaviour among intimates or part of fantasies which lead to sexual arousal.

Sexwatchers will be aware of the enormous variety of sexual tastes catered for by the pornography industry. For some, practices such as group sex, rubber or leather fetishism,

Quite the wrong reaction to the flasher in the park! The man, or very rarely the woman, who exposes all does so with the intention of shocking, not – as in this early twentieth-century cartoon – of entertaining.

sado-masochism, bondage and bestiality exist only in magazines and movies, but for others they are fantasies that enliven an otherwise unremarkable sex life. For some of course they are a necessary reality. A few of these practices are potentially very dangerous. Since they are minority preferences there is a genuine fear that unwilling participants might become involved if society makes no protest. The general attitude is therefore disapproving and legal or social restraints are placed on advertising and display.

Lastly, to round out our view of being different, there is a category of behaviour not often thought of as different: lack of interest in sex, abstinence, celibacy. In the West our attitudes to these are ambivalent: on the one hand we accept them as the mark of clerics, the devout and the virtuously unmarried, but on the other they are the subject of ridicule. Friends and family get concerned and try to change the situation, sometimes recommending psychotherapy. In most societies a lack of interest in sex is viewed with puzzlement.

The various behaviours discussed in this chapter demonstrate that the sexual landscape is as immensely broad as it is deep, and full of people quite different from one another. No consensus on 'normal' sexuality exists within or between cultures, or within sub-cultures or even families. Current emphasis in the West is on informed choice, mutual consent and mutual enjoyment □.

'On amène les ânes' *('Here come the donkeys'). The bestiality hinted at by illustrator Auguste Leroux in this Roman orgy scene was not, and is not, uncommon in farming communities. Today there are also magazines and movies that cater for 'animal lovers'. Paul Gebhard, past director of the Kinsey Institute for Sex Research, once remarked: 'If you butchered and ate your cow, no one would care. If you made love to your cow you would be put in jail.'*

9

That little word 'love'

A decade ago, while producing a television series called *Human Sexuality*, I asked a camera team to roam through the parks and beaches of Honolulu taking candid pictures of people expressing affection. It was my intention to use these little interludes more or less *passim* in the series, but in particular for the programme about love and intimacy. I had expected, considering that Honolulu is a destination for honeymooners and has a younger than average population, that it would be relatively simple to get pictures of couples expressing love – holding hands, embracing, kissing... I was wrong. Love and affection were indeed there, but expressed much more subtly. Far from being flaunted – and flaunted means different things to different people – love and affection are rarely openly displayed.

How does one recognize love? At its most fundamental love is a bond, a feeling of attachment between two individuals. It is an emotion that is common, as far as we can judge, to all higher order social creatures. It exists between animals that live in packs or troops and

among those whose infancy is prolonged. It enables individuals, especially young individuals, to learn from their elders and peers. It induces individuals to cooperate for hunting, defence, foraging and other purposes.

Higher social animals show bonds of all sorts – between adults of the same or opposite sex, between parents and offspring, between old and young, between siblings and age mates. Many primates and members of other species act as if they mourn the loss of an infant, parent or mate who dies or disappears. With that individual they display behaviour which, in humans, we would call love. The adults of many species, most notably birds, are monogamous and apparently mate for life; when the bond breaks, they do not easily establish a new bond. This relationship model, the pair bond, is the one in which humans feel some of their strongest loves and loyalties.

Love, then, is a utilitarian mechanism and not a quirk of nature or the monopoly of humans. It is one of evolution's most significant inventions; long, intimate relationships

Top right *Love is one of the most powerful and durable of all human emotions. It persists long after its object – a spouse, lover, parent, child, friend – has left.*

Right *Loving and being loved is unlike any other experience.We all learn how to express love in our own unique way.*

effectively ensure individual and species survival, and group cohesion. And in keeping with the complexity of the purposes it serves, love is itself enigmatic and complex. In some form or other it exists and has existed in every human society known, yet it has probably never been fully understood by any of them. Also, like many other feelings, it can be communicated in many different ways, or sometimes not at all.

Although the propensity to love, to form bonds, is in all of us, we require nurture for that propensity to be realized. American psychologist Harry Harlow and his colleagues found that monkeys brought up in isolation, without the contact of siblings, parents or human keepers, fear association with others; they behave aberrantly when in company or presented with unfamiliar situations. Harlow raised infant rhesus monkeys in isolation, using wire or cloth 'mothers' equipped with feeding bottles to feed and 'nurture' them. He found that their behaviour was closely tied to the amount of comforting contact they received from their 'mothers'. Monkeys mothered by the wire 'mothers' acted like psychotic children, crouching passively, huddling in corners, crying plaintively without provocation, and rocking back and forth hugging themselves.

When they grew up those monkeys deprived of adequate contact as infants and juveniles failed to relate normally to other monkeys. Males showed very little interest in copulation; if they did, they seemed to have little idea what to do, mounting the female from the side for instance, or thrusting against an arm or leg. Females isolated as infants would not present themselves to males in a normal manner or allow normal males to mount them. Nevertheless the drive to do *something* was sex-appropriate – the males clearly knew that they should mount, the females that they should be mounted. It was the 'how' that needed learning.

Harlow wrote of his monkey subjects: '... we had developed not a breeding colony, but a brooding colony'. The dramatic conclusions from this research were that the ability to bond (love) and perform sexually remains latent unless there are opportunities to socialize, learn and practise. Another highly significant finding was that if unmothered female monkeys were somehow inseminated and bore infants, they did not know how to

149

mother them. They abused or ignored them to the extent that none would have survived without human intervention. So, for non-human primates, not only is sexual and companionate 'love' something to be learned, but 'mother love' is too. Is it reasonable to extrapolate from rhesus monkeys to humans?

James Prescott, a developmental neuro-psychologist working with the US National Institute of Child Health and Human Development, has reviewed the work of Harlow and others and concluded that during certain critical periods of brain growth some kinds of sensory deprivation – an absence of rocking, hugging, and body warmth from a real mother – result in incomplete or distorted development of the neural programs involved in affection. He concluded that such studies

. . . have profound implications for human cultures that raise their infants with low levels of touching and movement. Children in these societies may be unable to experience certain kinds of pleasure – and be predisposed to apathy and violence . . . In one study of 49 primitive cultures, I found that when levels of infant affection are low – as among the Comanches and the Ashanti – levels of violence are high; where physical affection is high – as among the Maori of New Zealand and the Balinese – violence is low. I also found that restrictions on premarital sexual affection were associated with high violence.

Human loves

In the past it was left to philosophers and poets to probe the love experience. The Greeks of Homer's time, more than 3000 years ago, wrote of three basic types of love, *philos*, *eros*, and *agape*.

Philos meant supportive, companionate or brotherly love of the kind that develops between comrades in arms, team mates, fellow workers striving toward a common cause. It was non-sexual and most often homosocial. This is the love idealized in the relationship of Damon and Pythias, two youths willing to die for one another.

Eros represented erotic love, love born of physical attraction – what we would probably call lust today – but for the Greeks, *eros* did not have negative connotations. It was a healthy and normal sexual response, and could be hetero- or homosexual, and supremely satisfying and joyful. *Eros* certainly provides bliss

Toilet of Lampito *by Aubrey Beardsley. Eros, alias Cupid, is almost always portrayed as an irresponsible prankster, stirring the fires of passion in human hearts. Aphrodite, his mother, once took away his wings and arrows to punish him for having aimed at her!*

Below *The martyrdom of St Peter by Caravaggio. Martyrdom is the ultimate expression of* agape, *the love that is other-worldly and self-sacrificing.*

enough to be called love by many. However, the French-Thai Supreme Court Judge and author-poet René Guyon in *The Ethics of Sexual Acts* advises against confusing sexual desire with love. He writes: 'How many painful disillusions would be saved if, instead of thinking themselves obliged to say "I love you" men would content themselves with saying "I desire you . . ."'

Agape was considered to be the highest form of love – the love that is spiritual or altruistic. Love of democracy, truth, science or God would be *agape*. Martyrs of all faiths have expressed this form of love with their lives. As far as St Paul was concerned, *agape* was divine and so sacred that it could not be achieved by mere mortals.

Passionate heterosexual attraction allied to companionate feelings was certainly known in Ancient Greece, but was looked on as a mixture of *eros* and *philos*, or as a sign of emotions that came under the heading of neither. 'Losing one's head' over someone was seen as a sort of craziness, an illness for which no good treatment existed. Yet Plato, coming on the scene some centuries later, spoke of love as admiration of the good and the beautiful, as an asexual kind of *philos*.

Most of us like to think we know what love is. We will recognize it, we say to ourselves, when it happens to us. Yet when we suspect it might be happening we often ask 'Is this love?' It is when we think there is only one kind of love that difficulties arise; to think that there is any 'best' kind of love can lead to tragedy.

Recently a Canadian researcher, John Alan Lee, tried to codify love in all its guises and ended up with a blending wheel of six main categories (see next page). He felt these reflected all the loves spoken of by the ancients as well as the feelings of modern men and women. The latter he judged from the responses he got by asking 112 randomly selected adults from England and Canada several hundred questions that requested detailed descriptions of all those experiences that could, in some way, be called love. Summing all these loves he arrived at a list of nine, including *eros* and *agape*, and platonic love (*storge*), but also *mania*, *ludus* and *pragma*.

Mania is the love that is irrational, extremely jealous, obsessive and often unhappy; it seems to be out of the lover's control. It is the sort of emotion that attracts attention because of its intensity. Psychologist Dorothy Tennov

coined an alternative word, *limerence*, to describe this bond of love. She defines limerence as the one human interaction that eclipses all others, as a state of cognitive obsession in which, to quote Stendhal, one is 'unremittingly and uninterruptedly occupied with the image of the beloved'. This is the love of dreamers and the star-struck, of teenagers and the lonely. It is the love most likely to produce a throbbing heart, pallor or blushing awkwardness and shyness. It is the emotion that makes the lover stutter and falter when the beloved suddenly appears; it is the passion that doesn't even require the loved one to be aware of the lover's existence, let alone return the love. It is also the love that can leave one most vulnerable. One student of mine expressed her own limerent experience like this:

After I was divorced from my first husband, and before meeting my second, I met Greg. I'm not sure what there was about him but I fell head over heels. It was crazy! I wanted to be with him every moment of the day and he with me. When we were apart I kept thinking of him to the extent that my work and other relationships suffered. Actually, looking back, I can see that really this was a destructive relationship. He literally wanted to possess my every move and thought and I enjoyed his doing so. I thought it was romantic. He was insanely jealous. He would go off to do his own things expecting me to be ever waiting for him; and I was. In truth he was 'schizy' and I saw it as exciting. Reality came as a shock to me but at the time he seemed to be everything I could ever desire.

Ludus is another name for Ovidian love. The Roman poet Ovid, in his *Art of Love*, wrote of love as a game, the winning of which gives pleasure to the winner and often to the loser. Ovidian love is primarily tactical. Even saying 'I love you' can be a tactic to gain sexual or other favours, an admission fee both literally and figuratively. It was best, Ovid advised, to try to seduce a woman when she was aroused by a gladiatorial spectacle since one type of arousal might well predispose her to another (recall some of the twentieth-century research along these lines mentioned in Chapter 2?). The modern Ovidian sends flowers or cooks a special meal. Indeed Ovid's *Art of Love* has

Right *Ovid's game. Playful seduction, perfectly portrayed by Faye Dunawaye and Steve McQueen in the film* The Thomas Crown Affair. *One of the ground rules of Ovidian love is that, like alcohol, it should be enjoyed but never allowed to become a necessity.*

Below *John Alan Lee's 'blending wheel' of love. In the outer circle passion (eros) blends into game-playing seduction (ludus), which in turn blends into brotherly/ sisterly affection (storge), which merges back into passion. In the inner triangle are obsessive love (mania), self-sacrificing love (agape) and practical love (pragma). (Adapted from* Colours of Love, *1973)*

been called 'the classic seduction manual of Western literature'. Certainly he would have endorsed the saying 'all's fair in love and war'. Nonetheless tactics and tacticians breed caution. Bertrand Russell warned: 'Of all forms of caution, caution in love is perhaps the most fatal to true happiness.'

Pragma, as its name suggests, is the accommodation of one person to another for various practical reasons. *Pragma* is the spirit in which arranged marriages are entered into, with compatibility, mutual responsibility and companionship as their goals. A relationship that starts as pragmatic can evolve into one of great warmth, tenderness and deep mutual understanding. Or it may start with passion, and then take a companionate course. My father, close to 90 years of age and 60 years of marriage, expressed his feelings about love like this: 'Love to me is a feeling of closeness, the knowing that she is always there. Even when we argue we know it means we value each other's opinions and respect each other's ideas although we may try to convince each other otherwise. She is my best friend.' My mother, not much younger, says: 'Love is a feeling of wanting to do for another without regard for a return; a concern for the other partner's feelings.' An elderly couple walking serenely arm in arm is almost universally seen as a model of companionate 'true' love.

Other types of love have been described – puppy love and romantic love, addictive love and dependent love, and certainly mature and immature love. But, of them all, romantic love typically receives most attention in the West. Is it what 'makes the world go round'? Is it, as the publishers of romantic fiction and soap opera audience ratings would have us believe, what we all want?

This medieval stained glass window epitomizes holy matrimony, love sanctioned by religion and state. But there is a twist to the story of Sarah and Tobias, the couple portrayed here: Sarah's seven previous husbands were all carried off on their wedding night by the demon Asmodeus!

Romantic love

Romantic love is seen as an escape from the woes of the real world, as a magic carpet that can soar over such mundane barriers as race, religion, class, education, age and occupation. It is a state of permanent infatuation which poverty, intolerance and rotten luck cannot shake or sully. Romantic love fantasizes tenderness, intimacy, privacy and lust in just the right proportions at just the right time, fantasies in which every action is part of a courtship without end and in which the lovers are sought and desired, seeking and desiring. Sexual consummation is not necessarily achieved but is constantly anticipated.

Romantic love may be fraught with passion and suffering but the lovers always anticipate a happy ending, if not in the real world, then in some symbolic apotheosis – hence the romantic ideal of double suicide. Romantic love combines the sexual, the erotic, the sensual and the mystical. It is a brilliantly coloured, surrealistic and personal painting on a canvas framed by society.

Our modern concept of romantic love has much history behind it of course. As an incorrigible romantic myself I find it difficult to believe that romantic love was not the reason why Mugga chased Ugga, or Beep 'had a thing' for Bopp, in cave-dwelling times. Nevertheless historians such as Denis de Rougemont date the stirrings of Western notions of romantic love to the twelfth and thirteenth centuries, and specifically to the troubadours of the castles and courts of southern France. Up until that time, in the West at least, the dominant notion of love had been that promulgated by St Augustine: the highest form of love was asexual, dedicated to the service of Church, the glorification of God and the stability of the State.

The troubadours began to sing and write of new social and sexual arrangements and what they called 'courtly love' and their songs and writings were called 'romances'. In a romance, a troubadour or a knight swore fealty not only to his lord but to his lord's lady. In an age when all social strata knew their place and relationships followed strict expectations, this was a dramatic break with tradition. Traditionally love was expected to develop within arranged marriages hedged about with rules and roles. Freedom to love by choice was a new idea. In the twelfth and thirteenth centuries even one's choice of friends was limited by class and family.

Courtly love was ostensibly asexual and highly virtuous. The troubadour or knight hero sought favour in his lady's eyes by overcoming all manner of trials and tribulations by self-sacrifice, perseverance and pious acts. His reward was to wear her token – a ring, a handkerchief – on his travels. Sex he could obtain from any wench or from his wife as a marital right, but from his lady the most he could hope for was permission to lie beside her and chastely caress her naked body (or that was the theory).

Whether this perception of love was spread by the troubadours as an Ovidian ploy to seduce maidens, influence social mores or reflect current events, is debatable. Yet the model of romantic love inexorably spread. This was non-consummated transcendent love, erotic, heterosexual and adulterous. It fed on frustration rather than consummation. The troubadours and their audiences were in love with love, consumed more by the desire for the experience or appearance of love than by the desire for a particular person, precisely the kind of love that makes many people put up with totally inappropriate partners. The notion of romantic love also led to the idea that knights in shining armour (or their contemporary counterparts) are over every horizon waiting to rescue damsels in distress – a fiction that has wide appeal but cannot be relied on!

Abelard and Héloise

Quite different from the knights and damsels in the troubadours' songs were the lovers Abelard and Héloise. Peter Abelard was a 40-year-old scholar and tutor of great renown

Above Garden of Love, *from a fifteenth-century French manuscript of Boccacio's* Decameron. *A group of courtiers listens to a poet 'spinning a romance', descanting on the infinite nuances of courtly love.*

Left *Carried off, by a knight in shining armour! Gustave Doré's interpretation of the central episode in Tennyson's poem* Enid. *Such imagery remains an ever popular dream.*

and Héloise his teenage pupil. They first met in 1118. Disregarding all social, religious and legal constraints, their love blossomed and from their passion came a son. Despite their subsequent marriage the relationship so offended Héloise's uncle that he forced the lovers apart. Héloise entered a nunnery, at Abelard's suggestion. Abelard was castrated (without anaesthetic) at the uncle's insistence. Their infringement of contemporary social mores and the persistence of their love brought them general condemnation, but it struck a responsive chord in a few hearts. Disciples followed Abelard to his desert refuge to learn his philosophy. Héloise, within her convent walls, continued to consider herself Abelard's lover and intellectual disciple. Over distance, time and adversity their love prevailed. Abelard's letters advised Héloise to seek solace in God; she did so only because it was Abelard's wish. Her love was constant after the mutilation and separation, and for the twenty years during which she survived him. Legend has it that she asked to be buried with Abelard. When the casket was opened, Abelard extended his arms and they embraced each other for eternity.

This story, in the minds of the troubadours and poets who spread such tales, was indeed the ideal love. For the establishment of the day, however, it was heretical and dangerous. Sex, and certainly pregnancy, was sinful outside marriage. Marriage was to be entered into

The lovers Dante and Beatrice, from an early fifteenth-century Venetian manuscript. Legend has it that the poet Dante saw Beatrice once only; ever afterwards Beatrice was his love ideal. Note the balcony on which Beatrice stands, as on a pedestal; this was the romantic idealization of womanhood. Shakespeare was mindful of the balcony cliché in his stage directions for Romeo and Juliet.

by arrangement, prudently, not on the basis of fanciful notions called love. At the end of the sixteenth century, when Shakespeare wrote *Romeo and Juliet*, the concept of romantic love was sufficiently understood yet disapproved of for the play to be seen as tragic.

In an age when most people lived very close to poverty, illness, disease and sudden death, it was widely accepted that an emotion as strong as love ought to be reserved for bonding a couple together through life's vicissitudes; it

The tomb of Abelard and Héloise. Loves that have to run the gauntlet of social disapproval still form the hard core of problems put to 'agony aunts' and 'Dear Ann' today. The path of true love . . .

155

was not something to be thrown away or given to the first comer. Sexual favours and virginity, particularly women's, were seen as bargaining chips to be offered in exchange for marriage. Love was to be given, in marriage, to someone who had earned and merited it. Even today, in societies where hardship rather than affluence is the rule, the Western concept of romantic love tends to fall on stony ground. I should also add that even in the West romantic and pragmatic notions of love are still in healthy conflict.

Loves compared

Although it is difficult to look objectively at something as non-objective as love it is obvious that each type of love – if one accepts the broad descriptions I have just offered, and not everyone does – has both advantages and disadvantages.

Romantic love requires total commitment, companionate love understanding and give and take. Ovidian love involves planning and strategy, passionate love 'chemistry' and spontaneity. Loves are either stormy and ex-

A wedding in the old quarter of New Delhi, India. In both affluent and impoverished communities arranged marriages – with or without love between bride and groom – are a very practical way of creating social support networks and decreasing the likelihood of cultural conflict.

citing or dependable and predictable. Love either arrives at first sight or develops over time. It is the stuff of dreams or built on substance. It is either lustful or chaste. To some, love is measured by the strength of sexual desire, to others the true depth of love can only be gauged when it is purged of sexual desire; to the former love means sex, to the latter love and sex may be in conflict or have nothing to do with each other. (One advice columnist received a letter from a woman complaining of her husband: '. . . he insisted on making love to me four times. By nightfall I felt physically and mentally abused'. A strange mixture of language and feelings.)

Romantic love is unconditional, selfless, 'made in heaven'; pragmatic love is mutually beneficial, an exchange, something to be worked at. Love for some allows the fullest expression of self; for others it is the melting of two individuals into one; for others it is too profoundly disturbing to a fragile 'self' to be lived with for long.

Despite neat categories and labels, love is an emotional experience that defies easy description. To Socrates love was a seeking for something in others that we do not possess in ourselves. To Plato love was the admiration and contemplation of beauty, the loved one having no obligation other than to exist. To Aristotle love was a reflection of the self and therefore a form of self-love. To the poet Dryden it was 'a malady without a cure', to feminist Ti-Grace Atkinson 'a euphoric state of fantasy in which the victim transforms the oppressor into . . . redeemer', and to Eric Segal, author of *Love Story*, 'never having to say you are sorry'. In short, even among those who have devoted a good part of their lives to considering the matter there is no common definition. That is because love is not a thing but a very large collection of ideas.

Labelling love

Are attempts to give labels to various sets of ideas within this large collection helpful? In some ways, yes. Labels allow us to look at experiences and feelings and link them to others in ways which are patterned and communicable. We need to express our feeling to others, to tell and be told how we love and how we are loved.

Many of these labels are not directly descriptive but are metaphorical: love is like 'a bridge over troubled waters', like a madness, like a contract, like a burning and consuming flame, like violins playing, like all the wonderful things in the world rolled into one . . . and so on. Metaphors freeze feelings, images, experiences and ideas so that they can be more easily recalled and spoken of. They also help to convey the fact that experiences of love are varied and very personal; they allow us to feel unique. Other people's descriptions of love are not recipes but possible avenues to explore. Labels also help researchers in their attempts to probe love as they might probe any other complex phenomenon.

A love that keeps on growing. Lovers down the ages have expressed their passion in graffiti. In the West the heart is the symbol of a couple joined in love; in Japan lovers' names or initials are linked by an umbrella symbol.

Is it good or bad to be hit by Cupid's arrow? In reality, and in parody, it is often hard to know. Drawing by Mel Calman.

'He loves me, he loves me not . . .' The old petal-picking rhyme is more serious than it sounds. How do we know – especially when we are young, sexually inexperienced, and unsure of the qualities we most respect – whether what we feel towards others, or what they feel towards us, is love?

Studying love

Can scientists study human love? How do they – and the rest of us for that matter – recognize love and measure its intensity?

A very common way of measuring love is to test someone's willingness to have sex: 'If you love me, you'll have sex with me.' But the test can be used in reverse: 'If you love me, you wouldn't ask or you would wait.' Crude as such a test may seem, it is in many ways as good as any. The first version is more often applied by males and the second by females. But although both sexes desire intimate physical contact and orgasm, studies have shown that girls and women are more likely to think they are in love with their partner if they have had coitus than if they have not, although whether coitus is the cause or effect of love is not clear. For men feelings of love are less likely to be linked to coitus.

Social scientists such as John Alan Lee and Dorothy Tennov, Zick Rubin, Elaine Hatfield, Ellen Berscheid and others, claim that love is measurable both quantitatively and qualitatively and that measurement does not necessarily have to involve experimental situations or manipulation. They simply construct questionnaires and ask volunteers to answer them. Here are some sample questions.

On a scale of 1 (not at all true) to 9 (definitely true) indicate your feelings about the person you love/have loved most passionately.
A *Since I've been involved with . . . my emotions have been on a roller coaster.*
B *I take delight in studying the movements and angles of . . .'s body.*

On a scale of 1 (none at all) to 9 (tremendously strong) indicate your feelings for the person you are most in love with.
A *How much passionate love do you feel for . . . ?*
B *How much companionate love does . . . feel for you?*

When most in love I felt as if I wanted to run, jump and scream (underline as appropriate):
A *never* **B** *sometimes* **C** *usually* **D** *almost always*

During the time I was most deeply in love some of the things I did were:

Using questions like these, different definitions and intensities of love can be compared and correlated with various groups of people. Zick Rubin feels he comes closest to measuring love when he uses three scales, one to assess attachment (desire for the other's physical presence and support), another to assess caring (concern for the other's well being) and another to assess intimacy (feelings of closeness and being emotionally in tune).

Hypotheses about love can be tested by asking people to define and describe love, and say what they prefer in love and why. One study by R. Ellis and R. Harper in 1961 found that university students were more likely to call a relationship 'love' if it was still in progress, but more likely to call it 'infatuation' if it was in the past. Jon Jecker and David Landy, in 1969, found that givers come to love recipients more than vice versa; the giver of a necklace becomes more involved and has greater investment than the recipient. William Kephart, in 1967, found that contrary to popular belief men are usually more romantic than women. When he asked his respondents 'Would you marry someone you didn't love if they had all the other qualities you desired?', few said yes, but more men than women said no. In matters related to love women tend to make quite rational and practical (unromantic) decisions.

Awkward questions for measurers of love

Is someone who rates his passion as a 7 more in love than someone who rates her passion as a 6? How many people have a sufficient quantity of passionate loves or companionate loves, however defined, to make even personally valid comparisons? And can we rate feelings of involvement with other people on the kind of linear scale that might go from love at one end to hate at the other? Perhaps, in answer to the last question, we could, although most love scales do not yet include hate; most murders are domestic, committed by people who once loved their victims. Would a love that is rated 9 today become 3 or even a minus 9 next month? Is climbing two mountains more loving than climbing just one? Is a love accompanied by a ten carat diamond more intense than one accompanied by a single rose?

Much of the value of using such arbitrary measures is lost unless great care is taken in structuring the questions and test situations.

A major difficulty is that respondents and researchers rarely share a common background and perspective. There is no universal standard, no fixed value system, by which to measure 'the real thing'.

Humanist philosopher Robert Solomon derides the idea of measuring love. He cynically paraphrases Browning: 'How do I love thee? Let me measure something.' The somethings measured, he argues, are seldom meaningful. For example, does the counting of eye contacts between lovers have any more value than the verbal report 'He doesn't look at me like he used to'? Does defining something as 'passion' or 'infatuation' make it any more precise than calling it 'lust' or 'puppy love'?

One thing questionnaires do is obtain information about groups, even if that information is of limited relevance to individuals. If, as philosophers and psychologists agree, love is at least partly a product of social conditions and learning, tests can certainly mirror what the majority of questionnaire answerers think or have learned. Here Solomon makes a suggestion which I think helpful; he advocates that anyone attempting to investigate love scientifically should, as part of their investigations, describe his or her own experiences as well. He says: '. . . to analyse love, scientifically or poetically, on the sole basis of other people's experience, should strike us as odd, to say the least. The problem, in other words, is not the use of science but a certain emasculation of science . . .'

But I myself find it difficult to follow Solomon's suggestion. While I 'know' I love and want to be loved, I cannot, in my own mind, fix on what would be valid measures of the feeling – perhaps interest, caring, respect,

longing, missing the person I love, a desire to be with her, to share things with her. But I have no idea how to adequately scale or test these feelings. Strangely it would be easier to list how I would like such feelings to be measured in those who love me: 'If she loved me, she would...'

There is also the question of timing. Other life events – an argument with the boss, illness, a new relationship on the horizon – influence how love is rated. Also, we want to be loved for ourselves, as we are. We may *choose* to change in order to please a lover, but we don't want to *have* to change to meet his or her expectations. Also, what one person offers as proof of love may not be accepted as such by the person on the other end of the relationship. Commonly partners' 'trading items' are different. Many a couple has sat in my office exchanging comments such as:

'You don't love me.'
'Yes I do! I slave overtime at a job I detest to bring home a pay check and keep you and the kids warm and fed.'
'If you loved me, you'd spend more time at home.'

'And if you loved me you would understand that what I'm doing is for us, and you wouldn't put me through this guilt trip.'
'If you loved me, you'd tell me. You used to.'
'I thought you knew. You never asked straight out. Anyway, I thought by now you could take our relationship for granted.'
'I want to hear you say it. I want you to show some passion.'
'I want you to take my feelings for granted. Why do I have to keep proving myself?'
'We haven't made love in weeks.'
'I love you every day.'

The speakers have obvious difficulties but they also express feelings and actions that may be considered loving.

Eternal questions

Chekhov once remarked of love: 'When you read a book it all seems so old and easy, but when you fall in love yourself, then you learn that nobody knows anything, and each must

Not communicating any more? Or communicating all too well? The huge emotional and physical 'credit' that partners give each other in the first flush of love – and on which the seemingly effortless, intense communication of new lovers is based – can quickly go into overdraft. Why do we often reserve our strongest anger for those we love?

decide for himself.' The old, old questions pose themselves anew for each generation of lovers. Is it possible to love more than one person at a time? Can one love without being 'in love'? How are sex and love related? Why do some people reject love? Why do some loves persist despite time and distance and adversity? Why do others require closeness and intimacy to keep them alive?

Accepting that there are many types of love and that we ourselves are seldom the same with all people (I like to think we all have different facets that different people see and polish uniquely), the answers to some of the questions above become obvious. Certainly one can feel love for several people simultaneously. In fact doing so is common. A man's love for his wife is different from the love he feels towards his children or towards his friends or towards his parents. His loves vary in their content from erotic, to companionate, to nurturing, to competitive, to altruistic, and so on. Much depends upon his needs at a given time and the needs of those he loves. As we and our loved ones change the nature of our love changes.

Sex with or without love?

One of the most contentious topics in sexology today is the relationship between sex and love. There is a growing feeling in the West today that the 'sexual revolution' is entering a backlash phase; traditional values have survived the onslaught of sex on demand and for its own sake, and people now wish to return to more 'meaningful' sexual relationships. It is now fashionable to believe that the best and deepest relationships involve sex plus baring of the soul. Our hierarchy of romantic and erotic love is still headed by marriage; next come stable, long-term relationships; then come affairs, flings and one-night stands; last of all come 'quickies' that take no longer than orgasm. The higher reaches of the hierarchy belong to relationships likely to be based on many, rather than few, of the ideas we call love, and not merely on the physical motions we call sex.

To draw a physiological analogy, sex is rather like the nervous system of the body, love rather like the endocrine system. Both are communication systems, but one is fast and the other is slow. Sex brings about rapid and temporary interaction between people, but love works more slowly, dealing with the

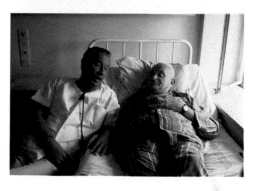

All of us, at all ages, are capable of many different loves, and each love enriches and adds meaning to the others. Though marriage – and the deep, single, sexual relationship it implies – comes top of our cultural hierarchy of loves, it is not sufficient. We all can benefit from loves which cross generations, which allow us to depend on others and be depended on.

longer-term functioning of relationships. The most 'healthy' situation is when both work in concert.

Many non-Western societies recognize the value of sex uncomplicated by the pressures and problems of emotional commitment. At an intellectual level so do many respondents to surveys in the West; they agree, in principle, that sex should be available to all, even if it is better with a little love thrown in. And at a fantasy level so do many married men and women; sex with someone else is a common fantasy, even during intercourse.

It occurs to me that people who object to sex without love may be objecting not so much to sex itself as to having to deal with an intimate relationship that cannot be labelled as love. Though it is often said that women demand love in return for sex, it may be truer to say that they are also interested in many other kinds of personal communication, and not necessarily of the highly involved or demanding kind.

One of the main arguments for sex with

Most marriages in the West today begin with love, not with convenience. Statistically Western love goes through its most testing time after five to nine years of marriage and again after twenty years – times which seem to be linked with the start of having children and their leaving home.

To paraphrase Freud: 'When two people are in love, there are at least four people present – the two in love and the two they believe each other to be.' The path of love might run truer if we did not project all our needs and fantasies on to a single person. On the other hand such interdependency may be what keeps many couples together through adversity.

love is simply that it is better, more meaning-ful, more satisfying, a whole experience rather than an optional extra. But sex without love has its own validity. First, since partners are chosen mainly for erotic purposes, there is a high likelihood of achieving sexual satisfaction; it can be a means of fulfilling fantasies. Second, non-involved partners can make demands on each other they would never dream of making on an emotionally involved other. There is less need to impress, to be consistent, to do the right things at the right time, all of which lessen sexual inhibitions. It doesn't very much matter what the other person thinks. Third, sex for its own sake cuts out the banalities, power relations and hidden resentments built into many relationships. If you don't like it, you don't have to continue. It does not impinge on other areas of life, so there is no need for apprehension or regret afterwards. This point of view is well expressed in one of Woody Allen's films in which Diane Keaton says: 'Sex without love is an empty experience.' Allen replies 'Yes, but as empty experiences go, it's one of the best.'

There are many reasons why people separate sex and love. For a married man or woman a casual affair may be a release from tensions within the marriage, or simply a desire for novelty. Uninvolved sex can also be a transitional phase after a destructive affair or messy divorce, a way of building new values and repairing self-confidence before making another emotional commitment.

Love: an infinite resource

Too often it is assumed that love is an exhaustible commodity of which there is only so much to go around. On the contrary love is an inexhaustible resource. Leo Buscaglia, or 'Dr Hug' as his fans call him, is a best-selling author on love. He writes: 'Since love is not a thing, it is not lost when given. You can offer your love completely to hundreds of people and still retain the same love you had originally.' The more one loves the easier it becomes. What is exhaustible is time, and the demonstration of love takes time.

There are those who have never learned to love, in the physical as well as the emotional sense, and those who have learned not to love. There are also those who have learned to repulse love. Love demands a degree of vulnerability with which not everyone is comfortable. Experience, wrongly or rightly,

teaches many people not to show love openly, not to risk embarrassment, attack, betrayal, desertion and pain. To honestly say 'I love you' may be one of life's most difficult decisions, but ultimately one of the most rewarding. And to be able to love another, one must first love oneself. We all know people who belittle themselves at every turn, who reject compliments, who mistake attention for condescension and patronage.

For sexwatchers the lesson seems clear. We should savour the eternal dialogue between generation and generation, culture and culture, scientists and poets, experts and raw recruits, for all of them have their different wisdoms. And we should be wary of portraying love in simplistic terms. We would do better to keep an open mind and explore for ourselves the meanings of love and be willing to gamble at love. It is truly 'better to have loved and lost than never to have loved at all'. In loving, the more you give, the more you may get □.

Ken –
FOREVER I WILL LOVE YOU,
LOVE THROUGH YOU,
LOVE AWAY FROM YOU,
LOVE BECAUSE OF YOU...
– PAULETTE
8·10·76

10

Relationships

*One who thinks he can live without
others is mistaken;
one who thinks others cannot live
without him, is even more mistaken.*
HASIDIC SAYING

ove, in the abstract, is heady stuff. For
most people the subject is only meaningful in the context of relationships. The
who and how of personal interactions give
flesh to feelings not only of love but of frustration, longing, jealousy, admiration, concern
and so on. The colourful doings of Elizabeth
Taylor with Richard Burton, the romance of
Prince Charles and Lady Diana, or even the
games of the next-door neighbours, are of
more immediate concern than the musings of
Ovid or the findings of obscure scientists. But
the workings of one's own relationships are
the most important of all.

Interest in relationships, particularly sexual
ones, and a natural curiosity to compare
oneself with others and to learn more, turn
most people into part-time sexwatchers.
What Sally sees in Andy, or what made Harry
leave Maud for Helen (or Henry), are the
common currency of every society. Such
stories are told and retold for their inherent
interest, for clues to behaviour, for scandalous
detail, for their instructive value.

Relationships mirror the values, aspirations,
successes and failures of a culture. Marriage
and divorce rates, for example, are seen as
barometers of morality and happiness. Relationships are regulated by and reflected in
property rights, titles, social responsibilities
and of course the laws on marriage, divorce,
adoption and guardianship. Civil or religious
law can intervene to prevent a union – on the
grounds of mixed race, mixed religion, incest,
homosexuality, bigamy – or to prevent divorce. In the West two people make a marriage,
but four wives are allowed in Muslim countries, and in some southern Indian cultures
women are allowed two husbands. In all
societies in which polygamy is institutionalized a man with several wives is a sign of
wealth but a woman with several husbands is a
sign of poverty.

Categorizing relationships

People are linked in an infinite variety of
relationships, ranging from the simple to the
complex. The link may be friendship or
kinship, great intimacy or brief acquaint-
anceship, convenience or necessity, contrac-
tual or voluntary. Some kinds of relationship
are reinforced, others hampered, by the society
one lives in.

Relationships can be categorized as sexual/
non-sexual, homosocial/homosexual,
heterosocial/heterosexual, ambisocial/bisex-

Above right *The eye
roves, even from a topless
friend to a fully clad
stranger. Yet sexual
opportunism in the West is
not as rife as we in our
fantasies might conjure or
visitors from less
permissive countries like to
think. Some degree of
intimacy typically precedes
a sexual relationship and
obligations are usually felt
or implied if not explicitly
stated.*

Right *'Harry, this is
Jane, my trial wife!' All of
us are curious about the
relationships between
other people. If no
relationship is stated, we
usually invent one.*

ual, or if one's focus is on marital status as marital/premarital/extramarital/post-marital/non-marital.

In most non-Western societies sanctioned sexual relationships are usually limited to marriage. Boys and girls, and certainly men and women, are often socially isolated from each other. Extramarital liaisons are clandestine, if they are possible at all. In Saudi Arabia, for example, the sexes work and live apart unless they are members of the same family. Even male and female university students rarely attend lectures together; a male professor lectures on closed-circuit television to his female audience in the next room. Women-only banks exist and one conservative spokesman predicted that women would be more willing to join the workforce if all-female parking lots were provided.

Western nuances

In the West there are no such extremes but rather a great number of possible male–female relationships, the nuances of which are not always adequately expressed in English. Here are some of them, in order of erotic involvement: friend (platonic is assumed), boyfriend–girlfriend, intimate, partner, companion, mate, spouse, lover–mistress. I have put lover–mistress after spouse because usually extramarital affairs have a higher sexual component than an established marriage. Referring to someone as a boyfriend or girlfriend usually indicates amorous, if not erotic, involvement, but full sexual involvement is implicit in the other terms. Of all the relationships listed only spouse, and perhaps mate, imply permanence. In less liberated times, when sex was assumed to occur only within marriage, the terms boyfriend–girlfriend were non-sexual. Today no such correlation is assumed. Many an embarrassing moment can be spent trying to find the right words to define the precise nature of a relationship: 'This is my daughter and her...', or 'My wife and I are separated but I'd like to introduce my...' The United States Census Bureau tried to solve the problem by introducing the classification POSSLQs (pronounced 'poss LQs'), Persons of Opposite Sex Sharing Living Quarters! A more common but equally awkward expression is 'significant other', as in 'All employees and their significant others are invited.'

For the vast majority of people some type of

relationship has to be established before sexual activity occurs. Rarely, except in prostitution, fantasy, pornography or the anonymous homosexual sex of a tea-room or bath, is sex devoid of any personal interaction. In *Fear of Flying*, the novelist Erica Jong described the 'rarer than the unicorn...zipless fuck', the uncomplicated meeting of strangers who, sensing each other's sexual magnetism, meld easily into sexual embrace, without embarrassment, guilt, or fumbling of zippers. Most people who want sex form a relationship in order to get it.

Forming relationships

Traditional societies may seem quaint and restrictive but one advantage of highly structured sex roles is that they remove the trauma and pain the West accepts as the cost of choice and chance. Arranged marriages and chaperoned meetings between young people may frustrate dreams and desires but they protect egos and ensure social approval.

During this century the West has evolved many ways of making meetings between the sexes easier. Initially boy met girl under the watchful eye of the family, or religious or community organizations. Then coeducation emerged, and instead of entering the labour force at puberty, adolescents were kept at school to gain job skills. In the aftermath of two world wars families and populations shifted, and job opportunities changed. Women, more from necessity than choice, left the home to enter a trying and competitive job market. The extended family which traditionally provided access to new acquaintances and prospective partners began to break down. Heads of family, once entrusted with providing social and marriage partners, were no longer reliably in charge. By chance and necessity, a freer system of forming relationships evolved. The American sociologist Roger Libby has put forward two models for the formation of relationships within this more open framework. The first he calls the 'Primrose Path of Dating' and the second 'Branching Paths of Getting Together'.

On the Primrose Path, boys and girls share certain notions about romance from a very early age. Today youngsters are likely to be sexually attracted to each other earlier than in the past. According to studies by Carl Broderick, even 10-year-olds now play teasing and kissing games, though pre-arranged

meetings are rare at this age. With puberty group dating begins. By seventeen or eighteen single dating is the norm, the assumption being that after a number of random dates one will go out several times with the same person and that will constitute 'going steady'. Initially, sexual activities are bland but they build in intensity, until heavy petting or coitus signifies that the relationship is 'serious'. Boy and girl strive for different things in a serious relationship, but both are eager for the social status that goes with heterosexual involvement. If one or other is unhappy, the relationship breaks and each looks for another serious involvement. The pattern repeats itself

Stolen kisses while Papa dozes – young love frequently found a way round the chaperone system. Today Western society no longer holds parents responsible for ensuring their children's chastity until marriage.

beyond adolescence. Fleeting or experimental relationships are gradually replaced by steady ones, which tend to be more and more exclusive, until finally the partners become engaged. When both think the 'time is ripe', because they have made the best match possible, they marry.

Along the Branching Path individuals are, at all ages, less fixed in their expectations and behaviour. To them exclusivity in relationships is less important and pairing off is more the result of individual needs than obedience to any sex role script. In Branching Path relationships, erotic exchanges do not necessarily mean commitment, or fidelity to a single partner. Relationships are seen as an ongoing process of change rather than as the fulfilling of a static set of expectations. Marriage is not necessarily the goal and if it occurs it is not always along traditional lines.

For most people in the West the path followed has a lot to do with age and upbringing. Older people, brought up in a less affluent and permissive age, tend to have followed the Primrose rather than the Branching Path in forming their relationships. But stretches of both are not uncommon in any individual's life. And there is no doubt that marriage, and being faithful to one partner, remains the goal for many.

In forging new relationships after divorce people tend to follow the same path that led to their marriage. For travellers along the Primrose Path, widening of sexual experience occurs through sequential monogamy (or should it be called serial polygamy?). For those of the Branching Paths, experiences broaden more quickly and simultaneously.

What do people want?

A book called *Marriage and Alternatives: Exploring Intimate Relationships* starts. 'It is no secret that emotional closeness, touching and caressing, sexual fulfilment and intellectual sharing compose the most basic needs and desires.' All of these things are certainly desirable, but it is parochial and part of Western romanticism to think they are universal desires. A decade ago, in Japan, a survey of young unmarried adults found that what women desired most in men was 'manliness' and 'income' (security), and that men, above all, wanted 'femininity' (which really meant someone to care for their home and have their children). Ten years later a repeat survey

found that women put 'kindness' at the top of their wanted list and men 'independence', 'kindness' meaning understanding of the difficulties of being a wife and mother, and 'independence' the expectation that the woman will go out to work to contribute to a tight family budget. Idealistic Western notions of a fulfilling relationship were not in high demand. So, the components looked for in relationships are highly time- and culture-dependent.

In England, in 1950, the sociologist Geoffrey Gorer found that the husbandly virtues most highly prized by women were: understanding and consideration, thoughtfulness, a sense of humour, and various moral qualities,

in that order. Men ranked the most important wifely virtues as: being a good housekeeper, being attractive in both the social and physical sense, and displaying understanding and consideration. In 1969, nearly two decades later, Gorer found that women put understanding and consideration at the top of their list, but followed them with love, affection and kindness, and then generosity. Men still put being a housekeeper first, but raised being a good and affectionate mother to second place, followed by attractiveness.

A *Playboy* survey done in 1982 showed that readers – whether they were single, married, remarried or cohabiting – felt that love and

How long will their marriage last? Perhaps a lifetime if they understand that marriage requires working at .

family life were the most important ingredients of personal happiness. So did divorced women, but not divorced men; they ranked sex as more important than love (which may, of course, have been a factor in their divorce). The study also found that friendship was mentioned as a major requirement by non-marrieds of both sexes. For those without legal ties, friends tended to replace family and recreational sex was important. Even if not possessed, love and family life were still highly valued.

'Opposites attract' or 'birds of a feather'?

Aristotle thought of love as representing the search for something lacking in oneself: Christopher who needs affection and reassurance, will be drawn to Sara, who wants to provide them. The traditional stereotyped roles of men and women appear to reflect the idea of complementarity: the man is strong and aggressive, the provider and protector; the woman gentle and conciliatory, the homemaker and mother who needs to be protected and provided for. In many parts of the world where marriages are arranged, much thought is given to partners being complementary and therefore relatively self-sufficient units.

The opposite of a complementary relationship is a homogamous relationship, one in which the partners' needs and behaviours are similar. This kind of relationship appears to be becoming more common, now that people are freer to choose their own partners. Given a free choice people do tend to marry into a similar background, class, education and religion. Many studies have shown that a large proportion of dating partners live within three or four miles of each other (usually indicating a similar socio-economic background) and end up getting married.

Like needing like makes sense. It would be destructive in a relationship if only one partner

A similar background and similar attitudes to life bring people together. Interestingly second marriages are often less homogeneous. They are more likely to be a union between what people have become rather than between what their early background made them.

craved frequent sex, or exotic food, loud music and religion. Marriage bureaux and computer dating services certainly work on the principles of homogamy; they try to match people's backgrounds, needs, interests and tastes.

In reality there is no either/or. People relate to each other for both complementary and homogamous reasons, for reasons both rational and quixotic, and these reasons vary with time and circumstance. A partner who fills a particular need at one time may not be appreciated at another, and as a relationship matures, different needs and desires come to the surface.

A question of trade-offs

Romantics like to think of relationships as predestined. To the more prosaically minded, relationships involve an element of planning and need to be worked at. In fact all of us, whether we are aware of it or not, tend to make and break relationships on a cost and benefit basis; we weigh the costs against the benefits and opt for relationships that bring us most and cost us least. When the benefits fall below an acceptable level, we start looking for a relationship that offers more. This is the so-called exchange theory or equity theory of relationships. Interestingly, some psychologists believe that being 'overbenefited' in a relationship can also be bad; it can lead to feelings of guilt and therefore stress. Of course, we do not always weigh benefits against costs consciously, and even if we do, it disturbs us to think of love and marriage in such mercenary terms.

The most obvious trade-offs between marriage partners are those made in arranged marriages (land, livestock, income and so on). In a romantic 'love match' the idea of a *quid pro quo* may be distasteful, but ultimately, when the passion fades, the relationship must depend on some kind of equity. Unfortunately there is no agreement as to what constitutes equitable trade. As one remarried woman remarked to me recently: 'My new husband is my treasure, but he is his ex-wife's garbage. I can imagine my ex-husband's new wife saying the same.'

When one has invested only a small amount of time, work, or emotion in a relationship, change may occur quite easily. But when one has invested years in a relationship, and it is inextricable from children, an extended fam-

ily, status and so on, it is likely to have a solidity and momentum of its own. That does not mean to say that all one's reactions to adversity or to the possibility of change are based on the investment principle; sometimes they are idealistic rather than realistic, irrational rather than rational.

In judging the quality of a relationship we tend to use such measures as intensity, intimacy, duration and sexual compatibility, but a high score in one or two departments says little about scores in the others. Some relationships last only a few days, yet are so charged with emotion that they are remembered for life. Others, even if they endure for many decades, may never have been close or passionate. Others have wonderful sex, but that is all.

Relationships and sex

Whether free or arranged marriages are the norm, most cultures assume that closeness and intimacy go on developing over the years. Maybe they should, and sometimes they do, but research and common experience show that neither time nor a long-term sexual relationship makes for greater intimacy, or indeed leads to more equitable relationships.

It has long been known that in any relationship frequency of coitus generally declines with time. Kinsey documented this some 30 years ago and the *Playboy* survey found it again in 1982. And yet many women say that the quality of coitus, as measured by the likelihood of orgasm, increases as a relationship continues. Feminists say this is because men are more willing to recognize women's enjoyment of sex as a marriage continues, others that women take longer to adapt to coitus, and that once they do they become orgasmically more responsive. Another view is that men are learning to take more time and care in coitus and are becoming less selfish. And yet another is that, with age, women become more responsive and men less 'driven' and slower to ejaculate.

In the 1982 *Playboy* study even the most sexually active respondents reported that after four years with the same partner frequency of intercourse dropped from four or more times a week to between seven and eight times a month. Other studies have shown that, regardless of the age at which people marry, frequency of coitus in the first year is rarely equalled in subsequent years. The major stimulus to continuing high frequency coitus bet-

When the picnic is over . . . Cartoon by Sempé.

ween partners seems to be novelty rather than intimacy or love, although other factors within in or outside the relationship may also have some effect.

Many studies post-Kinsey have tried to relate frequency of intercourse to overall sexual contentment. But an awkward chicken-and-egg problem is hatched: the more you like it, the more you do it, and the more you do it, the more likely you are to like it! Nevertheless certain correlations are apparent. Too much sex and too little sex (the definition of too much and too little is a personal matter) make people unhappy, but at every frequency and in every type of relationship men, more than women, are likely to desire greater frequency. This is most noticeable among single men but is also true of the majority of married men. Only among the divorced and those who are cohabiting do men and women seem equally pleased or displeased with their coital frequency. The *Playboy* survey found that, for their respondents, once a week was a sort of cut-off point; discontent was likely to set in once frequency dropped below once a week.

A very touchy and common dilemma presented to marriage counsellors is disparity in desire for sex play. The cliché answer is compromise. This certainly works for some couples but for many it is a recipe for both partners to remain dissatisfied. To suggest any 'suitable' frequency of coitus is presumptuous and arbitrary, and likely to cause as many problems as it solves. While the overall average frequency of two to three times a week for married couples has been around for some time, it is no measure of harmony, nor is it in any way prescriptive or suitable for everyone. Partners must work out their own ways of meeting their own needs, remembering that frequency of coitus, orgasm, or any other aspect of sexual activity is only one barometer of compatibility.

Primordial couplehood, carved by a Senufo artist. How are we in the West, with all our economic, social and reproductive freedoms, to go about reinventing couplehood? There are signs that the 'Me' generation of the 1960s and 1970s is giving way to a 'We' generation.

Marriage on trial

Marriages are made for many reasons, sex being only one of them and sometimes not the major one. In fact social and economic reasons predominate if one looks at marriage on a worldwide basis. Marriage is more than a relationship: it is also an idea, an image, a public announcement of commitment, an institution sanctioned by society, a package of rights and responsibilities. And it is the only relationship that all societies approve of as being a proper setting for coitus, and the bearing and rearing of children.

It is difficult for most people under 40 years of age in the English-speaking West to accept that only several generations ago, among their grandparents and great grandparents, arranged marriages were fairly common. Marriage was thought too important to be left to chance. Arranged marriages are still the rule in most of the Islamic world, Africa, Southeast Asia, and even in modern India and Japan. Youngsters in these societies may chafe at such non-romantic practices yet they continue not only because of cultural resistance to change but also because they seem to best serve the population's needs. In Japan and India, modern societies by many measures, love marriages are accepted, but they account for fewer than half of all marriages.

The fact that people in the West today are cohabiting more and marrying later suggests that the choosing of a marriage partner, when one has freedom of choice, is no easy matter. The wisdom and accumulated experience of well-intentioned elders has been dispensed with and is not easy to replace. Eligible young men and women feel they need to experiment with alternative lifestyles, 'try their wings', 'live a little' before they settle down. Women, especially, want to develop a career before they marry.

Cohabitation is a solution that fulfils both the sexual drive and the need for affiliation to a 'significant other'. It still carries a stigma – the expression 'living in sin' is often used and still has the power to wound and hurt. In the United States, the Census Bureau estimated that the number of cohabiting couples rose from about half a million in 1970 to just under two million in 1982. And according to a study by C. L. Cole in 1977 about 23 per cent of US college students had had a live-in sexual relationship with someone, however briefly, at some time in their lives.

Rapidly rising divorce rates in the last fifteen years show how the forces maintaining marriage have changed. Marriage used to be a partnership between male breadwinner and female housekeeper. Now it is more likely to be a union of free choice and greater flexibility. However while either partner can raise a child or go out to work the stereotype roles of our parents' generation still hold, by and large, for our children. The formal wedding sets in train a lifetime marriage pattern.

Does the testing of relationships by cohabitation eventually lead to marriage, and does it lead to better or more durable marriages? A 1982 survey among the generally conservative and happily married women readers of the *Ladies' Home Journal* found that 25 per cent of those who responded, who had on average been married for 12 years, had lived with their husbands before marriage. Incompatible couples separate before marriage of course. Many get married and then divorce. One cannot help suspecting that those who feel the need to test a relationship so extensively before marrying may have valid doubts about themselves or their partner which eventually, even when marriage has taken place, prove insurmountable.

A strong commitment to marriage is perhaps the best index of whether or not a partnership will endure. Most marriage and sex counsellors, as well as married people themselves, say that no matter how long a couple lives together it is not the same as marriage. The institution, with its myths and realities, strengths and weaknesses, pleasures and sorrows, sets in motion special feelings and forces.

A geisha putting on traditional make-up (in Japan the nape of the neck is considered very sexy). The geisha is not the institution she used to be. Today only the most affluent clients can afford her. She offers a type of entertainment – conversation, singing and dancing – not expected of a wife. Sex is a very expensive extra and, if desired, must be separately contracted for; but it is not always available.

Marriage should be...

The expectation of most people marrying in the West today is that marriage will supply almost everything they need – a comfortable home, sex, affection, companionship, children, security, entertainment, ego support, psychological counselling... and all with the approval of the family and society at large. Marriage is expected to provide a safe harbour from the storms and currents of the world outside. If it truly does provide all these things, why are only 50 per cent of adults in the United States married and living with their spouses?

The reality of marriage is very different, because it involves two people with different needs, and must accommodate the career development of one or both partners, and the needs of children.

In Japan, where I lived and worked for several years, marriage is surrounded with very few of the expectations typical in the West. Husband and wife are expected to occupy separate social spheres, and their sex roles are starkly divergent. For a Japanese girl, even in the 1980s, marriage is still the primary goal. She expects to marry, be responsible for the home, raise two children, and cater to her husband's needs. Her security and social rank will depend (as they still do to a large extent in the West) on how well her husband does. But her emotional support and companionship will come from her original family, her children, and female friends. Her sexual desires and fantasies may be met by her husband, but probably only partly so; she will satisfy the rest by reading and watching television.

The world of the Japanese husband is very different. His job, not his wife, will occupy the greater part of his life. He will probably relax and enjoy himself with his chums and a bar hostess. He will be more willing to share his sexual and other intimate thoughts with an old school friend than his wife. He will have sexual relations with his wife but satisfy his erotic fantasies and other sexual needs with a hostess or a prostitute, if he is wealthy probably with a regular mistress. If he is homosexually oriented, he is still likely to marry, and seek male partners outside his marriage. Mistresses are no longer as accepted as they were in the past but they are still part of the fabric of affluent Japanese society. The West certainly has its share of bar companions, prostitutes and mistresses but they are part of an uneasy sub-culture, spoken of in embarrassed or defiant tones.

Adjusting to a sexual relationship

In the West more people are becoming sexually active earlier, and more are having sexual experiences with more than one partner before they cohabit or marry. But these facts tell us little about the sexual sophistication or satisfaction achieved by wider and more precocious experience. Even with premarital sexual experience, most people bring to marriage two to three decades of sexually inhibiting influences. Society does not look on sex before marriage as a training ground for the gaining of sexual expertise and yet somehow people are expected, when they marry, to become sexually proficient and sexually fulfilled.

Several recent studies suggest that, particularly for women, the earlier in life one starts having orgasms, the more likely one is to have orgasms in a married or stable relationship. And the more one masturbates the more sexually responsive one will be in such a relationship. However, these findings are not borne out by all studies, and in any case women's overall satisfaction with a relationship correlates only to a minor degree with sexual compatibility, and even less with orgastic satisfaction *per se*. Even regularly orgasmic women (apparently in the minority) say that orgasm is no guarantee of sexual satisfaction.

Judging by many well conducted studies, for women the consensus seems to be: 'If the relationship is good, the sex will feel good. The better the relationship, the more likely I am to come.' For men the consensus goes like this: 'My orgasm is almost inevitable in any case. And if the sex is good, the relationship will feel good.'

The other man and the other woman

Among the most ogled sexual statistics are those concerning extramarital sex (EMS). They are looked at with apprehension ('It's almost bound to happen at one time or another, isn't it?'), with regret ('Yes, I was one of those statistics'), with relief ('Yes, it happened to us but it was a long time ago'), confidence ('Our marriage is too solid for that to happen') or pleasure ('It was wonderful while it lasted'). Actually the likelihood of extramarital sex, or sex outside stable cohabitation, is quite high as we shall see, and male-female double standards being what they are, more attention is usually paid to her experiences than to his.

Statistically the 'other' woman or man in an extramarital affair has backed a loser – more marriages survive infidelity than break because of it. Typically meetings are restricted, often hurried, often tainted with guilt and apprehension. Yet, if it did not offer such powerful satisfactions and serve such varied functions, why should EMS thrive?

A quick run-through of EMS surveys in the popular press reveals the following:

Year	Survey	Women % EMS	Men % EMS
1970	*Psychology Today*	36	40
1975	*Redbook*	39	n/a
1980	*Cosmopolitan*	69 (over-35s)	n/a
1981	*Hite Report*	n/a	66
1982	*Playboy*	34	36
1983	*Ladies' Home Journal*	21	n/a

n/a = not asked

What these figures show most obviously is the disparity in the readerships of the magazines concerned. But it is interesting how closely the *Psychology Today* and *Playboy* figures tally, even though the surveys were twelve years apart.

How are such statistics to be interpreted? The first difficulty is that the surveys rarely make clear just what it is they are asking. A question like: 'Have you ever engaged in extramarital sex?' may be interpreted by some to include petting, by others to mean only coitus. Even when the question is: 'Have you ever engaged in extramarital intercourse?', some respondents will include homosexual affairs or sex with prostitutes, others may only mention heterosexual encounters with significant emotional involvement. Also in Western society, extramarital sex is usually clandestine, or the subject of bragging, so the truth of some answers will be in doubt.

The second problem involves the profile of the responding populations. The bulk of replies to such surveys come from men and women in their twenties, thirties and early forties. But we know that there are significant differences in behaviour among age groups, more so among women. At present, for example, younger women are more likely to have affairs than older women. This raises the female average. On the other hand, most of the respondents were not yet at the halfway mark in their sexual lives. This tends to lower all averages.

Kinsey's data is much more reliable, but it is now nearly 40 years old; it reflects the behaviours of the grandparents and great grand-parents of the present generation. In the early 1940s about 50 per cent of married men and 25 per cent of married women had experienced heterosexual extramarital intercourse by the age of forty. Present estimates of EMS in the United States are that by the age of sixty some 75 per cent of both men and women will, at some time in their marriage, have had coitus with someone other than their spouse.

Information about other countries is scarce and probably not comparable. Often the figures reported seem unrealistically low. For exam-ple, in a 1961 study of French women by the French Institute of Public Opinion, only 7 per cent admitted to adultery; the investigators felt that at least 22 per cent would have been a more realistic figure. A 1971 survey of married couples in the United Kingdom, by G. Gorer, found that only 8 per cent admitted to extra-marital sexual experiences. In 1979 the British magazine *Woman* put the figure for British men at 25 per cent. A 1980 survey reported that about 15 per cent of Italian women admit-ted to EMS; another Italian survey found about 40 per cent of Italian men making the same admission. A 1983 survey in Japan found one in forty women had had extramarital affairs compared with one in five men.

Adultery is the legal term for EMS. In English, the word 'adultery' has more moral overtones than 'extramarital sex', and 'infidel-ity' even more; both imply a breach of trust, and are surrounded by a constellation of words such as 'unfaithful', 'stray', 'cheating', 'fooling around', and so on. However, in many societies adultery is not illegal or clan-destine, and even if it is considered immoral, extenuating circumstances are recognized: 'With a drunk of a husband like that, who can blame her?', or 'If I had a shrew of a wife like that, I'd do the same.'

Context and reasons for EMS

A 1983 review by Anthony Thompson, an Australian psychologist, found that in the United States no particular social class, ethnic group or educational level has a monopoly on extramarital relations. For women, however, there do seem to be some links between EMS and generation (those born in the 1950s and 1960s are more likely than their mothers or grandmothers to engage in EMS), also politi-cal persuasion (conservatives are less likely than liberals to engage in EMS), residential

'Darling, we can't go on meeting like this!' Cartoon by ffolkes.

area (rural inhabitants, less likely), and occupation (those working outside the home, more likely). None of these factors is clearly identifiable for men. Nor does the fact of being of one religion rather than another seem to be of importance, either for men or for women. But devoutness is significant. The devout of all persuasions are least likely, and the re-ligiously unaffiliated or inactive most likely, to engage in EMS.

However, when it comes to the characteris-tics of the primary relationship there are clear correlations with the frequency and nature of

Prelude to intimacy. The prospect and possibility of getting to know someone new, emotionally and sexually, is highly exciting, not easy to pass up. Though fantasized about by those both in and out of extramarital relationships, frequent and easy indulgence demands a depth of personal understanding rarely found or accepted in the West.

extramarital relationships for both men and women. EMS is more likely to occur when one or other partner considers the marital relationship poor and unsatisfactory and the frequency of coitus too low. However, some authors claim that this does not lead to EMS unless feelings of personal alienation are also present.

For men, the most common reasons for EMS are the desire for novelty and the desire for ego enhancement – either or both can be provided by an uncritical and flattering partner. For women, however, the reasons seem to be more varied:

○ to find greater emotional satisfaction, a more vibrant and communicative relationship, a release from emotional boredom;

○ to gain social status;

○ to retaliate for real or imagined mistreatment, sexual or nonsexual;

○ to find a new and perhaps more skilful and exciting sexual partner;

○ to accede to the wishes of a respected or valued friend;

○ to assert independence, or regain self-esteem by being desired by someone new.

The most common single reason given by both men and women in one study was 'constant fighting at home'.

The temptations of opportunity

Opportunities for extramarital sex are now greater than in the past. Both men and women have more mobility and more disposable income. Women, now in the workforce in greater numbers, spend less time at home. Families live in neighbourhoods where they have relative anonymity. More children are leaving the family nest earlier. Certainly the media, with their frequent focus on extramarital affairs, encourage people to think the grass may be greener on the other side of the fence. Also, in the last two decades, reliable contraception has reduced a major disincentive to extramarital coitus. And, significantly, most of these factors have impinged mainly on women – men never have been particularly hampered by children, money, environment or the fear of pregnancy.

The moral climate has also changed. More so than in the past people recognize that not all extramarital relationships are wrong or detrimental. It is more accepted that individuality and personal growth may not be totally satisfied by one other person. 'Emotional independence', 'sex role egalitarianism' and 'humanistic expansion' are more than sociological buzz words; they actually mean that more people are doing more of 'their own thing'.

EMS: the idea and the reality

Does EMS weaken the primary bond? Does it disrupt trust and intimacy? Might it, in some instances, strengthen some aspects of a relationship? The answer to all these questions is a qualified 'yes'.

Many couples who cohabit rather than marry do so on the tacit or explicit understanding that sexual relations with others are 'allowed'. Partners who enter into marriage usually do so on the understanding, again tacit or explicit, that affairs are not allowed. When it comes to it many cohabiting couples find their partners' affairs just as hard to take as married couples do. Understandings and expectations do not always tally. The reality of a partner's EMS is often more difficult to cope with than the idea.

A significant difference exists, however, between homosexual and heterosexual couples. Among gay male couples in established relationships expectations of sexual exclusivity diminish rapidly after the first year together. Not infrequently homosexual couples will have relationships in which new sexual partners are individually enjoyed or even mutually shared. The term 'comarital' sex would in fact be more appropriate.

More frequently than not husband and wife become ready for an affair independently. Early in the relationship the couple may discuss sex with others: 'It's OK when you're on a trip away from home', or 'It's OK if I'm out of action or somehow unavailable for a long period of time', or 'It's OK as long as you're discreet and I don't know about it,' or 'It's OK as long as it's just for kicks and you don't get involved'. Nevertheless EMS is seen as a powerful threat. Some 85 per cent of US couples in a major study done in 1979 admitted as much. The breach of trust was seen as fundamentally damaging.

When a relationship has endured for a number of years the idea or the reality of extramarital affairs may be more tolerated, especially by those who have had extramarital experiences themselves. But it is still easier to accept one's own behaviour than a partner's. Acceptance may imply that EMS does not represent an impending break to the primary relationship or a lack of care and concern for the family as a whole. 'I know he loves me and the children. If he has a fling now and then, I know it's just that and of little lasting significance.' Many men and women see extramarital relationships as necessary safety valves for pressures and needs which build up within or outside a marriage. The partner having the extramarital relationship may even see it as a way of helping to preserve the marriage.

In fact most research finds that wives are more tolerant of their husbands' affairs than vice versa. One study of divorced people by Kinsey and his colleagues revealed that only a quarter of those women who knew of their husbands' extramarital activity thought it a significant factor in the break-up; half saw it as a moderate factor. Among the men, however, half thought that their wives' infidelity was the chief reason for the break-up and a third thought it an important, but not the main, reason. An interesting sidelight on the subject is provided by a 1983 study of some 200 separated and divorced individuals by Graham Spanier and Randie Margolis. More than 80 per cent of both the men and the women in this study felt that their own extramarital relations were the result of marital problems but that their spouses' were the cause of such problems! Selective sex-watching indeed.

Too often the subject of extramarital relations is first broached when suspicions are already flickering or feelings have already been hurt. Anger and jealousy are stock reactions. Several studies have found that women's immediate reactions to EMS are somewhat different from men's. Women usually try to patch up or improve the primary relationship; they try to 'beat the competition' by making themselves more attractive to their partner. Men are more likely to go out and seek consolation with an affair of their own. Assaults on lovers are not rare, but despite such images as bull elephants charging one another, stags locking antlers, and gentlemen drawing swords at dawn, the emotionally wounded human male in contemporary Western

society does not usually confront his rival.

Gay couples tend to deal with jealousy and sexual competition rather differently. With lesbians the tendency is for the *couple* to deal with the 'competition' and possibly draw closer as a result. Among gay men the tendency is for the primary relationship to break; partners generally prefer to 'switch' rather than fight or work it out.

In a US study of 3880 married people done by Anthony Pietropinto in 1979 some 19 per cent of the husbands and 14 per cent of the wives said they would demand an immediate divorce if they found their partner was having an affair. About half the women said they would calmly confront their husband with his adultery, and about 40 per cent of the husbands said they would do the same. In practice, however, many husbands and wives avoid confrontation and live with repressed jealousy, hurt and insecurity until either circumstances force open acknowledgement or the situation resolves itself. Sometimes the status quo, the sharing of a partner with another, is preferable to losing a partner altogether. Only for a minority of couples are extramarital adventures acknowledged and accepted as unthreatening.

Open relationships

When both partners feel similarly they may, by word or deed, contract to allow each other sexual intimacy with others. The term 'open' marriage or 'open' relationship is often used to describe such arrangements. Ideally it

'It was hard bargaining – we got the milk and honey, but the anti-adultery clause stays in.' Punch cartoon. People often accept clear-cut rules even if they bend them occasionally.

Right *Swinging party, California style. Though mate swapping receives a lot of media attention, attendance at swinging events seems to have peaked or be on the decline. Sexual experimentation is still most likely to occur in twosomes, or among three or four people, rather than in a large group.*

The Swing, a Bazaar-style Indian painting (c. 1830) showing the exuberant possibilities of group sex. The central pair of lovers sits on a swing composed of other couples.

is a relationship of equals where neither 'owns' the other and both enrich the union by contributing gains from their own experiences, sexual or otherwise. Only 4 per cent of Pietropinto's respondents thought open marriage possible or practical, and in my own professional experience I have met few people capable of it for long. Some renegotiation of the contract usually becomes necessary: the nature or frequency of the outside sex becomes more restricted – only with or not with a certain partner, only during separate vacations or work trips or not while the children are on the scene, and so on.

Swinging

Further from the mainstream are couples, known as 'swingers' or 'mate swappers', who engage in mutual and consensual EMS as a form of recreation. Sex may involve a third party, more often female than male, or another couple or a whole group. For the

majority of swingers the stated goal is novelty and sexual pleasure. A small minority participate from a utopian philosophy that society should be free of sexual jealousies and frustrations. In the United States the total number of swinging couples is estimated at between 1 and 5 per cent of all married couples. In Japan the number is near 0.3 per cent. Figures for other countries are not known. In New York and San Francisco there are swingers' clubs where couples, for an entrance fee, disport themselves with others in unabashed sexual games and gymnastics.

Swingers, by the nature of their behaviour, which titillates some and repels others, attract a great deal of interest. Yet most studies have found them to be little different from most of their neighbours, except in their sexual arrangements. In fact in many ways swingers are remarkably conservative socially and politically. The majority begin swinging at the husband's urging, or sometimes intimidation, though it seems that wives become more enthusiastic once they get involved. Women can obviously participate longer, with more partners, and without the obligation to 'perform' that men feel. In the past rather biased etiquette allowed single women, but not single men, to join in. Now women are demanding that unattached males should be allowed to take part too. The more the merrier.

The effects of swinging on a marriage are debated. Participants often say that sharing EMS adventures strengthens their relationship. Researchers are not so sure. Masters and Johnson, for instance, mistrust swingers' positive statements, and say that jealousy is probably repressed. Yet no study has revealed more divorces or more marital battles among swingers than among any other comparable group. Indeed a 1977 study carried out in the United States by Brian Gilmartin found that swingers were generally happier with their lot than most.

Divorce and remarriage

Alone among modern nations that allow divorce, Italy is the only Western country that does not depend heavily on it as a solution to marital strife. Perhaps it is only a matter of time – divorce did not become legal in Italy until 1974. Italian men reject divorce mainly for financial reasons (alimony awards are high and taxes soar). Italian women reject divorce mainly out of fear of ostracism. One woman described the social ordeal of divorce like this: 'I was abandoned by my friends, who were afraid I would seduce their husbands, and chased by their husbands, who thought I would be an easy target. I discovered that a divorced woman in Italy has to renounce both love and sex if she wants to lead a quiet life.' To maintain social networks but resolve marital woes, Italians separate. Not uncommonly the husband moves in with a mistress, whom he has probably been seeing for years, and the wife retains her respectable married status. Divorce is something that happens to less than 2 per cent of Italian couples.

In the United States three to five marriages in ten end in divorce, though it is often the same people getting divorced over and over again who raise the statistics. Until the early 1970s, in most of the states in the USA, adultery was the only justification for divorce accepted by the courts – many a photographer and model made good money providing 'evidence'. Currently 'no-fault' divorce laws are in force in 48 out of the 50 states. It is now, for better or worse, almost as easy for Americans to get divorced as married. Approximately one third of marriages in the Soviet Union end in divorce before the first anniversary. In Britain the divorce rate is about one in four though the marriages last longer.

Sexual problems are not usually the main reason for divorce or the severing of a long-standing relationship. But the importance of sex in a relationship is very relative and subjective. As one of my clients remarked: 'When everything is going right, sex is only 20 per cent of my marriage. When things are going wrong, it's 90 per cent.' More usually break-ups happen because of a gradual growing apart over the years.

Separation and divorce are seldom easy on the emotions. They provoke feelings of anger, blame, guilt, hurt and failure. The intention to

Here comes the bride, ferried along the famous canals of Venice. If her marriage to Signor Bruno fails she is not likely to remarry. She may, discreetly, take a lover, but to the neighbours she will remain Signora Bruno.

divorce must be uncomfortably explained to children, parents, friends and colleagues. But when it actually happens it is often a welcome escape from hopeless or neurotic entanglement into a brighter, freer world. Some people positively blossom once the initial anguish is over. Though some remain bitter, most eventually look back on their union as a learning experience rather than as a period of pain and failure.

Divorce is often followed by a period of sexual experimentation and exploration. There may be a frenzy of different sex partners in an attempt to regain confidence and self-esteem, particularly if the problems in the marriage were mainly sexual. Or there may be a desire to make up for lost time. But for many divorcees, however, starting the dating game again is frightening and disheartening. It requires purposeful re-integration into the world of the unattached, a catching up on social and sexual mores which may have changed a great deal in the intervening years.

The majority of divorced people remarry and find their second marriage much more satisfactory than the first. Most second marriages seem to avoid the sexual problems that may have bedevilled the first. People enter into second marriages with more amorous and erotic experience, more confidence about making their preferences known and enquiring about those of their partners, more willingness to be adventurous in their love-making. In fact there is more flexibility all round. Second-time-rounders may do things with lovers or new spouses they never dreamed of doing with their original mates. They are more likely to know what it takes to make marriage work and to have learned the spirit of compromise so necessary to all successful relationships.

Motives for remarriage usually echo those for first marriages: sexual needs, companionship, love and intimacy, desire for commitment, obedience to social pressures and the belief that it takes two to raise a family. Reasons for not remarrying are lingering bitterness, fear of failing a second time, and fear of hurting the children or others. In the case of divorced women another reason is the numerical deficit of available or desirable partners. The number of heterosexual unmarried men over thirty is significantly less than the number of unmarried heterosexual women over thirty. This is so in most of the affluent

nations of the West. Contemporary calculations of the United States' population, for example, show that for one in five women over thirty no male partner is available, and the disproportion affects black women even more. In fact two-thirds of those who live alone in the United States are women. In 1982, in the United States, more than 25 000 marriages took place in which one partner was over sixty-five. Women may be having to settle for men considerably removed from the *beau idéal*.

Most women today put closeness and shared feelings a long way before tight-lipped virility. If there is dissatisfaction in a marriage, the wife usually tries to draw closer to her husband; he, for his part, is more likely to seek satisfaction outside the marriage.

Improving relationships

If words were deeds, or individuals as predictable as machines, the end of this chapter would be a pleasure to write and a greater pleasure to read. There is no shortage of advice on how to improve sexual relationships – 'how to' recipes pour out of women's magazines, newspaper advice columns and TV and radio shows. 'Kiss your partner daily on waking', 'Smile when you greet him/her', 'Be open to change', 'Don't welcome your lover with a string of problems'... good pieces of advice all. But a successful relationship is like a chess game, full of nuance and subtlety, the moves of one player influencing the moves of the other, and so on. Even the doyen of behavioural psychology, B.F. Skinner, said of his relationship with his wife Eve: 'There is a problem doing things together. I walk faster and longer than she. She needs entertainment (movies, TV, plays) that I can do very well without. What is a fair deal then? How much should be done to make her happy in spite of the fact that it will make me less happy?' Can we lesser mortals solve our relationship problems any more easily? Can we even agree on what constitutes a good or ideal relationship?

In this chapter I have mainly talked about marriage and long-term relationships. Marriage of course has the support of law, tradition and convention, and the strength of stated, overt commitment, and its guidelines and obligations, observed or not, are understood by all. But what happens when partners are not married? They have to evolve their own rules. Any relationship, as it develops, undergoes continuous examination and reassessment by the parties to it. What does a cohabiting couple measure or assess their relationship against? In my opinion both cohabiting and marriage need working at but the former more than the latter.

At one level relationships can be improved by technical measures, such as earning more money, or making sure the children are happy, or spending more time boosting one's partner's ego, or reaffirming commitment to the relationship, or making more time for sexual and non-sexual togetherness. But at a deeper level it is not technique alone that will most enhance a relationship but willingness to change attitudes. As one marriage counsellor said to me: 'I can improve a couple's sexual technique and easily solve problems of ignorance, shame or inhibition. I am most stymied, however, by how to change motivation, attitudes and basic behaviour.' Couples who go for counselling or who buy 'how to...' books usually want to know 'How do I go about changing him/her?' rather than 'How do I go about changing myself?' It is no easier to permanently change sexual behaviour than it is to change smoking or eating habits. Nevertheless people do manage to stop smoking and control their weight, and many people do manage to improve their relationships.

Recipes for loving change

The easiest place to start is to *emphasize the positive in the relationship*. When you are pleased with something, say so. 'I like it when you do that', 'You look sexy in those jeans', and so on. Also, *emphasize your commitment to the relationship*. Don't threaten to walk out or get divorced, and never resort to physical violence. Tell yourself that everything you say and do must build towards improving, not weakening, the relationship.

Give yourself and your partner permission to ask, question or comment on things that may help you understand each other better. 'You know, I've always wanted to ask you if...', 'I've never

told you before but I'd like you to...', 'Do you know what turns me on/off the most?', or 'Which do you like better,... or...?'

Perhaps the most important permission is to *allow yourself and your partner to be honest*. Tell each other, clearly and lovingly, what you like and don't like, want and don't want. Don't always expect your partner to take the initiative in the honesty game, and don't expect him/her to know intuitively what you prefer. If you want to try something old, new or special, give yourself permission to say so. 'Let's do something different tonight. What would you like to do?', or 'You know what we've never tried that I would like?' One of the reasons men most frequently give for visiting prostitutes is they they want sexual favours denied them by their regular partners. Oral-genital play is high on the list. A reason frequently given by women for trying new sexual relationships is that they want a level of intimacy, communication and patience their regular partner does not provide.

Years of habit may make new practices seem strange and suspect. But novelty in an established, secure context can be particularly pleasing, erotic and enticing. *Give yourself and your partner permission to say 'Let's spice up our love life a little'.* Said warmly and

Many partners, even those who have been together for a long time, can reach new trust and intimacy through massage, a unique way of giving and receiving pleasure.

at the appropriate moment it should be well received.

Telling your fantasies and erotic desires out loud is a very effective way of initiating new sexual activities. You are not obliged to put them into practice, but on the other hand do not forbid yourself to make them a reality. Even if they only serve to break the ice they will have served their purpose.

Give yourself permission to interact with your partner in different ways. If he always initiates sex, you can. If she always asks for a massage, you can. Game playing, flirting and seductive behaviour, perhaps unused since dating years, can be an exciting return to sexual yesterdays.

Important too is the need to *make time to be together; to be loving and erotic.* Often the excitement of planning and expectancy are lost in a welter of chores and obligations.

A willingness to *improve communication skills* is also important. This means more than speaking with a smile, shrug, sigh, laugh or frown, messages which are not always as clear as they might be. To keep communication open and clear:

○ Don't beat around the bush. Say what you like and don't like. Let your partner know just what you have in mind, but be considerate about his/her feelings.

○ If you want to say no to something, say why and what you would rather do instead.

○ When requesting something you think your partner might not agree to, be patient and understanding if you are turned down. Try to find out why he/she feels that way. Remember, sometimes you have to agree to disagree.

○ Don't dwell on past grievances. Talk about anticipated pleasures instead.

○ If in doubt about your partner's meaning, intentions, or desires, ask rather than guess. He/she will generally appreciate your interest.

'Oh no, the neighbours never complain – it turns them on.' Cartoon by ffolkes.

Here are four final guidelines – they require thought and work but they will pay huge dividends:

○ Relate to your partner as a person, not just as a body.

○ Be willing to please and be pleased.

○ Be flexible, courteous and considerate.

○ Balance trust, seriousness and play.

One of the wonders of human sexual relationships is that satisfaction often comes as much from giving erotic pleasure as from receiving it. The same is true of love. Therein lies a powerful truth: in love and sex the greatest gain may come from the uninhibited offering of oneself, the sweetest feelings from putting aside inhibitions and self-control. Passion and receptivity to passion are potent aphrodisiacs □.

CHAPTER
11

Reproduction and birthwatching

One of life's most significant events, heralded by nine months of advertisement and watchful waiting, typically goes unwitnessed even by the individuals most intimately involved: childbirth. Despite moves to humanize childbirth in the West, most mothers are drugged, not fully aware of the birth process, and from the supine delivery position get a distorted view of the moment of birth. Fathers are not usually present. Although fathers are positively encouraged to attend deliveries in Scandinavia and the Netherlands, and tolerated in delivery rooms in a few other countries, in the majority of developed countries, as in the United States and Japan, fathers are excluded by hospital fiat, physician's whim or social custom. Birth typically takes place in the presence of strangers from a select professional class, not in the presence of relatives or friends, and in the anonymity of a hospital rather than in the familiar surroundings of the home. In some cultures, Mayan Indian for example, the pregnant woman's whole family, including the men and boys, attends the birth. But birthwatching *en famille* is rare. Most societies, even those where medicine is primitive, bar male relatives and children from the scene, and leave support and assistance of the mother to an older experienced woman or female relative. Many a father wishes he could attend the birth of his child and many a mother would welcome his presence.

Why the privacy and secrecy? Modesty and embarrassment certainly enter into it, as do considerations of hygiene, but so do mystery and magic. And the more the process of bringing new life into the world is seen as something women alone are responsible for the more exclusively is it kept the preserve of women. Among paleolithic people, who seem to have had only the vaguest appreciation of the male's part in reproduction (as far as we can judge from aboriginal societies still in existence today), birth was a secret female rite, the counterpart of secret male rites. Even in societies that had some understanding of the male's part in reproduction the process of birth tended to be looked on as a physical and spiritual experience proper to women, as a privilege of the female gender; that it took place in secret had nothing to do with sexual shame or modesty and everything to do with the special and fragile magic of the event. Even today some societies believe that at the moment of birth the spirit enters the child's body. It is quite logical therefore that only a few special individuals should be present, and those selected few must have the power to aid the process physically or spiritually. With minor variations and some notable exceptions, societies all over the world admit only the privileged few – midwife, priest, doctor, witchdoctor – to the drama of birthwatching.

Right *The creation of new life, an ancient and universal image. Bas relief from a temple in southern India.*

In North Borneo birth is watched by the whole community, and the father takes an active part in helping the baby to emerge. In the West attending a birth is a rare privilege.

The rise and fall of the midwife

In the West this heritage of secrecy and magic has been complicated by two other factors: modesty, and professional jealousy between midwives and physicians. For many centuries it was taboo for women to be seen naked by strangers, even by doctors, and until the eighteenth century almost all births were attended by midwives. Midwives offered, as Elizabeth Nihell put it in her 1760 *Treatise on the Art of Midwifery*, '...a certain shrewd vivacity, a grace of ease, a hardiness of performance, and especially a kind of unction of the heart...' Even so midwives in earlier centuries were often subject to abuse, and sometimes hanged as witches if they had attended a birth where the baby or mother died or the child was born deformed.

Today, in the developing world, between 60 and 80 per cent of babies are delivered at home by midwives whose abilities run from the primitive and unlearned to the highly skilled and trained, often reflecting the social status of the mother. Even in the developed countries the midwifery profession is enjoying a resurgence.

The systematic development of obstetrical knowledge can be credited to the Frenchman Ambroise Paré. In 1551 he wrote a treatise on obstetrics in which he encouraged fellow physicians to master 'podalic version', the manual turning of the foetus to facilitate delivery, an art relatively ignored since the days of Hippocrates. The few physicians who mastered this technique were often called in by midwives when they encountered the not infrequent situation of a baby ill positioned for delivery, its life in danger. Otherwise men were not admitted to the delivery of 'honest' women. In 1522 a German physician, Dr Wortt of Hamburg, dressed in women's clothes in order to be present at a birth. For the double indiscretion – curiosity and cross-dressing – he was burned at the stake.

In 1663 Louis XIV of France summoned his physician to attend one of his favourite mistresses in childbirth, thus giving royal approval and snob value to male supervision of delivery. The fad soon spread throughout the French aristocracy; the services of an *accoucheur* became a status symbol and physicians were not slow to play the role of male midwife in return for fat fees. This was the beginning of obstetrics as a specialized medical discipline and the beginning of the end for midwifery as the only profession concerned with women during pregnancy and birth. Women were denied access to medical schools and therefore excluded from full knowledge of a process of the most intimate importance to their sex.

Calculating the risks

Pregnancy and birth have always been risky. Even today, with modern medical knowledge, the leading causes of death among women between fifteen and fifty are pregnancy and birth. United Nations statistics for the decade 1970–80 show that for every 100 000 live births in developed countries such as the United States, England, France and Israel, about fifteen women died from complications during pregnancy, delivery or puerperium (the period immediately after delivery). Scandinavian countries do rather better, because they pay more attention to maternal care, but in most countries around the world fatalities during pregnancy and birth are so high that they are not usually reported accurately. Estimates for some African and South American countries, and for some Indian States, are that more than one in a thousand women dies from pregnancy-related causes, and that more than one in a hundred infants die at birth or very soon after. In countries that decline to report or, due to poor record keeping, cannot report such statistics, pregnancy-related deaths could be as high as one in every hundred.

Obstetrics

Obstetrics became a medical speciality precisely because pregnancy and birth can be life-threatening. One of the most frequent problems it must deal with is a 'poorly positioned' foetus. Due to quite natural causes, some four in every hundred babies get stuck in the pelvis in a position that makes birth impossible. If they cannot be dislodged by being turned within the uterus or birth canal (vagina), the lives of both the mother and baby are in danger.

French Huguenot physician William Chamberlin seems to have been the first to develop obstetrical forceps, spoon-like tongs that grasp the foetus in cases where there is no room for hands or where hands cannot get a grip. After emigrating to England to escape religious persecution, Chamberlin and his sons perfected their forceps but kept their use

and design secret. In fact they guarded their lucrative monopoly by blindfolding the women they delivered. In 1721 a more public-spirited Belgian barber-surgeon named Jean Palfyne made public to the world, through a speech to the Paris Academy of Sciences, his version of obstetrical forceps, otherwise known as *mains de fer* (iron hands).

Until the nineteenth century physicians had

In primitive and Third World societies pregnancy deaths and infant mortality remain high. But even against a background of endemic disease and poor nutrition, rudimentary hygiene and health care can have a positive effect.

Medieval midwifery, hedged about with mystery and superstition. Unfortunately most accounts of birth in the Middle Ages were written by men, excluded from birth itself and more concerned with the spiritual welfare of the mother and baby than with their physical and psychological wellbeing. Here a woman sits on a birthing stool shaped something like a modern toilet seat. It gave her support and allowed gravity to help the delivery.

only the vaguest concept of hygiene or how diseases were transmitted. Most mothers who died in childbirth died of infections contracted during or immediately after delivery. The raw uterus or ripped vaginal canal offers a ready site for infection. By then many lying-in hospitals had been established but it is a macabre fact that these facilities brought with them a dramatic increase in puerperal or childbirth fever and death. Hospitals became unwitting reservoirs of disease, transmitted from patient to patient by doctors, nurses, unsterilized instruments or contaminated bedclothes. The magnitude of the problem was such that in the Lombardy province of France in the 1860s few women who went to hospital to have their babies survived; in 1866, in the Maternité Hospital in Paris, around one in four women died. Voices such as those of Ignatz P. Semmelweis of Vienna, the Scotsman Alexander Gordon and the American Oliver Wendell Holmes, cried in the wilderness. Without yet comprehending the reality of germs, they held that 'contagion' was probably passed person-to-person and was not the result of sin or chance. Gordon published in 1795 and Holmes in 1843 but the medical world in general closed its ears against their contagion theories and their plea for greater cleanliness. Semmelweis, writing in 1861, was even more pointedly rejected when he suggested that everyone attending women in labour, including physicians, should cleanse themselves before entering the labour room, especially if they had been in contact with a diseased or dead person. He advised at the very least washing the hands in a chlorine solution.

It is partly to ensure cleanliness and to prevent the spread of infection that non-professionals are excluded from most delivery rooms today. The anonymous privacy of modern hospital delivery has a sound medical basis. But there are other reasons for privacy. Delivery is often painful and distressing, something many women would rather go through in privacy, and which others would rather not intrude upon.

Pain-free birth did not become a possibility until the mid-1800s when James Simpson, a Scot, demonstrated the use of chloroform during labour. Queen Victoria had chloroform for the birth of her seventh child in 1853 and made the practice socially acceptable. Today we have better methods of pain control but still the majority of women bear their

babies in ignorance of the physiological processes involved and lack the psychological, social and emotional support that can make childbirth a more positive experience. Ignorance, pain and psychological isolation are not necessary requirements of birthing; they are the sour fruits of tradition.

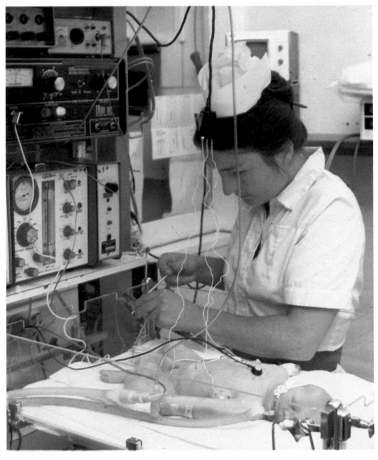

Left *Torture, ignorance, or merely enlisting the help of gravity? This medieval woodcut shows a woman in labour tied to a trestle being bounced up and down by two strong men to speed things up.*

Below *About 6 per cent of all Caucasian babies weigh 5½lb or less at birth. Considered premature regardless of their gestational age, the majority of such babies survive thanks to modern hospital facilities.*

Feelings about pregnancy

Birth (parturition) is the culmination of a growth process that starts nine months (or about 266 days) earlier when sperm and egg unite in a process called fertilization. Once the egg has been fertilized it is called a zygote. Most women are not aware that fertilization has taken place until some two weeks later, when they miss their period. Missing a period is never a neutral matter; a woman who wants a child will be elated but if pregnancy is unwanted or unexpected she may be frightened or depressed. Even for women who want children the knowledge of being pregnant is often greeted by very mixed emotions. The experience brings joy, melancholy, pride, apprehension, an added sense of responsibility. One woman I know, who wanted a child but did not plan her pregnancy, expressed her feelings like this: 'Well, I suppose I ought to feel happy, but right now I feel more numb than elated. I wanted this day to come, but I feel as if I'm somehow becoming part of the establishment, as if I'm approaching middle age earlier than expected. It also means I'm no longer the free spirit I like to consider myself. Yet deep down I know it's what I really want. And I know Larry will be ecstatic.'

The only way to be sure of pregnancy is by a home or laboratory test. These tests diagnose pregnancy at various early stages, but their

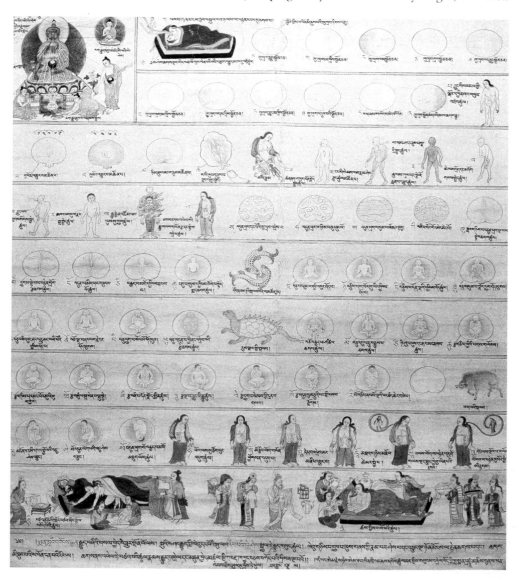

A Tibetan scroll used for teaching purposes. All stages from conception to birth are carefully shown. Note that new life is thought of not as a rapidly dividing collection of cells but as a steadily expanding soul, an offshoot of the life force of the universe.

accuracy increases as pregnancy advances. False negatives are possible, as are false positives. If the results of the test are unsupported by other signs, a repeat test about a week later is in order.

To a biologist a pregnancy is first a zygote, then an embryo, then a foetus and only after birth a baby, but to almost every onlooker and certainly every hopeful parent a pregnancy is a baby right from the start. Every pregnant woman is viewed as a future mother. This social view of a biological event is highly significant. Studies done in many developed and technologically advanced countries reveal that, for more than 50 per cent of women, pregnancy is unplanned. While some women accept the fact fatalistically, an increasing number do not. More and more women are choosing to abort, and in many societies they are supported in their decision. Parental responsibility really begins before pregnancy rather than after, but contraception requires an effort not all people are able or wish to make. In many societies, pregnancy is still seen as the natural outcome of sexual activity for women.

Which sex is the baby?
The units of fertilization contributed by each parent are called gametes. The male gametes are sperm produced by the testes and the female gametes are eggs, or ova, produced by the ovaries. The sex of the zygote, potentially the new human being, is determined at the time of fertilization. Since all ova contain an X sex chromosome, the male's sperm is the determining factor; if it too contains an X chromosome, the zygote will be female (XX); if it contains a Y, the zygote will be male (XY). For reasons we do not yet fully understand, more male zygotes are produced than female. The ratio is approximately 130/150:100, but since male zygotes are more fragile, by the time of birth the ratio has fallen to about 106:100. There are also more deaths among infant males than among infant females.

The knowledge that it is the sperm of the male that determines sex is being widely disseminated in countries such as China where, traditionally, female babies have been looked on as worthless and wives brutally abused for 'producing' them. In 1982 a newspaper report from Peking told of women forced from their homes, beaten, poisoned, strangled and driven to suicide for the 'offence' of giving birth to girl children.

Despite popular recommendations for douching with vinegar or a solution of baking soda, or having coitus in certain positions or at certain times of the menstrual cycle, there is no simple or reliable method of ensuring that a baby is of the desired sex. Folk nostrums abound because many people would like to choose, and because in many cultures boys are usually preferred to girls. Researchers are now working on ways to separate X sperm from Y sperm. Parents in scientifically advanced countries in the 1990s may be able, in certain carefully defined circumstances, to choose the sex of their children.

Various hospital techniques are now available for determining the sex of a foetus. Amniocentesis, which can be performed from the fifteenth week onwards, involves inserting a needle into the abdomen and uterus, and extracting some of the amniotic fluid surrounding the foetus. The cells floating in the fluid can then be analysed to reveal the baby's sex. Uteroscopy is a more complicated procedure which involves inserting a flexible, pencil-thick endoscope into the uterus; using optical fibres and with its own light scource, the endoscope enables the genitals of the baby to be examined. But knowing whether a foetus is male or female, and using that knowledge as a basis for maintaining or aborting a pregnancy, is not considered a medical advance by all. For some, it is an affront to God, a tampering with nature. To others it is social engineering at its most beneficial.

Neonaticide, the killing of newborn children, has been adopted by some cultures as a way of disposing of children of the 'wrong' (usually female) sex. This practice horrifies most people in the West; it shakes our belief in the strength of the bond between parent and child (and as the father of four daughters, I cannot imagine any sons providing more joy).

Early days and weeks
Fertilization usually occurs in one or other of the oviducts, the short tubes that lead from the two ovaries to the uterus, rather than in the uterus itself. Soon after fertilization, the zygote begins to split (cleave) into two cells, then four, eight, and so on. As it does so it is propelled towards the uterus. Two or three days after entering the uterus, the embryo, as it is now called, implants itself in the uterus wall. On average only one in two zygotes actually gets as far as this; the rest, presumably the least

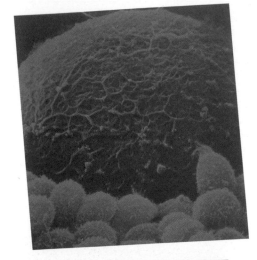

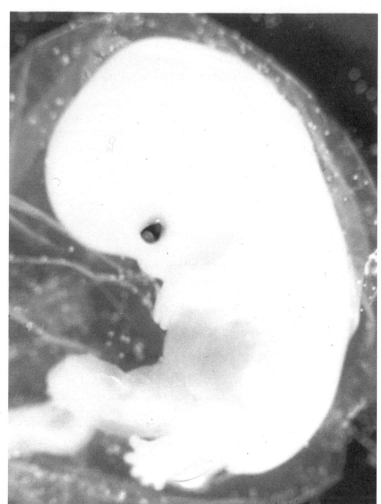

healthy, those least likely to survive, regress or disintegrate.

The uterus (womb) is the specialized female organ that carries, nourishes and protects the developing foetus. Once implantation has taken place, the woman's body becomes aware of its own pregnancy and changes to meet the demands of the developing embryo and foetus. Periods stop and the uterus begins to enlarge. The placenta and other tissues develop at the site of implantation to support the developing embryo, attached to them by the umbilical cord. Nutrients arrive and waste products leave via the placenta.

The embryo develops most rapidly during the first eight weeks of pregnancy, from a single cell about the size of the dot at the end of this sentence to a mass of cells about 1 in long and weighing about ⅓oz. By the eighth week all the systems the baby will need at birth have

started to develop. The brain and nervous system are among the first to develop, hence the disproportionate largeness of the head. From about eight weeks until birth, the head represents 40 per cent of body length; in the adult it represents only 15 per cent. By eight weeks the limbs begin to form. A tail appears during the fourth week, only to disappear by the ninth. This tail is a remnant of the evolutionary history of our species. In rare cases the tail remains at birth, but it is easy to remove surgically.

By the ninth week the embryo is recognizably human, no longer nondescript and grub-like. It has now become a foetus. Between the seventh and twelfth weeks, the sexual organs and reproductive system begin to develop; up until this time male and female foetuses look alike.

Spontaneous abortion (miscarriage) during

Above *A six-week-old embryo, in reality no bigger than the nail on its mother's little finger. The heart is already beating.*

Top left *The heads of hundreds of sperm massing around a single spherical egg.*

Left *Another electron microscope photograph, this time of the inner surface of the womb, as beautiful as a bed of coral and sea anemones.*

the first three months (first trimester) of life is not uncommon; in fact it occurs in 10 to 30 per cent of all pregnancies and, although an unpleasant experience, is probably fortunate since in most cases the foetus is seriously defective. If a woman is unaware that she is pregnant she may experience spontaneous abortion as a late, if somewhat heavy, period.

The symptoms of pregnancy

A recent newspaper article told of a 44-year-old Minnesota woman, Cathy Mountain, who, after spending a full day at work as a book-keeper, and four hours of volunteer work as a women's crises helper, went to bed at 11 pm and woke in pain at 3 am to find herself in labour with her 7 lb 9 oz sixth child. Apart from noticing some weight gain around the hips, she claimed 'she never felt anything' to make her suspicious. For most women, however, there are clues enough.

Although most women stop menstruating when they are pregnant, one in five continues to show some bleeding for several months after conception. This is usually light but sometimes sufficient to mask pregnancy if other signs, such as weight gain, nausea and tiredness, are ignored. Other signs of pregnancy are enlarged breasts and areolae which are deeper in colour than usual and develop small bumps, and nipples that are more sensitive to the touch. Some women, soon after conception, say they 'just feel different' for vague, undefined reasons. Morning sickness, a period of nausea, vomiting or dizziness on waking or at night, occurs in three out of four women at some time during the first three months. The cause and cure are both enigmatic. Some women link their sickness to car or train journeys, to certain foods and odours, or to being emotionally upset. Eating dry biscuits or toast before getting into bed at night or out of bed in the morning sometimes helps.

Very, very rarely a woman thinks she is pregnant when she is not, and may show some of the signs and experience some of the symptoms. Cases of false or pseudopregnancy (pseudocyesis) have been known throughout history. Hippocrates reported a dozen cases; in the Middle Ages pseudopregnancy was a state experienced by some nuns who yearned to be true brides of Christ. Mary Tudor, Queen of England from 1553 to 1558, also experienced pseudopregnancy. One research team wrote of her: 'Mary, finding herself without her expected baby, imagined herself deserted by God... During the time of her supposed pregnancy, Mary showed signs of pregnancy and experienced the symptoms of vomiting and enlargement of the abdomen. During this period her favourite amusement, other than attending Mass, was counting on her fingers the number of months she was "gone".' Pseudopregnancy is not a phenomenon easy to investigate scientifically, but it does seem to be associated with intense fear of coitus, intense guilt about having had intercourse when it is forbidden, or an intense desire to be pregnant.

The birth of the Virgin Mary, from a fifteenth-century English manuscript. St Anne reaches out to receive her newborn daughter. Mary, in her turn, gave birth to Jesus. Insistence that Jesus was 'immaculately' conceived owes as much to prudery and sexual guilt as to belief in the miraculous.

From three months to term

During the second trimester the woman's changing shape, and the fact that in the fourth or fifth month the foetus' heart starts to beat and it begins to move, confirm the reality of the pregnancy. Most women carry on a dialogue of sorts with the foetus, slowly making it a part of their daily lives. Expectant parents, if they have not done so earlier, think of a non-person but affectionate name for it – 'marshmallow', 'gumdrop', 'monster', even 'ET'. They often enjoy 'listening in' and looking for signs of movement.

By the end of the second trimester, the foetus may weigh 2lb but the mother may have gained 10lb. Some women show patches of temporary skin discoloration on the face, stomach and breasts. A clear yellow secretion (colostrum) may seep from the nipples. These changes are all harmless but undue weight gain should be controlled.

During the final trimester the foetus continues to grow, gaining about 1lb a week during the last two or three weeks. By the eighth month all the foetus' systems are well enough developed for it to be capable of precarious life outside the womb. The ninth month in the womb ensures extra strength and better resistance to the traumas of life outside. As the foetus takes up a head-down position in the womb its movements become increasingly noticeable to the mother. As the head enters the pelvis it pushes against the mother's bladder, making urination a more and more frequent necessity. 'Most of the time I feel great, but all I want to do is eat, sleep and go to the toilet' is a common comment from mothers nearing the end of their pregnancy.

Countdown to birth

As the foetus enlarges and moves down, the diaphragm is pushed upwards, making rib cage and breasts more protuberant and breathing more audible. As birth approaches, the foetus can be felt pushing down against the pelvic muscles and cervix. This is variously called engagement, lightening, or dropping. Gradually the cervix (neck), or exit from the womb, becomes thinner and thinner (a process known as effacement) and the woman's pelvis begins to relax. This makes walking awkward and sometimes painful but it is part of the preparation for birth and a sign that labour will soon begin.

Labour is the passage of the foetus and

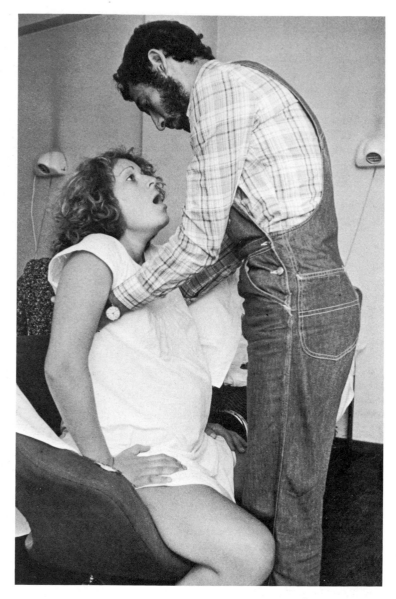

placental tissues from the womb, via the vagina, to the outside. It is usually described as having three phases: the first is the foetus' movement into the vagina or birth canal; the second is its passage to the outside (delivery); and the third is the expulsion of the placenta and its associated membranes (afterbirth).

The process of labour is extremely variable from woman to woman, and even in the same woman first, second and third labours may be very different. First births generally take longer and are more painful than subsequent ones. Despite cosy assumptions to the contrary, women in primitive cultures do not necessarily have quicker, less painful or less

A husband as a vital part of the delivery team. He can give a lot more than emotional support; he can breathe with his wife through each contraction, encourage her to relax and move about between contractions, and help her to squat, kneel, sit or stand in the position she finds most comfortable.

complicated births than women in technologically advanced ones.

The first stage of labour is marked by contractions of the uterus. These complete the process of effacement of the cervix and cause it to start widening (dilation). Other signals of the onset of labour are the discharge of a plug of mucus tinged with blood ('bloody show') from the cervix and discharge of the fluids ('waters') surrounding the foetus. Any of these signs indicate that it is time to head for the hospital.

Early contractions will typically occur at intervals of 10 to 20 minutes and last for 20 to 40 seconds. Later contractions occur at intervals of 3 to 5 minutes and last some 30 to 60 seconds. Contractions may last from 2 to 24 hours but 12 to 15 hours is average for first pregnancies; later pregnancies may take half that time.

When dilation of the cervix is sufficient to allow the foetus to enter the vagina – generally the diameter of the cervical opening is about 4 in or 'five fingers' in width – the contractions push the foetus through the vagina and delivery occurs. The average newborn baby weighs about 7 lb and is about 20 in from head to toe. A Caucasian baby is considered medically premature if born before week 36 or, regardless of gestation age, if he or she weighs less than 5½ lb at birth. The afterbirth is expelled some 15 minutes to an hour after delivery. In many cultures great magical significance is given to the placenta and umbilical cord. Before the turn of this century, for example, Hawaiian people used to hide the afterbirth (placenta and umbilical cord) in case it fell into the hands of an evil wisher. In the Solomon Islands the umbilical cord was kept safe in the lime-pot containing the mother's chewing nuts.

The assistance the mother receives during labour and delivery depends of course on her own needs and preferences in the matter, but also on local custom and on the physician or midwife in attendance. She may or may not be offered pain relieving drugs or an episiotomy (a surgical incision to enlarge the vagina to facilitate birth). There is no 'best' way to deliver because women and their babies are so variable. No woman should try to live up to some artificial standard of maternal performance. The sole criterion is the best possible physical and psychological health of both mother and child.

The couvade syndrome

The phenomenon of husbands suffering sympathetic labour pains and undergoing ritual delivery was a feature of many primitive and ancient cultures. 'Couvade' rituals (from the French *couver*, to hatch) were described by Plutarch in his histories of Greece and Rome and in Marco Polo's tales of China and India. The custom still exists, though not in societies which regard themselves as modern. Among the Solomon Islanders, for instance, it is still quite common, when the mother's labour pains begin, for the husband to stop work, go to the hut of one of his other wives or neighbours, and sit idle, refusing to lift anything

A rush of intense emotion as the baby takes its first breath and is held close. The blood still pulses through the umbilical cord. When the blood flow stops, which takes a few minutes, the cord can be cut. The bonds established in these early moments are considered fundamental and long lasting.

191

heavy or handle anything sharp or pointed. All this is supposed to facilitate birth and protect the infant, and may continue for at least three days after the birth. He may then visit the mother's hut to see the child. He may even continue to rest and not go outside the village for another two days. Rituals like this are rooted in a belief in sympathetic magic and in good and evil spirits, but they also establish the father's paternity in a very public manner. A few cynical observers have interpreted couvade as male one-upmanship, or as an attempt to deny women the sole pain and glory of childbirth. Many women would be only too glad to share some of it.

More intriguing are those instances of couvade which are not mere ritual. Many men wish they could take a fairer share in their wife's pregnancy and delivery, but a few actually feel real pain and exhibit real physical symptoms. In 1972 the British psychiatrist W.H. Trethowan estimated that the couvade syndrome, in some guise or other, probably occurs in about one in four or five expectant fathers. Common symptoms include nausea, alteration in appetite, toothache, indigestion, heartburn and abdominal pains. Though they are seldom serious these sympathetic sufferings certainly create a greater bond of concern and care within a family.

Pregnancy and sexual activity

In developed countries most couples continue to have sexual relations during pregnancy, but coitus is generally less frequent, and may cease altogether during the last month or so. Studies of Third World or non-technological societies show that practices are extremely variable. Some societies – the Abelam and Lesu of New Guinea and New Ireland, the American Indian Arikara of North Dakota, the Dahomeans of West Africa, the Nandi of the Sudan and the Masai of Kenya and Tanzania – expect coitus to stop as soon as the woman has missed one or two menstrual periods. More than thirty of the sixty societies in the same study expected coitus to cease by the seventh month, but fifteen of them had no inhibitions or prohibitions even in the ninth month. Generally, in societies that expect abstinence during pregnancy, it is the woman who is enjoined to abstain, not the man; he can usually have sex with another of his wives or with a prostitute. Even in the West, expectant husbands are disapprovingly allowed a certain licence: 'His wife was pregnant at the time, you know.'

Even today sex during pregnancy is something many physicians and their patients refrain from discussing. There may be a cursory warning about not having intercourse from six weeks before delivery to six weeks or so after, but apart from that very little informa-

An earth crib for a baby in southern Sudan. Childbirth in the Third World is seldom the swift, painless idyll that Western women imagine it to be. Malnourished mothers can suffer a great deal. On the other hand a natural and open approach to pregnancy and birth can relieve much anxiety and fear.

Left *Keeping up appearances during pregnancy. Some women are deeply concerned that maternity will destroy their sexual attractiveness. It seldom does. But a relationship can deteriorate if the husband feels shut out by his wife's growing concentration on their baby. It is important for a woman to feel physically loved in pregnancy. In some cultures coitus may be used to induce labour – the prostaglandins in male semen can cause the uterus to contract. But there is no firm evidence that semen, or orgasm on the woman's part, triggers labour unless it is already imminent.*

tion is given. Left to work things out for themselves, most women 'play safe'. Modern knowledge tells us that all usual sexual activities may be engaged in until birth without fear of harming the foetus or the mother, as long as there is no vaginal bleeding, the mother has no history of premature deliveries and is comfortable, and the process of delivery has not started. Having said that, pregnancy quite naturally brings with it certain changes in sexual activity. For most couples during the first trimester it is 'sex as usual'. In the second and third trimesters, though there are exceptions, most couples have intercourse less often, and in the final months may abstain altogether. Although much depends on previous levels of sexual activity, many women report that they lose interest in sex during pregnancy, masturbate less frequently and have fewer orgasms.

These changes are due to many factors. As pregnancy advances, women produce more and more of the hormone progesterone, which can act to depress libido. Also, many women feel increasingly uncomfortable physically and are afraid of harming the foetus. Husbands can also lose interest in sex; they too may be afraid of harming the foetus or their partner. And there are men and women who simply find the condition of pregnancy unattractive or who feel sexually unsure or frustrated at their partner's lack of interest. This is the situation most likely to cause men to seek casual affairs or visit prostitutes.

As pregnancy progresses, there is a shift from the man-on-top coital position to woman-on-top or side-by-side or 'spoons' (rear entry). There is also an increase in oral sex

and mutual masturbation. Pregnancy is a time to learn the value of non-coital sexual contact and of non-erotic touching. Both partners want and need and enjoy TLC (tender loving care), especially the woman; despite the great confirmation of femininity that pregnancy bestows, she has to cope with a new self-image as a mother, weight gain, and probably some change in her lifestyle.

Another behavioural change during pregnancy deserves mention. It is by no means uncommon for enthusiastic expectant parents to engage in a flurry of 'nest-building' activities. It seems, all of a sudden, that there is a need to paint, clean, sew, store food and so forth – preparation behaviours we share with our animal cousins.

Childbirth: adventure or ordeal?

The medicalization of childbirth in the West has often been inveighed against; also the privacy and secrecy traditionally associated with childbirth. Home deliveries with the whole family in attendance are being experimented with and special birthing centres are being established. In such centres, women can have their medical needs taken care of and also take advantage of emotional and companionate support for delivery without drugs, mechanical restraints or isolation. Traditional medical practices have certainly demonstrated many advantages to mother and child, but many feel other ways may be better.

The modern Western version of 'natural' childbirth is far removed from the fancied 'naturalness' of childbirth in primitive societies, which, as we saw at the start of the chapter, surrounded it with secrecy and ritual. For a start, delivery at home or in birthing centres is attended by medically trained male or female midwives, with physicians and an arsenal of modern pharmaceutical and intervention techniques available if complications arise. The essence of the modern concept of natural childbirth is that women need not deliver in isolation, ignorance and fear.

Pioneers of natural childbirth

The natural childbirth movement is not new, but it has been slow to grow. In England in the 1930s a physician called Grantley Dick-Read challenged his colleagues to make childbirth a great adventure rather than a painful ordeal: 'Childbirth should be accompanied by a sense of maternal achievement and satisfac-

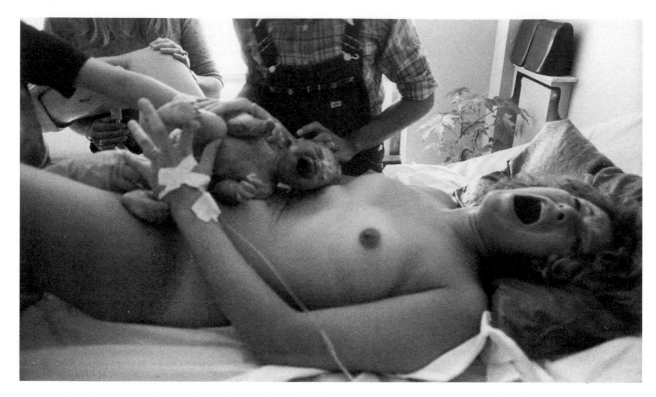

A first howl, and a howl of victory. Positive feelings about birth are far more frequent among mothers who remain conscious throughout the proceedings than among women who deliver in a state of semi-consciousness In the United States high rates of general anaesthesia in childbirth apply, but in Britain and Europe general anaesthesia is only offered to 5-10 per cent of women, usually for caesareans and difficult forceps deliveries. For such a common procedure, birth is subject to a great deal of fad and science mixed in unknown proportions.

tion and . . . the mother–child relationship should be enhanced by pride and pleasure and not tainted by resentment or distressing memories.' The first step, he said, was to reduce or remove the ignorance and fear that surrounded birth. How? By offering prenatal instruction and exercise classes, stopping or minimizing the use of anaesthetics, and resorting to surgical practices such as episiotomy only when absolutely necessary. His book *Childbirth Without Fear* became a public sensation. Predictably it was attacked and disparaged by two strong Establishment forces: doctors too lazy to learn the new techniques or reluctant to see their powers demystified and their fees diminished; and clergymen who thought it only right for women to bring forth children in pain and agony, as they interpreted the Bible. There were also objections from many earnest obstetricians who were all too well acquainted with the sufferings of many women in labour and who felt that anaesthetics, episiotomy and privacy suited their needs best.

The next major impetus to the natural childbirth movement came in the 1970s from two French physicians, Fernand Lamaze and Frederick Leboyer. They too proposed that women should be given instruction and exer-

cises to remove fear, ignorance and trauma during labour and delivery. And, like Dick-Read, both proposed birth in hospitals, but with a minimum of mechanical or technical assistance and little or no use of anaesthetics.

Lamaze insisted that fathers, as well as mothers, should attend birth classes and, more controversially, that the father should be present at the delivery to give his wife emotional support and remind her to relax and push and breathe as in the exercises. Leboyer was primarily concerned with the sensitivity of the newborn infant. In his book *Birth Without Violence* he advocated that babies should enter the world with as little trauma as possible. At birth they should be kept warm and secure, treated tenderly, washed in warm water and rocked so that the transition from the womb to the world is as gentle as possible. After delivery, instead of separating mother and baby, the baby is given to the mother for loving and cuddling so that a strong mother–child bond is established immediately.

Is birth an erotic experience?

All three physicians, Dick-Read, Lamaze and Leboyer, promoted maximum human concern for the emotional and psychological needs of mother, father and newborn. But

A Thai mother and baby. Breast-feeding mothers spend more time than bottle-feeding mothers talking to their babies, and the talk tends to be more affectionate too. Technologically advanced societies have dropped breast-feeding with the advent of packaged milk products. It is now recognized that for early nourishment nature knows best. The mother-baby bond is more easily formed with breast-feeding, and natural milk ingredients are important for the baby's health. Also mother's milk is always handy and at the right temperature.

Leboyer went further: 'Childbirth is also passion . . . an ecstatic experience.' Indeed, the famous Japanese poet-novelist Kazue Morisaki has written that birth provided her best orgasm. Many obstetricians say that the experience of orgasm is not rare in undrugged and uninhibited childbirth. There are, as sociologist Niles Newton has pointed out, remarkable similarities in breathing, vocalization, facial expression and many other bodily responses during orgasm and uninhibited childbirth. The sensuousness of the experience may also have physical advantages.

In those societies that viewed sex and birth in a more relaxed way, like the Siriono of Bolivia, birth was a public event and labour relatively short and painless. This can be compared with the long and painful process of labour and birth seen among the Cuna of San Blas, Panama, who learn facts and legends about coitus and delivery only after marriage. But it is impossible to say which is cause and which effect. It is easy to be open and public about an ecstatic, pleasant experience and understandable if elders prefer to shield youngsters from matters they know to be potentially traumatic.

No philosophy or method of delivery is best for everyone and not all options are universally available. What is possible every-where, however, is for each woman to discuss pregnancy and birth with her husband and physician and decide which method suits her best, and work with them to make birthing as positive and as fulfilling an experience as possible.

Mother's milk

In most developing countries almost all women breast-feed their children, at least to begin with. In developed countries, the practice is far less common, yet it is increasing. In 1970 only about one in four women in the United States breast-fed their children; today the figure is more than one in two. In general, in the West today, the higher the educational level of the mother, the more likely she is to breast-feed. From a nutritional point of view breast milk is the best food for infants – no milk substitute exactly duplicates it. It is free, highly palatable and provides immunological protection. Common reasons for not breast-feeding are that it is difficult to fit in with work schedules and embarrassing if it has to be done in public. Some women also have difficulty or fear they will have difficulty in providing enough milk. Actually, almost all women can breast-feed adequately if they allow time for the needs of their body to synchronize with those of their baby.

Occasionally a nursing mother will experience orgasm and frequently a nursing woman in orgasm will expel milk. This is a natural consequence of overlap in the physiological processes involved. Nursing a baby has no particular effect on erotic preferences; nonetheless many couples enjoy 'adult' nursing as part of sex play. It is perhaps not surprising that those who accept breast-feeding are significantly more relaxed about sexual matters in general.

All in all, birthwatching from conception through pregnancy to delivery and nursing can be a highly emotional and rewarding experience for all concerned. Shared knowledge of what is happening, and what can be expected, and loving preparation, are good insurance against fear, pain and isolation. Properly planned for and understood, birth can be the most exciting of all life's events. The mother, especially, will gain from this approach, but so will the family as a whole. Birthwatching is certainly a major component of sexwatching □.

12

Sex yes, children no

Since 1960 more than half the families in the world have voluntarily and success-fully imposed a limit on the number of children they have. What is more, these changes have taken place in spite of strong opposition from various religious groups, particularly the Roman Catholic Church, and political forces as diverse as the Chinese Red Brigades and Gang of Four, Eastern European Communist Parties, and the Eisenhower, Nixon and Reagan administrations in the United States. These changes have been both cause and consequence of women's greater sexual and social freedom.

Until 1960 India and China were the only governments willing to consider, let alone adopt, a national policy on family planning. For most governments the topic was taboo. An increase in population was often considered desirable for political reasons: more people meant more fighters and workers ready to defend and support national interests. A few countries gave medals to prolific mothers, and some still do. In the 1950s even the United Nations refused to discuss population control or family planning for fear of irreparable divisions within the organization.

Times have changed, but not for humanitarian reasons. Change was the result of technology and the realization that economic growth and standards of living are intimately linked to population and family size. By technology I

Two approaches to family planning: the famous 'pregnant man' poster which appeared in Britain in the early 1970s and a roadside billboard in Pakistan. Both appeal for greater male responsibility.

Would you be more careful if it was you that got pregnant?

mean the development of oral and depôt contraceptives, the improvement of the intrauterine device (IUD) and of abortion techniques, and an explosion in communications. In the 1960s and 1970s television became a worldwide medium, and telephones and radios linked villages and tiny settlements to distant capital cities and to events all round the world. News of effective and acceptable methods of birth control spread quickly.

Before 1960 legal abortions and contraceptives were unavailable or difficult to obtain almost everywhere. By 1975 however almost every developed country and more than sixty developing countries had made it official government policy to reduce population growth or had expressed government support for family planning. At a meeting in Bucharest in 1974 all but one of the 135 delegates from governments and organizations around the world voted to accept family planning as a basic human right, a right which governments should give their citizens the means to exercise (the term 'family planning' was felt to be less negative than 'contraception'). The exception was the Vatican representative, who abstained. Now more than 90 per cent of the world's population lives in countries that offer some form of family planning. The nations most often held up as models of humane and successful family planning policies are Korea, Thailand and Sweden.

The United States remains one of the few developed countries that has not formulated any consistent national family planning policy. Full family planning services are not equally available to all. Private bodies such as the International Planned Parenthood Foundation exist expressly to help those thwarted by the obstacle course created by the policies of different governments. Until 1967, when a Supreme Court decision changed the law, it was illegal for physicians to offer contraceptives to their patients and illegal to send them through the post.

Contraception and abortion are among the hottest of political and religious hot potatoes. In the United States party attitudes towards the availability of contraceptives and abortion are geared to catching votes at election time. Various countries in Eastern Europe have put the brakes on abortion whenever the rate has threatened to tarnish the national image. Occasionally abortion and contraception policies reflect the self-interest of the medical

In Britain the first birth control clinic opened in 1921; in the United States the first such clinic opened in 1916. Even today contraception is not always easily available to those most at risk and with most to lose – unmarried teenage girls.

establishment; in India, for example, where the pill was not legalized until 1974, and in Japan, where its use is still restricted to the treatment of menstrual disorders, abortion is extremely lucrative for physicians. Sometimes restricted availability of contraception and family planning services can be traced to the erroneous idea that easy availability encourages promiscuity and social upheaval. There is no evidence for this whatsoever. Most studies have shown that people are already sexually active when they first seek contraceptives. Fear of pregnancy merely postpones or takes the enjoyment out of coitus; it does not prevent it.

The governments of most Western states today, whatever their political or religious hue, make consultation with a registered physician a legal requirement for obtaining an abortion. Only in a handful of countries – the United States, Italy, Japan, India, China, Yugoslavia – is the decision to terminate a pregnancy left solely to the woman herself. In China and India it is not necessary to consult a physician to obtain most methods of contraception but in every other major country in the world it is.

Choices

Many people, even well educated people, are uninformed about conception. They do not realize that pregnancy can occur from a single act of intercourse or that the few drops of fluid that sometimes appear at the tip of the penis during the excitement or plateau phase contain sperm which can be transferred by hand or penis to the vagina. Nor is it widely recog-

nized that ovulation, though cyclic, is often irregular. Whenever a woman is ovulating there is the possibility of conception. And contrary to popular belief ovulation can occur even during a period.

Reproduction can be prevented at any stage of the reproductive process, before or after conception, or after birth. Celibacy and virginity are one solution. Social approval of virginity, especially in females, has traditionally postponed reproduction until marriage. In many countries – India, Spain, and most Islamic and Latin American countries – young men and women are discouraged from spending time alone together before they are married; it is not 'proper' for an unmarried woman to be seen in mixed company in public. Later marriages have also had a powerful population-decreasing effect. This has been especially true in Europe and Japan in the first half of this century and in a number of Asian countries since World War II. In China young people are advised to postpone marriage until after the age of 25. Abortion and infanticide are late and drastic preventives, but for centuries they have been the main method of limiting family size, and abortion still is.

Not everyone feels comfortable about using contraceptives. Many women, and some men, prefer to think of sex as spontaneous and unplanned: 'I don't like to seem prepared because he/she might think I'm promiscuous/ presumptuous.' Others just pray and hope. Nevertheless the most reliable temporary methods of contraception are those used with confidence and consistency, and until effective and acceptable male oral contraceptives are invented it is women who will continue to bear the main responsibility for not getting pregnant.

Certain contraceptives are seen as inconvenient, aesthetically unappealing or likely to spoil sexual concentration. Condoms and vaginal creams come into this category. Condoms can be awkward to slip on and creams messy to use, but if contraception is seen as a shared responsibility they can be made part of sex play, opportunities for erotic stimulation. Condoms can be sensuously applied by the woman and the man can erotically insert foam or a piece of sponge. For many people the worst distraction from sexual enjoyment is fear of pregnancy itself.

The ideal contraceptive is well known: it is completely reliable, inexpensive, can be used by both sexes at any time (preferably not

during sex play), lasts as long as required and has no detrimental side or residual or long-term effects. Unfortunately it is still waiting to be discovered. All currently available contraceptives have some drawback or other but by and large the disadvantages are trivial compared with the advantages. Pregnancy and childbirth are far riskier for women than any standard method of contraception, and having a child is too large a responsibility to be left entirely to chance. Contraception means less risk, more choice, and freedom from unnecessary anxiety. The kind of trade-offs acceptable to one person – ease of use versus reliability, convenience versus possible long-term side effects, aesthetic appeal versus low cost – are not necessarily acceptable to another.

A nun of Mother Theresa's order in Calcutta teaching 'natural' birth control to a group of Indian women. Other methods are more effective, but anything is better than nothing.

Rhythm methods

Abstinence is the only contraceptive that is free and available without legal or medical restriction, and periodic abstinence, the so-called rhythm method, is the only method of contraception sanctioned by the Roman Catholic Church, which considers all other methods unnatural. Coitus is avoided at times when conception is likely, the 'unsafe period', and reserved for times considered safe. But determining these periods is difficult. It requires the woman to keep a very careful check on her menstrual cycle. The two more reliable rhythm methods require that she checks, daily and without fail, either her body temperature on waking or the nature and amount of mucus around her cervix. Both methods are highly unnatural practices for most women and require not only a regular and predictable lifestyle but also a strong degree of motivation and discipline; unfortunately sexual desire rarely coincides with the calendar. These routines are inconsistently used even among Roman Catholics.

The temperature method cannot be relied upon until the woman has recorded her temperature daily for a minimum of six months; she then has to determine when, within each cycle, there is a consistent rise in temperature following after a consistent low. Three days after the rise has peaked, coitus is allowable until the onset of the next period. The cervical mucus method monitors daily discharges from the cervix. A day or two before ovulation mucus taken from the cervix turns from cloudy and sticky to clear and stringy in consistency. The safe period starts four days after the clear mucus appears and lasts until the onset of the next period, after which the mucus changes back to cloudy.

Another method of determining a safe period is to monitor the menstrual cycle for six to twelve months and then, assuming that subsequent cycles will be similar, 'guesstimate' the danger zone, usually ten to nineteen days before the start of the next period. The remainder of the cycle is 'safe'. Unfortunately predictability is poor since most women have highly irregular menstrual cycles affected by stress, illness, nutrition and other factors.

It is difficult to evaluate the relative reliability of these methods since more depends on the user than on the technique. Best estimates are that, regardless of the method used, within a year between twenty and forty women in every hundred using rhythm get pregnant.

Rhythm couples, despite the quip that 'abstinence makes the heart grow fonder', generally find that enforced abstinence dampens sexual ardour and increases anxiety. Some women remain obsessively concerned with pregnancy. But the really serious drawback is that rhythm methods are very unreliable and result in many unplanned pregnancies.

Temperature taking, one of the rituals of rhythm. Even with a close daily watch on body temperature to determine when it is safe to have intercourse a woman runs a 20-40 per cent risk of getting pregnant within a year.

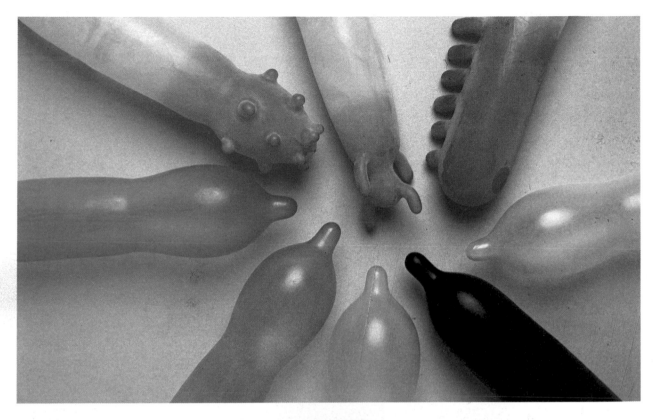

Condoms

The origin of the word condom is not known; it may honour the French town of Condom in Gascony, or a Colonel or Doctor Condom said to have perfected the device to protect King Charles II from the rapacious claims of mistresses and illegitimate children. The French picturesquely call the condom the *redingote anglaise* or *capote anglaise* (the English riding coat or overcoat) and the British call it the French letter. Japan is the world leader in condom use – condoms are sold door to door by women to women like cosmetics. In Britain and Denmark some 40 per cent of married couples use condoms, as compared with only 8 per cent in France.

Condoms have been in use in one form or another for hundreds of years. The modern condom, to which no one has ever laid a patent claim, is made of latex rubber or plastic, though versions made from animal intestines are still in use and now considered special. The condom prevents sperm from entering the uterus, and also acts as a partial barrier to disease. It has to be fitted over the erect penis but should not be stretched so tight that it splits from coital friction. After coitus it must be

carefully removed to prevent leakage of semen. Carelessness on both counts can lead to unwanted pregnancy.

Some couples claim that condoms reduce sensitivity, an effect welcomed by men who ejaculate quickly. But the major drawback of the condom is inconsistent or careless use. Otherwise it is reliable, inexpensive, safe, convenient, and one of the few methods for which men can take the major responsibility.

Condoms, plain and fancy. Sheaths that only cover the tip of the penis – known as 'tips' or 'tops' – are unsafe; they easily get left behind in the vagina.

Left *The ultimate give-away – condoms in bags of rice in Thailand. The bigger the bag of rice the more condoms you get – the more mouths you have to feed the more contraceptive encouragement you need!*

Cervical caps and diaphragms

These are also barrier devices made of rubber but to be maximally effective they need to be used with spermicidal vaginal jelly. The idea of placing a device in the vagina so that it covers the cervix or entrance to the uterus is not new either. One of the recommendations of the great Casanova (1725–98) was to squeeze the flesh from half a lemon and insert the cup of rind over the cervix; any juice (acidic) remaining in the lemon acted as a spermicide. The Egyptian Petri Papyrus (1850 BC) advises a vaginal pessary of crocodile dung and honey, or fumigation of the vagina with fumes from burning wax and charcoal. From India and Asia there is also evidence of early barrier devices made from small wads of feathers, sponges, lint or cloth soaked in acacia extract, honey or citrus juices.

The German physician C. Hesse, under the pseudonym Wilhelm P.J. Mensinga, seems to have been the first to write about a rubber version of the diaphragm. That was in 1882. Thereafter use of the diaphragm spread from Germany to Holland, and then to England, where it is still known as the Dutch cap. But actually the cap and the diaphragm are quite different. As known today, the diaphragm is a flat barrier covering the cervix and posterior end of the vagina, and the cap is a dome-like covering for the cervix alone.

Spermicidal jelly is applied to the cap or diaphragm before either is inserted into the vagina. Correct size and fit should be determined by a physician or a trained nurse, and correct placement is crucial or either may get dislodged during coitus. Either can be inserted some hours before coitus and the cap can be left in place from the end of one period to the beginning of the next. With both, jelly should be applied each time intercourse is likely to occur. Unlike the cap, the diaphragm should not be left in place for more than 24 hours. Neither should it be removed until at least six hours after coitus.

Caps and diaphragms do not suit all women; they are often considered 'messy' and unaesthetic and some women dislike the idea of having a device specially fitted. Nevertheless they can be inserted well before intercourse, are highly reliable, and do not interfere with any body functions. Use of the cap is quite common in Britain and Europe but less so in the United States where the diaphragm is overwhelmingly preferred.

An awkward moment for the conquest-hungry Casanova, credited with using various types of contraceptive. Was his 'reproductive responsibility' one of the reasons for his success with women?

Left *The diaphragm requires a degree of discipline, care and forward planning, but is well accepted.*

Creams, foams, jellies and suppositories

These are chemical contraceptives that either kill sperm or make conditions inside the vagina hostile to their passage. Inserted with the fingers or using a simple applicator, they are the only female birth control methods that do not require medical supervision. Many couples feel they interfere with sexual pleasure because they have to be inserted shortly before intercourse and most of them taste bad, which makes oral sex unpleasant. On the other hand they are easy to obtain and insert and need not be used on a permanent basis. They also provide extra lubrication and a degree of protection against certain types of VD.

Researchers have now developed a modern version of the small natural sponges soaked in citrus juice that Egyptian, Roman and Hebrew women once used: small plastic, disposable sponges permeated with a common spermicide. Initial tests show them to be as reliable as the diaphragm or cap and pleasant to use. They can be left in place for longer than the diaphragm and do not need additional spermicide no matter how often coitus occurs.

Injectables and implants

These are hormone preparations that are given in a single injection, become effective within 24 hours, and provide up to six months to a year of 99 per cent effective contraception. Also available are implants effective for up to five years. The preparations injected are long-acting artificial progesterones, known by such names as Depo Provera or Norplant, which inhibit ovulation and increase the viscosity of the cervical mucus so that sperm find it difficult to enter the uterus. Removal of implants returns normal fertility.

Depôt contraceptives are relatively new but have gained rapid acceptance, especially in rural and less technologically advanced societies. This undoubtedly has something to do with the mystique of total effectiveness attributed to any treatment given by needle or syringe, but it is also the result of not having to bother about remembering and counting days and pills. In areas where a woman's only access to medical care is when she delivers a baby, a single injection or implant immediately afterwards can provide months or even years of protection against another pregnancy.

Injectables are now in use in more than eighty countries, particularly in Latin America and Southeast Asia. In Europe they are available in Belgium, Denmark, West Germany, Holland and Spain, but they have not yet been accepted in Great Britain or the United States. The main reason for caution is fear that they might cause permanent infertility or cancer in some women, or congenital malformations in infants inadvertently exposed to them in

Bottom *The vaginal sponge; a fresh sponge should be inserted every 24 hours.*

Below *Spermicidal foam and a special applicator for placing it in the vagina.*

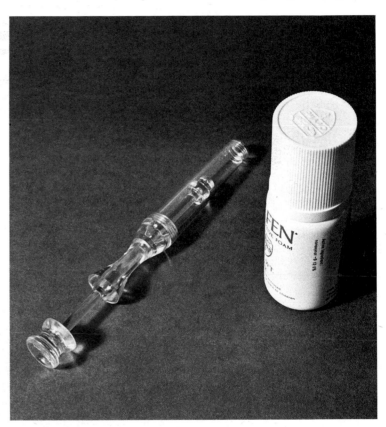

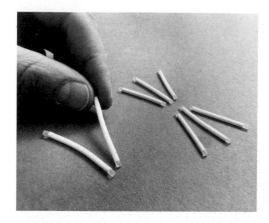

utero. With two decades of clinical data behind us, however, there is as yet no basis for these fears. The main disadvantage of injectables and implants is that they can upset menstrual patterns, which is not harmful *per se* but is often disturbing. After two years of use about 40 per cent of women lose their periods altogether and may gain up to 9 lb in weight.

Various injectables have been tested on men. While they are effective at reducing sperm production, they have many undesirable side effects, including breast development, dizziness, nausea and a decrease in libido and potency. But research continues.

Intrauterine devices (IUDs)

These are plastic or metal devices which are placed in the uterus and stay there for a period of months or years. They come in many shapes – rings, bows, Ts, Xs – and would probably work even if they looked like mini-spoons or toy battleships. The elongated S-shaped Lippes loop is the standard device against which others are compared, but each shape has its pros and cons. Attempts to make the perfect IUD have now produced 'active' IUDs, with added copper or hormones. The knowledge that foreign objects in the uterus prevent conception is not new; camel drivers in the Middle East are supposed to have protected their mares by inserting pebbles or peach stones into the uterus. How intrauterine devices work is not clear. What they do is reduce the likelihood of the zygote implanting itself in the uterus wall and make the intrauterine environment more hostile to sperm. They may also alter transport mechanisms for both eggs and sperm.

The IUD, more or less as we know it today, was developed in Germany in the late 1920s by Ernst Grafenberg (later of G-spot fame) and in Japan in 1934 by T. Ota. It was enthusiastically received at first, but then storms of protest erupted from the medical profession in both countries; they feared that unnatural devices, kept in the body for long periods, would be harmful. In 1936 the Japanese government prohibited IUDs and in Europe pioneering stopped when Grafenberg and others fled from the Nazi regime. Reluctance to revive its use continued until 1959, when new and favourable studies were reported from Israel and Japan.

The main attraction of the IUD is that it is easy to insert into the uterus, cheap, does not interfere with body chemistry and can be left in place for long periods and forgotten about except for the occasional check. It is also easy to remove if pregnancy is desired. It can be put in place immediately following delivery or abortion, or just after a period. One of the main reasons for its popularity in Third World countries is that anyone can be trained to insert an IUD; the procedure does not have to be done by a physician.

The thread attached to the IUD hides inconspicuously in the vagina and makes it easy to check that it is still in place. For some women an IUD is not suitable because it

Left *Slow-release hormone implants. These can give up to five years' effective contraception. Though treated with suspicion in some European countries and the United States, they are widely used in South America, Africa and Asia.*

Below *Various intrauterine devices in the form of a spiral, a 'T', a '7' and a loop. IUDs are second only to chemical contraceptives in efficiency – up to 98 per cent as compared with nearly 100 per cent. Being able to 'set it and forget it' is much appreciated.*

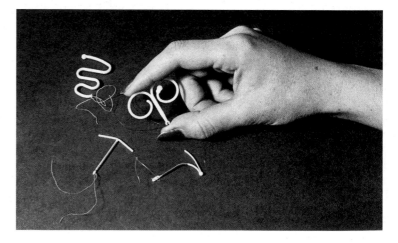

causes heavier than usual menstrual bleeding, occasional cramps and, in a few cases, interferes with sexual activity. Some women, and their partners, say they can feel an IUD during intercourse and orgasm. Though it is unusual, an IUD can be spontaneously expelled during a period or intense sexual exertions. IUDs rarely cause infection and cases of IUDs perforating the uterus are very rare.

Oral contraceptives

What could be easier than swallowing a pill or a potion to prevent pregnancy? The modern pill is the fulfilment of thousands of years of wishing. The Chinese *Book of Changes*, dating from 2700 BC, advises drinking fried mercury on an empty stomach, and other ancient writings encouraged prostitutes to take potions containing lead. In fact metallic brews have often been recommended for contraceptive purposes; in AD 540 Aetius of the Upper Tigris described a drink containing copper; in the Middle Ages women in the Alpine region of Austria swallowed concoctions of arsenic. Such preventives did more than stop conception; they often killed those desperate enough to try them.

Almost every society has its folk contraceptives, foods or herbal preparations, traditionally supposed to prevent pregnancy. Modern pharmaceutical companies and research institutes continue to investigate such nostrums in the hope of discovering the ideal contraceptive. In fact most modern oral contraceptives are based on diosgenin, a synthetic progestogen extracted from wild barbasco root, a plant native to Mexico. Attempts at large-scale cultivation of barbasco root have not been successful so far but there is a fortune waiting for the shrewd farmer who achieves predictable yields.

Development of the pill, now the most widely used form of temporary contraception in the world, came about through dogged research and concerted effort rather than any sudden, chance discovery. The research that ultimately proved successful was encouraged and supported by Margaret Sanger, a pioneer advocate of birth control, and was funded by Katherine Dexter McCormack of the McCormack tractor family. Gregory Pincus, H.C. Chang and John Rock of the United States put in place the final crucial pieces of the puzzle contributed to by researchers all over the world. In essence their work involved close analysis of the female reproductive system and the mechanism of ovulation. They realized that during pregnancy, when ovulation and periods cease, levels of oestrogens and progesterone in the blood are naturally high.

A Masai warrior decorates his girlfriend before a dance ceremony. Among the Masai unwanted pregnancies are sometimes terminated by drinking fermented cow dung.

If they could manage to produce a state of pseudopregnancy by giving extra doses of these hormones, ovulation would be halted and conception could not occur. It remained for them to work out how to make these hormones active when taken by mouth and to establish a safe and convenient dosage. In 1960 their work culminated in the launch of Enovid. Now there are well over a hundred different contraceptive pills in use worldwide.

Provided it is taken regularly for a fixed number of days within a 28-day cycle, the pill is almost 100 per cent reliable. It is inexpensive, separates contraception from coitus, and very rarely has any adverse effect on sexual activity. Some women feel side effects such as nausea or changes in menstrual flow. Thrombosis is a rare side effect and it is women who are confirmed, long-time smokers who are most at risk; this is why smokers are advised to come off the pill after the age of thirty-five. In fact the pill is not normally recommended to any woman after the age of forty.

All in all, pregnancy and birth are much riskier undertakings than using oral (or any other) contraceptives. There is no evidence that the pill encourages breast or cervical can-cer; on the contrary it may actually reduce such risks. This protective effect, partly the work of progesterone, seems to last for at least a decade and is most noticeable in women who have never borne children, the group most at risk of these types of cancer. Recent research has also shown that sexually active women aged bet-ween eighteen and forty-four who are on the pill have a 50 per cent reduced risk of develop-ing pelvic inflammatory disease (PID), a lead-ing cause of hospitalization and infertility.

The Chinese, among whom birth control research has high priority, have been active in developing many new types of oral contracep-tive. One is an edible paper permeated with hormones; the woman chews a piece the size of a postage stamp each day for 22 days in 28. Another type is a large-dose pill, the 'visiting pill', for use by women who see their partners infrequently. One pill provides short-term protection. The Chinese are also exper-imenting with gossypol, a cotton seed deriv-ative, as a male contraceptive; it is not yet dependable and still has undesirable side effects, but if it, or something very like it, could be perfected then at long last there would be a male counterpart to the female pill.

The manufacture of spermicidal jelly foil in a laboratory in Nanjing, China. In China contraceptives are given free to all married persons. The foil, which dissolves at body temperature, is either inserted high in the vagina by the woman or put over the top of the penis by the man before penetration.

Withdrawal and other methods

These usually involve withdrawing the penis from the vagina just before orgasm so that ejaculation does not occur in the vagina. The technical term is *coitus interruptus*. But even if withdrawal is properly practised, there may be sperm in the fluids released from the penis prior to ejaculation and therefore the risk of pregnancy. The only advantage of withdrawal is that it is better than nothing. With practice it is also possible to refrain from ejaculating but allow orgasm to occur inside the vagina. This is *coitus reservatus*. Most men know when ejaculation is about to occur so both methods are feasible. Unfortunately the experience of witholding ejaculation or withdrawing before orgasm is often, though not always, intensely frustrating. Even with the best of intentions neither method always prevails over the temptation of the moment.

Other behavioural methods, such as oral or anal intercourse, are much more effective, though they too cause frustration and are not to everyone's liking. Breast-feeding is sometimes regarded as a method of birth control too, but it is highly unreliable. At best it might help to space pregnancies. In most women breast-feeding postpones ovulation and therefore the possibility of conception for about six months after childbirth. Another pregnancy commonly follows if nursing is the only method relied on.

Douching is a useless contraceptive procedure; by the time it happens, many sperm have already entered the uterus and begun their journey towards the oviducts.

Sterilization

Though sterilization has been technically possible for many years it was not widely or confidently recommended until the late 1960s. Now it is the most effective and widespread method of controlling fertility, more popular even than oral contraceptives. In developed countries about one in three couples over the age of thirty opts for sterilization and the practice is fast growing in the Third World. In China and India sterilization is fashionable among all classes, rural and urban. In many Third World countries sterilization procedures are carried out by mobile clinics.

Sterilization methods differ for men and women, but in both sexes they usually involve cutting and tying the tubes leading from the gonads, the vasa deferentia in men and the oviducts in women. A trained doctor can do the operation in ten to twenty minutes. After it men are advised to take it easy and refrain from intercourse for several days, but otherwise they can go back to work or continue with their usual routine within hours. Since live sperm remain in the vasa and urethra for some time after vasectomy, contraception must continue to be used for at least fifteen or so ejaculations or until the ejaculate is free of sperm. Sterilization procedures for women are a little more complicated, and several days' to two weeks' rest are usually advised, depending on the method used. During this time intercourse must be refrained from.

A New Year greetings card from Thailand. Thailand has one of the most sophisticated, and effective, family planning campaigns in the world. A special 'family planning' skirt is distributed free to Thai women; when not worn as a skirt it can be used as a curtain, a table cloth or a wall hanging.

An old French advertisement for the 'Marvel rotary douche' or vaginal syringe. The theory is that douching — with warm water containing vinegar, salt, soap or a special spermicide — washes sperm out of the vagina after intercourse. It is not effective, but is probably better than nothing.

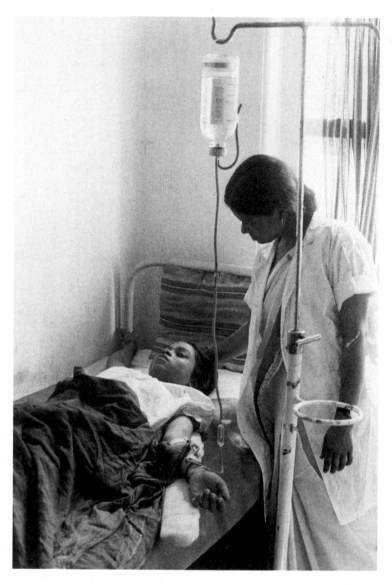

A young Indian woman recovers in hospital after sterilization.

Though it is a safer procedure for men than for women, more women are sterilized than men, which is not surprising since women bear the brunt of pregnancy. Feelings of inadequacy or depression after sterilization are not unusual. After all, fertility is a strong symbol of femininity and masculinity. Unfortunately for some couples the erroneous belief that sexual drive fades after sterilization becomes a self-fulfilling prophecy.

Researchers are now developing sterilization techniques that do not involve surgery. The sterilizing agent may be a vaccine which incapacitates sperm and eggs, or a substance which causes constriction and closure of the tubes leading from the gonads. A technique I worked on for several years involves the drug quinacrine, also used in the treatment of malaria. In liquid or paste form, quinacrine can be injected into the uterus or oviducts via a tube passed up through the vagina. Once inside the uterus it causes the oviducts to close, preventing the passage of eggs or sperm. Many scientists are now working on quinacrine and similar drugs (tissue adhesives) but their safety and reliability have not yet been adequately proved. Mechanical plugs are also being developed that essentially do the same thing, block the passage between uterus and oviducts. Some or all of these alternatives to surgical sterilization should be available within the next ten years.

Interception

This is analogous to blocking the stable door when the horse has bolted, since it involves halting the reproductive process after conception rather than before it.

The 'morning after pill' is an interceptive. Actually a series of high-dose oestrogen pills taken for three to seven days following coitus, it alters the hormone environment of the female reproductive system so that it becomes inhospitable to the fertilized egg. The morning after pill is highly effective although it makes some women nauseous and often disturbs the following menstrual period. It is not intended for regular or repeated use.

A late period worries most women, especially if they are sexually active and pregnancy is unwanted. 'Can you help me bring on my period' is a common euphemism for 'I suspect I may be pregnant; can you do anything about it?' In many countries it is perfectly legal, whether or not pregnancy is suspected, for a

Hysterectomy, surgical removal of the uterus, is a common procedure and is usually done for reasons that have nothing to do with contraception – unusual or frequent bleeding, prolapse, or painful tumours or growths within the uterus. The end result is of course sterilization. Psychologically, hysterectomy can be difficult to come to terms with; unlike sterilization it is usually a matter of necessity rather than choice.

Sterilization should be regarded as a once-and-for-all procedure. It is not generally or reliably reversible, though there have been more successes with reversing vasectomies. For couples who have decided that their reproductive days are over it is the ideal answer.

trained practitioner to insert a flexible straw-thin tube into the uterus through the vagina and remove the uterine lining by gentle suction. Menstrual extraction, or menstrual aspiration, as it is called, is becoming an increasingly common procedure. Against the advice of physicians, some women's groups in the United States have been advocating it as a routine procedure (even done by one woman to another) to shorten menstrual bleeding time and obviate the need for contraceptives.

Up until four to six weeks of pregnancy menstrual extraction is easy and untraumatic if done in proper conditions by a trained person. It takes just a few minutes. Normal activities can be resumed after a brief rest but the usual advice is to abstain from coitus for at least a week. If the woman is not pregnant, all that happens is that a period is induced. If she is pregnant, the process is, in effect, a very early abortion.

Abortion, certainly the most common method of interception, is now legal for more than 90 per cent of the world's population. In Belgium, Ireland, Spain and many Muslim and Latin American countries abortion is still a crime. But illegality does not mean that abor-

Left *This spiny plant which grows in the high Central Andes is extensively used as a native abortifacient. Almost every culture has its 'folk' contraceptives and abortifacients.*

Below *Abortion under acupuncture at a hospital in Xi'an, Shaanxi Province, China. China's one-child-per-family policy is seen as socially responsible and necessary for national survival.*

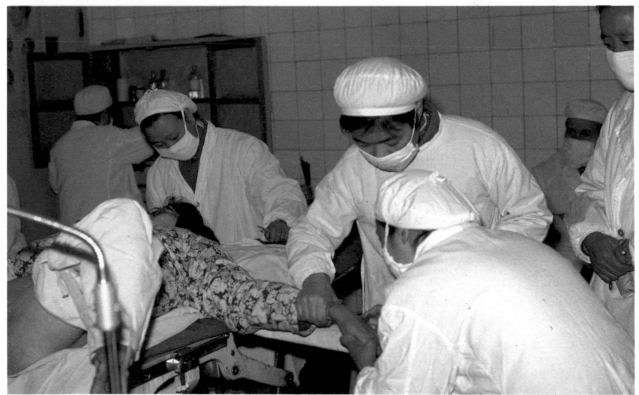

tion is not available, from trained or untrained practitioners, if one has the money and the contacts. Abortion can be an ugly and risky procedure if performed by a backstreet operator. Even done properly in clinical conditions it is not an altogether pleasant experience, although it is certainly less risky than delivery.

Until the twelfth week of pregnancy the abortion method most commonly used is similar to menstrual extraction. But after the twelfth week the foetus is too big to be simply sucked from the uterus. Thereafter the preferred method is to place prostaglandins (mentioned on the next page) directly into the uterus or vagina or inject a salt solution into the fluids surrounding the foetus. This brings on contractions and within hours the foetus is expelled. After a day or two of rest, most women resume their normal routine, although some physicians advise women to refrain from intercourse for at least a week.

Although there is a greater or lesser degree of psychological pain involved, almost all women who abort feel they are making the best decision in the circumstances. Follow-up studies have consistently shown 'no regrets' to be the predominant response, regardless of religious persuasion, marital status or nationality. Where abortion is regretted, who is to know whether having a child would not be even greater cause for regret? Where women have been denied abortions for governmental or medical reasons, research has shown that the children born are more likely to suffer social and medical problems than their wanted peers.

In 1979 approximately fourteen out of every thousand French and Italian women between the ages of fifteen and forty-nine had abortions. The figures for non-Catholic countries such as Canada, England and Wales were slightly lower; in Finland and Norway they were slightly higher. Another set of statistics for 1979 shows that in Western European countries between 20 and 30 per cent of all pregnancies were aborted, and in Japan, Romania and the Soviet Union as many as 70 per cent. In areas of the Chinese Peoples' Republic the percentage may be even higher.

When contraceptives are readily available abortion is not usually regarded as a substitute for them; rather it is resorted to by regular partners when contraceptive methods fail. Single and young women who get pregnant and have abortions are more likely to revise their ideas about birth control or seek a more reliable method in preference to repeated pregnancy and abortion.

Despite its prevalence and legality, abortion is seldom talked about openly, except in general political terms. Pregnancy and birth are greeted with social support and general rejoicing but abortion is done without fanfare or advertisement. Even close friends may be unaware of the event; if they are told later it is a mark of special intimacy. There is the underlying feeling of personal failure – as an adult, as a parent, as someone who ought to be contraceptively aware and responsible but somehow wasn't. Women in particular, but sometimes their partners and families too, undergo in private an experience that might be better borne with social support.

As yet there is no safe way for a woman, privately and by herself, to intercept a preg-

The original caption to this rather grim French cartoon of nearly a century ago reads: 'Lifting heavy objects is not recommended, but it is not forbidden'. Ineffective as a technique. In the absence of safe and legal abortion, even more drastic methods were resorted to.

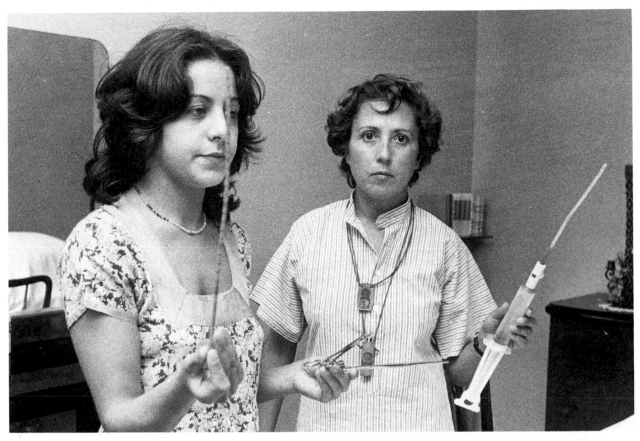

nancy, but the option is already on the horizon. Prostaglandins are naturally occurring substances that can be used to induce menstruation or miscarriage early in pregnancy. Applied as suppositories they terminate pregnancy very effectively. Side effects such as uterine cramps, vomiting and diarrhoea have meant that their use has been restricted so far, but one day, with the necessary refinement and supervision, they may give women the option of terminating early pregnancies themselves in their own homes. And I have little doubt that such a development will bring about a major change in social attitudes to reproduction. It will surpass even the changes associated with the pill.

For any sexually active and fertile couple conception is a potential reality that cannot be dodged. It is no good hoping that it won't happen. There is now such a wide array of family planning methods, especially in the West, that most couples and individuals should be able to find at least one that meets their needs. With continued research, the development of safer and more reliable techniques, and better means of educating people about them, unplanned and unwelcome births will become rarer and rarer □.

Abortion is never pleasant, least of all when it has to be done in secret. These two women, displaying some of the instruments of abortion, were members of CISA, the Italian Centre for Sterilization and Abortion, which fought hard to make abortion legal in Italy.

13

Sex as work

Newspaper and magazine headlines make hay while people cry. The large type heralds 'test-tube' babies and 'miracle' fertility drugs that give new hope to thousands. Those of us fortunate enough not to need or want such help can usually empathize with the feelings of those who seek it. There is a particular heartbreak for couples who for various biological reasons cannot have a baby of their own making.

Infertility is a condition that affects about one in ten to twelve couples and in countries where health care and general health are poor the figure is much higher. Other than being aware that a couple of our acquaintance has been 'trying' for an unusual length of time, most of us do not realize just how common infertility is.

Surveys have repeatedly found that more than 90 per cent of newlyweds plan to have children. Whether the reasons are psychological or biological, self-worth is often seen in terms of children. Children are wanted for many reasons – to satisfy family and friends and society at large, to achieve personal growth and fulfilment, to graduate from being a child of parents to being the parent of children, to conform to religious, political or cultural teachings, to swell the population of a group or tribe. Children are also a means of rationalizing sexual activities, a demonstration of sexual potency, an affirmation of masculinity or femininity. That said, many couples want children simply because they feel they have a lot of love to give and because they anticipate receiving great pleasure and joy from parenthood.

The search of the childless for children can become acute and obsessional. One infertile husband admitted: 'There is nothing that hits

Above right *To many couples the birth of a child is planned and welcome, and signifies the completeness of their relationship.*

Right *Prayer plaques outside a Japanese temple. 'My wife and I want a child' says one of them. For those without funds or contacts, what options other than prayer exist?*

into the very essence of what I am more than this.' One woman in Australia threatened suicide if her request for *in vitro* ('test tube') fertilization was turned down. Judy Carr, the first woman in the United States to benefit from this procedure, strongly criticized medical insurance companies for classifying it as 'elective' rather than necessary: 'They're saying this is an option. But for me it was not an option.'

For infertile couples sexual activities can become work rather than play, dictated by the thermometer and the calendar rather than by passion and interest. Schedules for sex may become as rigid as train timetables. To increase the likelihood of pregnancy, coitus must happen as close to ovulation as possible, regardless of when that occurs; and if sperm are in short supply, coitus should not take place except during ovulation. Strictures like these make every demand for erection or lubrication a test of self-worth and commitment. Reproduction, not satisfaction, becomes the goal. Sex as the expression of love takes second place to sex as a means to an end. Efforts to 'soften' the coital atmosphere with flowers, candles and other romantic images meet with varying degrees of success, for when reproduction becomes the only goal of sex, love is almost sure to be lost.

Causes of infertility

The causes of infertility are many but they fall into three main categories: blocked tubes from ovaries to uterus in women or from testes to urethra in men; sperm or eggs of poor quality or in insufficient quantity; and testicular or uterine problems.

Obstruction of the tubes, frequently the result of low grade but persistent and undetected infections or venereal disease, is an increasingly common cause of infertility. Obstructions can be removed by a technique know as insufflation, which involves forcing gas through the oviducts or vasa deferentia, or by microsurgery, now often with lasers (microsurgery is also used to repair or bypass the results of sterilization). But these techniques are not always successful. If they fail or are not feasible, and the woman is in good health otherwise, *in vitro* fertilization may be the last resort. Men whose tubes cannot be repaired do not have a similar alternative to enable them to achieve biological parenthood.

When not enough sperm or eggs are produced because the hormones that stimulate their production are in short supply, one possible solution is to take extra hormones, natural or synthetic. One or two weeks' hormone treatment is often successful in helping women ovulate, but because so-called fertility drugs can induce more than one egg to develop at a time, they are often responsible for multiple births. Men are less likely to be helped by hormone treatments, partly because sperm production takes much longer (about 60 days) and is a less understood and apparently more complicated process.

Endometriosis is also linked to female infertility. For reasons not properly understood the endometrium, the tissue that lines the inside of the uterus, overruns its normal boundaries and grows unpredictably, somehow impeding conception. In men, abnormally growing varicose veins, or varicoceles,

in the testes or ducts are also linked with infertility. One theory is that varicoceles hamper sperm development by raising the temperature of the testes. While the significance of endometriosis and varicoceles is not clear successful treatment is often followed by pregnancy.

In a few cases coitus occurs so infrequently that fertilization is a statistical improbability. Also if a couple is sexually and biologically naïve, ejaculation may never occur inside the vagina. There are even reports that in some men the regular wearing of tight underpants or the nightly taking of long hot baths is associated with infertility. (Because they raise the temperature of the scrotum?) In such cases the remedies are simple.

These labelled batches of plastic straws contain sperm frozen in liquid nitrogen. For obvious reasons, it is not known how long sperm can be successfully stored in this way.

New routes to fertilization

Infertile couples now have two main options if they cannot or do not wish to adopt children or if fertility drugs are not the solution: artificial insemination (AI) or *in vitro* fertilization (IVF). The first method involves collecting sperm from the husband or from a donor and introducing it into the uterus at a time when the chances of conceiving are greatest. The sperm sample, usually obtained by masturbation, may be fresh or it may have been frozen for several months. If the husband has a low sperm count it may be necessary for him to make several donations. Or his donations may be supplemented by those of a donor. If his sperm are defective, the sample used for insemination will come from a donor alone.

The alternative procedure, *in vitro* fertilization, is used when the woman's oviducts are irrevocably blocked. With painstaking care an egg is removed from or near the ovary, mixed with sperm and, after a period of development in a glass laboratory dish (nothing like the 'test tube' of media mythology), introduced into the uterus to await implantation. The first baby born as a result of IVF was Louise Brown in 1978. Her birth focused worldwide attention on the British medical team responsible, headed by Robert Edwards and Patrick Steptoe. Since then other 'test tube' babies have been born, including twins and, in both Australia and Great Britain, triplets. Efforts are now underway – amidst a flurry of controversy – to perfect techniques allowing women to give birth from frozen embryos. Meanwhile the Browns have had a second IVF daughter.

Attempts to make IVF more widely suitable and available are continuing in many countries, but the techniques are arduous and at present the chances of successful implantation are less than 50:50. Naturally the pleasure or disappointment of would-be parents is made even more intense by the effort and emotional investment that IVF involves. As many as 30 per cent of effortlessly normal pregnancies end in early miscarriage but the risks of losing an IVF pregnancy are higher still. Each menstrual period becomes, as one woman expressed it, 'like a little death'.

Artificial insemination and *in vitro* fertilization have been condemned by various church leaders. Pope Pius XII, in 1949, rejected IVF as 'immoral' and 'absolutely illicit'. Bishop John Reid of the Anglican Church of Australia

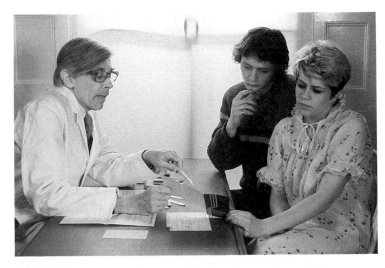

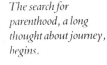

The search for parenthood, a long thought about journey, begins.

The Maaye triplets, the first triplets to come into the world thanks to in vitro fertilization, in the arms of Professor Ian Craft, the man responsible for the birth of Britain's first 'test tube' twins. The babies, two boys and a girl, were born by caesarean in January 1984. The Maayes had tried unsuccessfully for 11 years to have children.

Louise Brown, the world's first 'test tube' baby, as a romping three-year-old.

Sperm donors ejaculate into this special receptacle. Sperm is then introduced into the vagina by syringe.

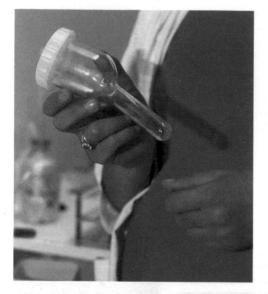

A little girl, awaiting a formal adoption order, gets to know her new family by looking at a photograph album. Adopted children have the privilege of being chosen, of knowing they are wanted.

Below *Fertility festivals survive even in the modern industrialized world. These phallic totems are part of Jibeta Matsuri, an annual Japanese fertility festival.*

has been quoted as saying: 'A reverence for life means that there should be absolutely no breeding in test tubes.' As in other matters of morality, the clergy may preach one way but their parishioners go another. Polls in England, the United States and Australia, the nations at the forefront of *in vitro* fertilization research, have all shown that the majority of those questioned approve of 'test tube' help for infertile couples. Some clinicians, in an attempt to defuse religious objections, recommend that couples have coitus soon after IVF or insemination so that the link between love, sex and reproduction is affirmed. Other clinicians say this jeopardises the chances of successful pregnancy if, for example, semen characteristics are poor or if there is likely to be undue movement of the uterus and oviducts during intercourse.

Adoption

In many cultures throughout history, childless couples have simply been given children by friends or relations. Among the Hawaiians and other Polynesian peoples this custom is known as *hanai*. To be a hanai child is an honour, a mark of great desire and great love; hanai children are given to couples with or without children of their own. But in industrialized societies, adoption is usually less simple. Although informal and private adoptions do occur, legal adoption is hedged about with obstacles. In the West it is no honour to be adopted, because the motives for putting a child up for adoption usually spring from poverty, inadequacy or unhappy circumstances. Many adopted children feel this stigma, even though they receive all the love their adoptive parents are capable of. The adopters also bear part of this stigma, as if the stigma of infertility were not enough.

Up until the 1960s much of the demand for children by infertile couples in Western countries was met by legal placement. Today better contraception, legal abortion and slow improvements in social support systems for single mothers are reducing the number of children available for adoption, and so illegal and private adoptions have increased to fill the need. Private transactions motivated by goodwill still persist even though they are frowned on by legal and religious authorities. Most adoptions involve healthy infants but children with handicaps are also increasingly welcome into new families.

Surrogate parenting

This highly controversial practice – one woman bearing a baby on behalf of another – is now becoming more common. It is, in fact, a practice recognized by the Bible: 'And Sarai said unto Abram, Behold now, the Lord hath restrained me from bearing. I pray thee, go unto my maid; it may be that I may obtain children by her. And Abram hearkened to the voice of Sarai.' (*Genesis 16.2*)

In some countries, notably in the United States, surrogate parenting is now becoming institutionalized. Women, married as well as single, are offering themselves for hire to conceive and bear children for others. In the United States, Surrogate Parenting Associates Inc. and other organizations have been formed to match willing mothers to hopeful parents. Dr Richard Levin of Kentucky claims to be the first physician to have established a surrogate-couple matching system; he screens the medical and psychiatric history and professional and educational background of the surrogates on his register.

In Britain, surrogate parenting is against the law if a fee is involved. In other words, it is illegal to charge for bearing a baby for someone else. Nevertheless it does happen and cases are known where the surrogate mother has changed her mind and wanted to keep the baby she has carried.

In themselves the technical advances and administrative procedures that have made it possible to match sperm donors with hopeful mothers, and 'wombs for rent' with hopeful fathers, are commendable. But with these New Age benefits have come some very hoary controversies – religious, moral, social and sexual.

In the past it was not unusual, although not widely announced, for infertile couples, husband and wife together or separately, to arrange for natural insemination. The wish to have a baby overrode the usual taboos about coitus outside marriage. A relative, friend or willing 'other' either bore the baby or acted as impregnator. One woman I interviewed described her feelings about surrogate fathering like this: 'I was past the age of thirty and didn't see marriage in my future. Yet I very dearly wanted to have a baby and to be a mother, more than I wanted marriage in fact. I also knew who I wanted to be the father. He was married but someone I admired and respected and thought would be ideal. I asked him and he said yes. The insemination was natural.'

There are certainly many men and women willing to offer surrogate services, free or for a price. Many women who would like to bear babies for others echo the comments of surrogate mother Carol Pavek, a midwife with a husband and son; she feels it would be 'wonderful to keep having babies without the responsibility of raising them'. Many of the men who donate sperm are medical students, simply because they form the bulk of the healthy male population in easy proximity to donor centres.

Should we concern ourselves with the intelligence, morality, and emotional involvement of sperm donors and surrogate mothers, or should we limit our interest to medically significant genetic factors? A student of mine

Peruvian slum children. Illegal trafficking in children such as these periodically makes newspaper headlines. Certainly a degree of profiteering is usually involved but the demand for children by childless couples in affluent societies is growing. Perhaps more important is the question: does it, or does it not, benefit the children?

who was a regular donor used to fantasize: 'My progeny are improving the general calibre of the population.' *Folie de grandeur* indeed! He was never the slightest bit concerned about the destiny of his sperm, an attitude common among other donors. However, some donors I have interviewed say they do occasionally think of 'their children' but most of them are not sufficiently uncomfortable with the idea to stop donating. Most admit they would masturbate anyway.

The emotional investment of the surrogate mother, who surrenders the baby she has been carrying for nine months, is easier to empathize with. Elizabeth Kane (a *nom de maternité* used by the first acknowledged surrogate in the United States) thinks more attention should be paid to the emotional needs of women like herself: 'We need support groups both during the pregnancy and after we give up our babies' she says. 'The first time I saw the adoptive mother hold the baby it

was thrilling. But I also went through depression... I cried for weeks every Sunday because he was born on a Sunday.'

Psychiatrist Philip J. Parker has made a study of 125 women before, during and after their surrogate experience. He claims that there is 'no evidence to support the notion that surrogate motherhood with or without a fee leads to serious psychological consequences'. Since these women embark on pregnancy knowing that they will give up the baby and that, in the meantime, their womb is 'for hire', they consider it 'the couple's baby' rather than their own and so reduce their emotional investment. During pregnancy a surrogate mother may refer to 'their baby', rather than to 'my baby'.

Currently, in the United States, surrogate mothers can earn up to $15 000 (£10 000) plus expenses for their nine-month assignment. In Britain, where it is illegal, charges vary considerably and so a figure cannot be put on what

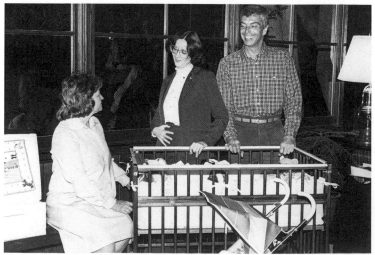

Left *Nina Kellogg, President of the Surrogate Parent Foundation in the United States.*

Far left *A surrogate mother signs a contract in the presence of a lawyer.*

Below *The expectant parents cheerfully discuss their forthcoming baby with the surrogate mother.*

The Emperor Napoleon was unable to have children. Would the course of modern European history have been different if artificial insemination had been available to Josephine?

'undercover' surrogate mothers typically charge. It is not only governments and religious bodies that oppose commercialized childbearing for others. Ellen Goodman, a Pulitzer Prize winner writing for the *Boston Globe*, was speaking for a large unaffiliated lobby when she wrote that surrogating 'encourages people to regard parents as customers rather than caretakers... We've learned to be wary of people who regard babies as just another product for an eager and vulnerable market.'

How do surrogate mothers themselves feel? One woman, who has two children of her own from a dissolved marriage, put her feelings like this: 'It's a business endeavour that satisfies monetary needs and emotional needs... I have very easy pregnancies and enjoy the idea of being able to provide for a couple that can't have a child by themselves. It's almost as if I'm being paid to be who I am and I can't think of anything more ideal.'

To couples that hire surrogate mothers the cost, including the surrogate's fees and expenses, and the fees of the physicians and lawyers involved, is high, sometimes nearly double what the surrogate mother receives. The expense involved in AI is high but not nearly so costly. Should the possibility of having a child by these techniques go to the highest bidder, or to those likely to be the best parents? Could governments be persuaded to foot the bill? Should the children born by means of such arrangements be permitted to know the identity of their biological father or their surrogate mother? 'I see no reason for anonymity', says Dr S.J. Behrman, writing for the prestigious *New England Journal of Medicine*. 'It's really only to protect the husband's vanity.' However, not everyone believes it is quite so simple.

The bond between partners

The marriage bed cannot for long, or happily, accommodate two lovers and a doctor who monitors their performance. If the partners see their acts of affection and play as acts of work, their relationship is almost bound to suffer. If they see their attempts to reproduce as opportunities to express their desire for each other, as expressions of love, they may achieve their goal without emotional damage and even find that the bond between them has been strengthened. Some couples who have tried for children and failed also say that the effort involved has brought them closer together. For those who are successful the effort almost always seems worthwhile in retrospect.

There are many legal and ethical problems attached to all the methods – AI, IVF, surrogate parenting – I have been talking about, and a lot more could be said about them. But to infertile couples who feel that full pleasure and satisfaction cannot be gained from marriage unless it includes children, they are secondary. For many people children are a unique and irreplaceable means of affirming manhood and womanhood. The quest for parenthood makes fascinating study □.

14

Watch out

Much of the time sex is pleasant and rewarding, but for a sizeable minority of people sex has its darker side. There are a number of diseases, some causing severe physical and mental distress, that are closely related to sexual behaviour. Many people react to this hard fact by refusing to think about the possibility of disease until they are personally infected or affected – a typical human trait, perhaps, but one which aggravates the problem unnecessarily. Nevertheless prevention rather than cure is in everyone's best interest. And although not all sex-related diseases can yet be cured, most can be controlled, and all are more likely to respond to treatment if detected early.

Sexually transmitted diseases (STDs) are those diseases that are passed directly from one person to another through sexual contact. They include those ailments traditionally called venereal diseases as well as many others. Usually it is possible to trace them back to a specific sexual contact or time period, and usually treatment requires the infected indivi-

dual to refrain from sexual activity at least for a while.

There are also diseases which, though not contagious as far as we know or specifically related to sexual behaviour, affect the sexual organs or parts of the body directly involved in sexual play – breast, uterine and testicular cancers for example. Again early diagnosis gives the greatest chance of cure. Sexual ability and desire can also be undermined by chronic illnesses such as diabetes, heart disease and arthritis, or by fatigue, pain and lack of energy, whatever their cause.

In the case of diseases that are transmitted person-to-person various simple precautions can be taken, but with the non-contagious kind, where it is not possible to predict who is most at risk, one can only watch for warning signs and be ready to seek expert help fast.

Sexually transmitted diseases

Lately the spread of sexually transmitted diseases has come to the attention of even the most casual reader. AIDS, for example, not

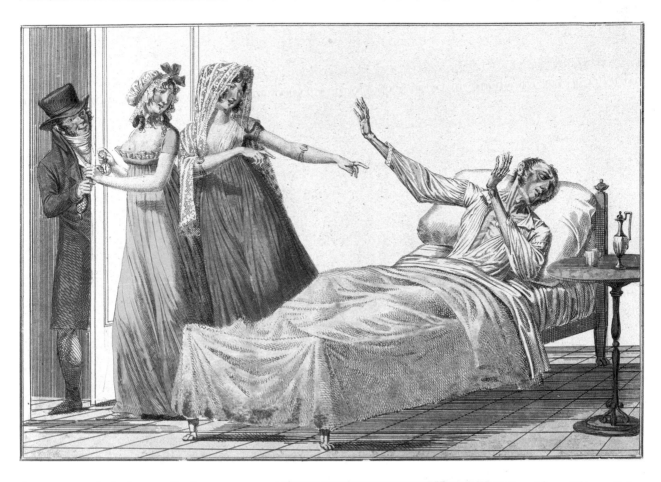

known to medical science until a few years ago, is now a household word, front page news both in Europe and the United States. Venereal diseases are not new. Both syphilis and gonorrhea are mentioned in writings from Ancient Egypt and China and also in the Bible. Syphilis, in medieval times, was known as the great pox, to distinguish it from smallpox which was considered a minor problem by comparison. At different times syphilis became known as the French, German or Italian disease and was routinely treated, usually ineffectively, with preparations containing mercury. Caused by a microorganism called *Treponema pallidum* which enters the body through a mucous membrane or a break in the skin, it causes skin sores and rashes. In the long term it also causes brain damage and paralysis and until the widespread use of penicillin in the 1950s more people were committed to mental institutions because of the ravages of syphilis than from any other cause. Penicillin and other antibiotics have now brought the disease under control.

MERCVRE.

Above *This moralizing nineteenth-century illustration shows the self-disgusted ravings of a victim of syphilis.*

Left *Preparations of mercury were used in early attempts to prevent and cure syphilis. Overprescribed they led to tooth loss and general poisoning. Fortunately syphilis readily responds to modern prescription drugs.*

Gonorrhea, caused by a bacterium that invades the mucous membranes, has also yielded to these drugs. Though not as devastating or potentially lethal as syphilis, untreated gonorrhea can lead to infertility. arthritis and closure of the urethra, making urination painful or impossible. At one time it was the most common cause of congenital blindness: babies would get gonorrhea in the mucous membranes of their eyes as they passed through the vagina and would become blind soon after.

Recent medical advances have certainly checked some of the worse effects of sexually transmissible diseases but the contemporary picture is a sobering one. According to the British Medical Association there are about half a million new cases of venereal disease in Britain every year – a new patient applies for treatment every two minutes on average. In the United States there are something like two million cases of gonorrhea annually, and another two million of gonorrhea-like disease, mainly among 15- to 30-year-olds. Elsewhere venereal disease may not affect such a high proportion of teenagers and young adults, but it is on the increase. A particular problem at present is the prevalence of several strains of gonorrhea that can be treated but not cured.

In men the first symptoms, pain during urination and a discharge of white pus, can occur within three to five days of infection. The large majority of women who have gonorrhea have no noticeable symptoms although they are affected internally; gonorrhea can quietly cause sterility. Between 10 and 15 per cent of men with gonorrhea are also unaware that they have it, although the results can be equally serious. Affected men and women can unwittingly pass the disease to new sexual partners, but sometimes the knowledge is there but not disclosed. Three out of ten respondents to *Playboy's* 1982 survey admitted to having had intercourse knowing they were infected but without telling their partners.

Some types of sexually transmitted disease, relatively rare in the past, have spread rapidly in recent times, the most common being herpes, a viral disease that periodically produces painful genital blister rashes. Not being a bacterium, herpes is resistant to penicillin and other antibiotics. Between 10 and 20 million people in the United States today have herpes

An AIDS counselling centre. Help is given in confidence and non-judgementally.

and it appears to be spreading at the rate of half a million people a year.

Certain sexually transmitted diseases seem particularly prevalent among homosexuals. Sexually transmitted hepatitis, for example, was found in one in two gay males tested in various clinics in the United States. Greater use of anal intercourse also means that, as a group, gays are at greater risk of diseases which attack the digestive system than of those which attack the genitals. And the incidence of AIDS (Acquired Immune Deficiency Syndrome), though not confined to gays, has been higher among male homosexuals than among any other affected group.

'Before we go any further, I'll need to see the results of your last physical examination and four or five character references.' This cartoon by Sylvester, in The Advocate, *a gay magazine, shows humour used to defuse a serious issue.*

AIDS

'Epidemic – the mysterious and deadly disease called AIDS may be the public health threat of the century. How did it start? Can it be stopped?' This was the headline on the cover of the 18 April 1983 issue of *Newsweek* magazine. In February 1983, in the gay newspaper *New York Native*, lead writer Harry Kramer warned, in an article prefaced with equally large headlines: 'If this article doesn't scare the shit out of you we're in real trouble. If this article doesn't rouse you to anger, fury, rage and action, gay men have no future on this earth. Our continued existence depends on how angry you can get.'

In 1981, with the help of Dr James Curran, who now heads the United States Government's effort to combat AIDS, I published a chapter on sexually transmitted diseases in an American Medical Association Handbook on Sexuality. I said not a word about AIDS, which was not identified until the summer of that year.

AIDS became the label used for a group of symptoms seen in a number of men who had been under observation since 1979. In just over two years, between summer 1981 and autumn 1983, AIDS attacked more than 2000 people, mostly male, in the United States alone and the number of victims in the United States, Canada and Europe, until early 1984, appeared to be doubling every six months. Fortunately there are now indications that this doubling rate is levelling off. However, all of those diagnosed as having had AIDS for more than two years have died. AIDS has now appeared in thirty-three countries and all inhabited continents. Though its main targets among Caucasians have been homosexuals it also particularly afflicts Haitians, haemophiliacs and heroin users, an alliterative mnemonic. In Africa it seems to affect heterosexual men and women equally.

Given the numbers of people affected and the nature of sexual epidemiology it is merely a matter of time before AIDS spreads among heterosexuals in the West. Unlike herpes, which is also spreading, AIDS is life-threatening. The body loses its normal ability to fight invading organisms. Bacteria which would normally be disposed of by the body's immune system go unchallenged. Various types of pneumonia and cancer (such as Kaposi's syndrome), and other rare or highly serious conditions, easily take hold. While the

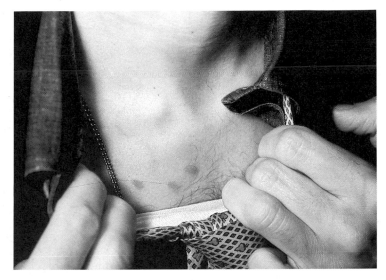

adult herpes sufferer, in spite of painful and occasionally disfiguring rashes and ulcers, can be fairly sure that he or she will recover, the outlook for the AIDS sufferer is unrelievedly bleak at present. The only way to prevent congenital transmission of herpes at the moment is to deliver pregnant women with active herpes by Caesarean section.

The effects of fear

Does fear of venereal disease prevent or change sexual activity? Yes and no. Herpes and gonorrhea were both known to the ancient Greeks. The Roman emperor Tiberius, in an attempt to stem herpes (probably the non-genital kind, better known as cold sores), outlawed kissing in public. He suspected kissing had something to do with the spread of the disease. But neither the law nor fear of infection have prevailed against sexual drives. Fear and prohibition deter some people but not all. Fear may be a factor in the incidence of AIDS levelling off, but as with cigarettes or car seat belts, there will always be a minority of people willing to gamble with their lives. A crucial factor seems to be how fastidious one is about health in general and the relative weight one gives to immediate pleasure and long-term risks. The flesh is notoriously weak. The diaries of James Boswell, biographer of the great Doctor Johnson, tell us that he suffered from gonorrhea at least a dozen times. He desperately tried to be selective about his partners, choosing 'perfect, sure people' and he tried using condoms, but as there was no cure for the disease in the eighteenth century the

The early signs of Kaposi's sarcoma, a rare cancer of the tissues beneath the skin, causing bluish-red discolourations which should not be written off as bruises, blood blisters or insect bites. Other symptoms of the lowered immunity associated with AIDS are: low-grade, persistent fever; a dry cough unrelated to smoking or a cold; shortness of breath with minor exertion; unexplained loss of weight; fatigue; blurred vision; persistent and severe headaches; swollen glands in the neck or under the arms; creamy-white patches on the tongue; persistent itching around the anus; persistent diarrhoea or stomach upsets; cuts and infections that do not heal as quickly as they should; persistent skin rashes and discolourations.
The best rule is 'If in doubt, check it out.'

malady kept recurring. I remember that when I was in the army one soldier in my unit repeatedly got gonorrhea from the same woman. With penicillin an ever-ready prophylactic he thought it no more serious than catching a cold.

Indeed familiarity is part of the problem. Gonorrhea is somehow neutralized and made acceptable by referring to it as 'drip', 'gleet' or 'clap'; syphilis becomes less alarming when vaguely referred to as 'syph' or VD. Yet both are much worse and much more serious than a cold. Herpes and AIDS are more difficult to sanitize and trivialize in this way, except in gallows humour. In fact they seem to be changing attitudes towards STDs in general. The motivation for this change is almost certainly fear or, more correctly in the case of AIDS, terror. People are becoming more cautious, taking longer between meeting and bedding. Baths where gay sex was common have closed and cruising is being done more warily. Word is spreading from those who are afflicted that sexually transmitted diseases can be debilitating, painful and even deadly.

These facts are presented not to encourage a negative attitude towards sex but to point out that sex has certain risks attached to it. But there are simple methods of minimizing these risks, and various steps one can take if a problem already exists.

Not letting it happen

Obviously sexual partners should be chosen with care. If you have reason to be suspicious try to discuss the subject. Be open about your own anxieties and encourage the other person to be open as well. After all, if you are prepared to share your body why not share your concern about its health? To broach the subject you might say, for example: 'I had a complete check-up last week and was glad to find I didn't have VD. Have you ever been checked?' or 'I had VD several years ago and had to give up sex until they cured it. I wouldn't want anyone to pass it on to me again.' Or with a half smile you might ask: 'Do you have anything I can catch?' The words are less important than the message.

If you decide to go ahead, protect yourself. Condoms and vaginal foam are partial barriers to disease. Check that your intended partner has no obvious signs of infection – unusual rashes, ulcers, discharges, odours. The best place to do this, and the most fun, is in the bath

Above *Casual pick-ups, though frequently seen as proof of sexual 'liberation' can lead to trouble.*

Left *Soap is hostile to many body invaders, but the most reliable defence against sexually transmitted diseases is 'no' or 'not until we know each other better'.*

or shower. Urinate and wash your genitals after coitus. Although good old soap and water are not wholly effective against disease they can do no harm and may do some good.

If your suspicions persist, postpone genital contact – have a diplomatic headache, think of a reason why you have to be somewhere else right away, or simply say no. This may nip a new relationship in the bud but you won't end up with gonorrhea, herpes or AIDS.

It is true that being wary and taking precautions interferes with spontaneity, passion and fantasy, but contracting an unwelcome disease is much worse interference. Be careful with any new partner, especially if you know he or she has had a lot of short-lived or anonymous relationships. Usually those whose sexual style puts them most at risk of disease are those least likely to take precautions. To be concerned about the possibility of disease hardly fits the 'cool' approach to sex that teenagers, macho males, swingers and promiscuous homosexuals like to project. The risk of disease is accepted as the price of sexual 'freedom'. And the popular myth that male and female prostitutes have regular check-ups and treatment for STDs is rarely true. Even if it were, disease can be contracted between check-ups and passed on to clients. If you promiscuously ride the sexual merry-go-round the odds are against you.

Treatment

First of all, not all genital rashes and odours or vaginal discharges are venereal in nature. Most of them readily respond to soap and water. If they don't, consult your physician; most often prescribed medication will solve the problem.

If you suspect you might have been infected, go and see your doctor right away. Don't wait for visible symptoms to appear, and do refrain from intercourse until you know you are in the clear. Your partner deserves the care and respect you would apply to yourself. Tests for STDs are painless, at most requiring a blood sample. The medical staff are not there to make judgements. In the long run you will save a lot of time and anguish if you act early on well founded suspicions. If you have a reasonably active sex life, especially if it involves frequent changes of partner, make sure that any regular health checks include tests for STDs.

How do you tell a current or prospective

partner that you have something he or she could catch? Naturally much depends on the nature of the relationship and the level of intimacy and communication between you. One herpes sufferer remarked to me: 'It's a funny topic to bring up early in a relationship. But if anything is going to come out of it – and I only go to bed with people who have that potential – I think, well, better safe than sorry and better early than late. So I tell them, usually before we get close to the bedroom. I would feel terribly guilty otherwise. So far two guys have said no thanks and bowed out, and two have said it's OK. So far neither has caught herpes from me, but we always use condoms and we never make love when the disease is active.'

There is no doubt that disease can act as a brake on casual or impromptu sex, but in valued and committed relationships it can strengthen intimacy and lead to alternative expressions of sexual love.

STDs are often accompanied by mental anguish. Fear, guilt and frustration arise not only from the diseases themselves but also from some of the behavioural changes involved. Psychological help can be just as essential to coping and recovery as medical help. Individual counselling is one option. Self-help groups, such as the herpes sufferers' group HELP in the United States, are another. At group sessions participants can express their real feelings, get information, learn how others cope, and gradually regain their self-esteem and sexual confidence. For many individuals, STDs can severely curtail sexual activity, whether with a regular partner or not, and depression and bottled-up aggression are common.

Instant rescue, American-style, for lovers stricken with disease, or just remorse or apprehension.

The need for public education

STDs still carry a stigma. Unlike other common ailments they attract moral judgements, spoken or implied. Embarrassment, guilt and secrecy hamper open discussion of STDs. For centuries the preferred method of control has been disapproval and public moralizing against any sexual activity outside marriage. With the increase in non-monogamous relationships and prostitution during and after World War I the emphasis veered towards accepting the behaviour and trying to prevent the disease. Condoms were advertised 'for the prevention of disease' (there was no mention of their possible use as contraceptives) and people were warned to be choosy about their sexual partners. There were public health drives against prostitutes as 'reservoirs of venereal disease'. Then, as antibiotics came into use, the emphasis changed again, from prevention to treatment. Many people now see the central problem not as an ethical one but as one of encouraging those at risk to come forward for diagnosis, treatment and advice.

In my view the wisest social response to the rising incidence of STDs today would be a better level of public education. The coverage that TV, radio and newspapers give to other public health concerns such as smoking and drinking should also be given to STDs, and their prevention, detection and treatment. I would advocate the slogan: 'Cool to care, risky to dare, sexy to be aware'. Individual responsibility should be strongly stressed – the individual may succeed where the forces of religion, law and public health have failed. At the same time more funds should be made available for research and treatment of STDs.

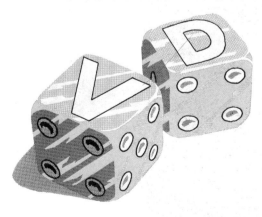

Doing the monthly breast test. Here it is being done in the tub, but it is best done in front of a mirror. Things to check for: 1 Is there any change in size or shape or hang? 2 Does either nipple turn in on itself or protrude upwards or outwards unusually, or show signs of bleeding or weeping? 3 Is there any unusual swelling or dimpling, or do the veins stand out more than usual? 4 Is there any unusual puckering, discolouration or rash, or any thickening or lumpiness?

Cancer and sex

There are a number of cancers which affect the sexual organs, but as far as we know they cannot be passed from person to person by sexual contact or otherwise. Nor is it possible to predict which individuals are most at risk. Only cervical cancer in women has been related to any particular type or frequency of sexual behaviour (frequent coitus with many partners from an early age). About one in every dozen women develops breast cancer; uterine, vulva and vaginal cancers are less common. In men cancer can affect the testicles and penis, but these types of cancer are much less frequent than those that specifically affect women.

Self-examination maximizes the chances of detecting cancer early. Any change in colour, shape, size or texture in the breasts or genitals should be noted, not ignored. Compare one side of the body with the other, the left breast or testicle with the right, any swelling or tenderness on one side of the body with the corresponding area on the other. Often a lump or noticeable change is not evidence of cancer, but worth investigating for your own peace of mind. If it is cancer, the earlier it is diagnosed the more successful treatment will be.

Women should examine their breasts once a

month. Once a year they should have a smear (Pap) test for cervical cancer; in fact some clinics recommend a twice-yearly smear test for women over thirty-five. Men over forty should have an annual check for cancer of the rectum, a common site of cancer in men.

Cancers of the sexual organs affect the most private and personal aspects of self-image and behaviour. Those parts of the body we seldom discuss are often the focus of our deepest anxieties and insecurities. How do you tell your partner that you have breast or genital cancer? How do you cope with his or her fear and anxiety as well as your own? How do you both feel about the changes that the disease or the treatment may make to your lifestyle and sexual activity? There are a number of self-help organizations that offer precious advice and support to cancer patients and their partners, and some specifically aim to help with sexual problems. Accepting that cancer is not contagious, not something that can be passed on during sexual contact, is a positive first step.

Where treatment involves surgery, pre- and post-operative counselling is especially important. Dealing with a partner's changed appearance can be very difficult. Discussing the treatment options together can be constructive, as can looking at the scars together while they are healing.

As with STDs greater public knowledge about the detection and treatment of cancer would mean earlier diagnosis and much less pain and anguish.

A final comment

This chapter has mentioned only the most obvious and life-threatening illnesses to watch out for. But any medical or physical handicap – from heart problems, strokes and arthritis, to amputation or disfigurement – can severely influence sexual practices and attitudes. Those individuals unfortunate enough to have to bear these burdens are no less deserving of love, sex and affection. Indeed, tender loving care can revitalize a person physically as well as emotionally and spiritually.

Despite the arguments of some religious fundamentalists, sex-related illnesses are not scourges sent to afflict unrepentant sinners. Like tuberculosis or dysentery, they are communicable public health problems; they spread most easily among individuals in frequent or close contact, or they appear spontaneously from causes we do not yet understand. The future will no doubt bring cures for these ills as it has for so many equally malevolent ills of the past □.

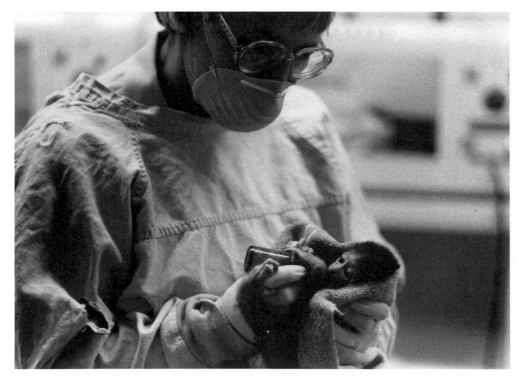

AIDS research. A 15-day-old monkey under intensive medical care to prevent it being infected with AIDS. American and French investigators now believe they have identified the virus or viruses that cause AIDS.

15

The contemporary scene

So far it has been my intent to alert sex-watchers to those aspects of sex which surround us in ways less emphasised by the media but nevertheless pervasive in their importance. In this chapter I am going to focus on a cross-section of sexual topics – rape, pornography, prostitution, sex discrimination and the media's coverage of sex – that not only constitute a quite sensitive barometer of changing attitudes towards sex in Western societies today but also find expression in many of our laws.

An infinite variety of sexual expression occurs behind closed doors and glimpses of that variety are occasionally seen in public. But social rules about the kind of sexual behaviour that is acceptable and unacceptable in public evolve because groups of people come to a consensus. Rules or laws become set formally in the case of educators and legislators, and informally in the case of almost everyone else. However, as social codes and laws are made to apply to all, many laws about sexual behaviour, whether based on moral, economic or demographic principles, constantly conflict with actual sexual behaviour and with fashions in sexual behaviour. But whereas fashions come and go, laws and the consensus principles on which they are based change much more slowly.

A lot of technically illegal behaviour goes unremarked and unprosecuted unless it is flourished in the face of authority. Where oral and anal sex are banned, for example, straights as well as gays may have to break the law to have any active sex life. But if enough people actively oppose a law or cease publicly to uphold it, the law may get changed. An example of this is recent legislation against sexual harassment and sex discrimination, and legislation decriminalizing same-sex activities. Even so, legislation takes a very long time to change intolerance and prejudice. Whenever there is a radical change in the law, there may still be a battle for approval to be won in the immediate community.

Religion and custom are also powerful moderators of sexual behaviour, even though they do not always have the force of law. Roman Catholic and Muslim traditions, for example, are powerful bastions against change. More subtle is the inertia provided by social custom. In Thailand, for example, it is traditional for the younger daughter and her husband to stay with her parents to support them in their old age and take over the home. In China and Japan the eldest son and his wife are expected to take this role, but living in the home of the son's parents. Naturally arrangements like this affect sexual intimacy in the home. In Cuba, Japan and many other countries where privacy is at a premium, young couples often resort to renting hotel rooms by the hour.

Above right
A 'streaker' in the arms of the law at a rugby match at Twickenham, England. At the time streaking was a faddish way of knocking social values; even so, 'public decency' was more amused than outraged.

Right *Rape, violent and violating, and the violation may continue in court where the victim can find her (rarely his) whole life, morality and credibility on trial. Only a fraction of all reported rapes come to trial and only a fraction of these result in conviction.*

Rape: proof and provocation

One category of sexual behaviour commonly legislated against is that which contains a large element of intrusion or assault. Rape is assault, but rigorous proof is needed to make a rape charge stick. There are many legal loopholes and ambiguous standards that allow accused rapists to escape conviction, not the least being interpretation of the word 'consent'. Do rape victims 'consent' if they are too terrified or tired to struggle?

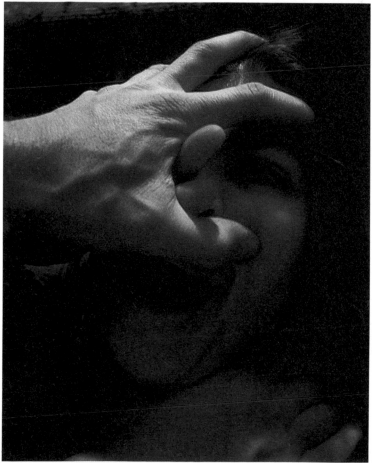

Combining as it does current Western fascinations with sex and violence and the acting out of a very common sexual fantasy, rape makes good media copy. Of course a fantasy victim remains in control of the rapist and of the level of violence; in real life the victim is not in control. Reading the newspapers one might be excused for thinking that rape is on the increase, but it is hard to be sure. Certainly it is more frequently reported, because women's attitudes towards their sexual rights are changing, and because society now expects rape victims to speak up, not suffer in silence.

Traditionally rape has been thought of as a crime by males against females. This is true in the majority of cases, but lately there have been more reports of men raping men and a few of women raping men. The incidence of reported rapes in the United States as a whole tripled between 1964 and 1970. Now it is crudely estimated that one in fifteen Amer-

The aftermath of rape. A secure counselling situation lets victims explore their feelings and regain their self-esteem. Even after some time has elapsed counselling can help to ease emotional damage.

ican women is likely to be attacked. At the time of writing about 3 per cent of the rape victims attending the Hawaii Sexual Abuse Center are men who have been assaulted by other men. No reliable figures exist for men raped by women, probably because the men concerned are reluctant to face the loss of dignity involved in admitting to such an experience or the sheer disbelief they expect to encounter. Disbelief and shame are potent factors for female rape victims too.

Why is it so difficult to prove a charge of rape? Police and prosecutors tread warily if the evidence is not absolutely sound. False accusations are infrequent but they do occur. More at issue is the question of whether or not the victim somehow provoked the attacker. Did something in her/his behaviour express willingness to have sex? The old cliché that women say no when they mean yes has a lot to answer for. Rape victims often suffer a sense of self-blame, or feel that society is pressuring them into accepting responsibility for having been raped. As one woman remarked bitterly: 'My father always said that whatever a man did to a woman, she provoked it.' Wearing flamboyant clothes, having a drink too many, entering a bar alone, walking in the street at night... all of these things can be construed, and often are construed, as 'asking for it'. The fear of being assaulted, sexually or otherwise, makes a significant difference to the way many women live their daily lives. Many would agree with Israeli Prime Minister Golda Meir when she said, in reply to a male colleague who

proposed that women should be kept off the streets after dark to protect them from rape: 'No! Keep the MEN off the streets after dark!'

The victim victimized?

Methods of investigating rape charges and conducting rape trials have been a special target of the women's movement. They represent, say the campaigners for reform, a closing of male ranks to protect men and red tape excuses for male violence against women. A common defence ploy in a rape trial was to cast doubt on the morals of the female victim; from proving that she had had 'sexual experience' it was a short step to concluding that she had 'led the man on'. Faced with this line of reasoning, what chance would a prostitute have of proving rape? Male gays, transvestites, drag queens and male prostitutes who are raped are also likely to be met with the comment 'What did you expect?'

Evidence of considerable physical violence does not always help in obtaining a conviction for rape. In fact most victims of rape delay reporting it, either through shock or fear. Often they rush to cleanse their bodies, even if they cannot purge their minds. Insisting that a competent medical authority examine them and record the event and the damage is often the last thing they think of. But, for legal reasons, that is precisely one of the first things they should do. Victims are faced with a nasty choice, to fight their assailant and risk even worse violence, or not to fight and perhaps later be accused of having consented. Actually, most authorities believe it is best to yell for help and attempt resistance. But the decision is still the victim's; so much depends on the rapist, and the situation in which the rape attempt takes place.

Some victims of rape appear better equipped to deal with its aftermath than others. From my own clinical experience, and from the reports of other professionals, I would say that a positive view of sex is a powerful aid to recovery. Although the person may have experienced physical fear and gross bodily insult, she (or he) is not usually traumatized as a person who has a generally negative view of sex sometimes is. The psychological damage that can accrue in the case of the latter is yet another reason why I feel it is important to erase the guilt, fear and secrecy that still tends to colour individual and social attitudes to sex in the West.

Coercion and aggression

Now a new concept is filtering into public consciousness on both sides of the Atlantic, that of rape within marriage. This concept directly confronts the traditional view of sex as a duty of marriage, and the associated idea that married partners are each other's sexual property. However, as of the early 1980s, marital rape laws are on the statute book in only two American states.

How sexual are acts of rape? Should rape be classed as a sexual crime at all? Should it not be regarded as physical assault? Evidence suggests that where assailants and victims are complete strangers, the assailant is more concerned with aggression than with sex. The act is a power play, a means of dominating and degrading another human being; gratification

A gang rape, even more brutal and horrible than ordinary rape. The perpetrators are usually adolescents or young toughs insecure in their own sexual status. The target may be male or female.

is achieved by thoroughly violating the emotional and physical privacy of the other person. Rape perpetrated by a spouse, lover or friend is more complex; what it represents is an extreme failure of communication as well as power play.

The majority of men sincerely decry rape, but that does not and will not stop them from seeing women, in fantasy and in real life, as objects of flirtation and lust. Women see men that way too. It is not hypocrisy to decry rape and continue to lust. In fact a great deal of lust is deflected from its object by humour – jokes, banter, *double entendres* – by pornography, and by rape fantasies.

But if one looks outside Western culture one gains quite a different perspective on rape as a category of social behaviour. Rape is scarcely known among the Mbuti of East Africa, because sex is not a restricted commodity and is in any case looked on as an extension of cooperative social activity. By contrast, the Gusii of Kenya routinely practise what we in the West would regard as rape; normal sexual coupling involves overcoming resistance and inflicting a degree of pain. For The Arunta of Australia, gang rape of a fourteen-year-old girl marks her transition to marriageable status. Despite such examples anthropologist Peggy Reeves Sanday observes that 'in societies where nature is held sacred, rape occurs only rarely'. The implication here is that rape is an 'unnatural' act and most likely to occur in societies (such as our own highly industrialized model?) that have lost touch with nature.

Pornography and its effects

Pornographic books, films and videos are often accused of encouraging sex crimes. Whether they actually do is a moot point – there is no good evidence that they do. But for the moment let us concern ourselves with the thorny question: what is pornography?

To some people a picture of a nursing woman with one breast exposed is pornographic; to others, scenes of oral and group sex are no big deal. A film or painting may be highly arousing for some, a powerful focus for sexual feelings; for others it may have no reasonance at all, or for others be plain squalid, depressing or offensive. The legal problem is to arrive at a definition that reflects a majority standard of decency or offensiveness without infringing the rights of minorities. Until recently, the definition of pornography in the United States included the words 'utterly without redeeming social value'. This is now changing. Now erotica must have 'serious literary, artistic, political or scientific value' to pass muster. In England the courts struggled for years to decide if various publications were obscene on the basis of the definition that obscene material 'tends to deprave and corrupt'. The confusion resulting from all these definitions was well summed up in a remark made by US Supreme Court Justice Stephens in 1977: 'A nuisance may merely be a right thing in the wrong place – like a pig in the parlor instead of in the barnyard. Whether a pig or a picture is offensive is a question that cannot be answered in the abstract.'

Pornography is a manifestation of the large fantasy component in human sexuality. That is why there is no universally true definition of the word. Material intended to arouse is as varied as the people it arouses. Many of the readers of this book may be less than tempted by an evening of *Lady Chatterley in Tokyo, Lust in the Swamps,* or even the all-time bestseller *Deep Throat* but those atttitudes contribute to denying or condoning another person's pleasure. Objecting or not objecting to erotica influences its availability.

The function of porn

Pornography is unequivocally a substitute for sex for people who don't have or don't want a real sexual partner or who see it as more pleasurable and less bother than othe... It can also be a means of arousi...

Standards of pornographic display in Thailand (above) and Japan (left). In Thailand it is illegal to display genitals and nipples; in Japan whole-body views of the genitals are not permitted. Note how the censors deal with the offending items – with a pen, and with an eraser.

Does this painting have 'serious artistic value' or is it merely pornography in an art gallery? Does it arouse you or not?

partner, a welcome aphrodisiac. It can be as diverting and as fascinating as a detective movie, a romantic novel, a science fiction story or a painting by a great master. Indeed many artists have turned their pens and brushes to erotic art. One need look no further than James Joyce and Picasso. Nor is all pornography laced with ropes, whips and knives; a lot of it takes place in elaborate, fairytale settings. Some even constitutes useful sex education. As assessment of pornographic materials illegally taken into Japan in 1982 showed that 48 per cent of offenders were honeymoon couples, not the depraved or deprived flashers or rapists so beloved of popular myth.

In fact reliable research shows little evidence that pornography encourages sex crimes. Data from Denmark, where porn laws were abolished in the early 1960s, show a significant decrease in sex offences registered by the police, not I hasten to add because of any new laxity in reporting sex crimes but because pornography actually appears to have acted as a substitute for intrusive sexual behaviour. Exposure to pornography is no predictor of sexual crime; indeed if one compares male sexual offenders with males convicted of non-sexual crimes, more of the latter are likely to have been consumers of pornography than the former. Pornography seems to be a displacement activity rather than a spur to overt behaviour. Those concerned with the relationship of pornography to crime might more profitably direct their attention to the role played by organized crime in its production and distribution.

Sensibilities and susceptibilities

Social pressure to get rid of pornography comes mainly from two groups, the basically right wing, self-appointed guardians of public morals, and radical socialist and feminist organizations – somewhat strange bedfellows. Members of the first group simply take a strict line on sex in general and view pornography as one of its more depraved manifestations. Members of the second group object to it as an instrument of male oppression, as a symptom of broader social forces that undermine the status of women. Ostensibly to pacify the women's movement, and to give 'liberated' women 'what they want', publishers and movie makers have created pornography aimed at women. But is yet more 'sexploitation' what women want? Porn

Sex without the effort? If anything, pornography seems to defuse sexual urges rather than promote them.

Pornographic magazines on open display in Denmark. Do you think they are pornographic? Would some of your neighbours?

for women has not taken hold in the same way as porn for men, nor does anyone seem sure exactly who its consumers are. While it is enjoyed by many women, one woman described it as the same old rubbish revamped, nothing but porn for men, in 'drag'. Interestingly, gay male groups defend gay pornography on the grounds that it portrays males as sex objects, which they applaud.

Regardless of whose sensibilities it offends, pornography flourishes because there is a huge market for it. People vote for it with their wallets and purses. But in every country, city and village, standards of display vary. Page three of one of Britain's popular daily newspapers regularly shows female nudity; but few communities in the United States would stand

for such blatant and cheerful exposure. Even in major cities in the United States the covers of magazines such as *Playboy*, *Penthouse* or *Hustler* are usually covered on display racks, although much more salacious offerings may be available under the counter.

The oldest profession: prostitution

In the public mind pornography and prostitution are closely linked, and with good reason. So-called red light districts usually contain or are contained within areas where pornography is freely available. Indeed prostitution and pornography are occasionally part of the same business empire. Also, in many countries, prostitution shares with pornography the same illegal but half accepted status. For example, prostitution is illegal in all but one of America's fifty states, but is rarely severely punished. In England, West Germany, Holland, Korea and Sweden it is legal. Only in a few societies is prostitution an honour, not a disgrace. Punishment is harshest in Islamic and communist countries where it conflicts sharply with basic ideologies.

People's feelings about pornography and prostitution usually go hand in hand: those who find sex *per se* distasteful disapprove and those who see sex positively either approve or don't much care.

Forty years ago, according to Alfred Kinsey and his colleagues, the majority of men in the United States had their first experience of sex with a prostitute. This is no longer true, but it remains true in Latin American countries. Prostitutes in the West today are usually partner substitutes, hired to provide more sex than

Above *Feminists – and also many women who do not think of themselves as feminists – feel that some advertising is offensive, if not pornographic. Is the suggestion of bondage in this advertisement really necessary to sell jeans?*

Above right *The first copies of* L'Echo du Macadam *go on sale in the streets of Pigalle, Paris, in 1981. L'Echo, the first newspaper to be run by and for prostitutes, fights for better working and living conditions.*

Left *This 20-ft-high phallus deeply offended the residents of Vevey in Switzerland and was quickly removed by the town council. It was put in the park by two young artists eager to advertise their talent!*

Far right *Prostitute and client at the Chicken Ranch, a well known legal brothel in Nevada, USA. Sex is good business and credit cards are welcome.*

is usually available or sex of a kind not available from a regular partner. The number of male prostitutes, mostly servicing other males, seems to be on the increase. Male prostitution is not new of course, but it is more openly acknowledged today than it used to be. In Japan there are male prostitutes who cater to women. Japanese society is highly sex-segregated and during the day affluent women can easily find the time and freedom to pay for sex without their husbands' knowledge. A new and popular institution in Japan is the 'mistress bank', supplying female companions for rich men on a regular but part-time basis; many of the women are housewives or students supplementing their incomes and some have the approval of their husbands or regular partners.

Mistresses and 'call girls' occupy a rather different social niche from street prostitutes or 'house girls'. They are usually less visible and better paid, and may even live quite well. The clever ones may even enjoy a certain amount of power, notoriety and status, although most lead a shadowy existence. Street prostitutes, as opposed to independent call girls or house prostitutes dependent on 'madams', are still largely dependent on pimps to protect their interests, although they are more or less exploited in the process. Theirs is a hard life. But in the United States, Britain, France and elsewhere prostitutes are forming pressure groups, collectives, even trades unions, to provide mutual support and protection of their rights. One such organization in the United States goes under the acronym COYOTE (Call Off Your Old Time Ethics).

Women unite

The unionization of prostitutes is one of many symptoms of the current assertiveness of women in search of the same personal rights and civil liberties as men. The ways in which rape, pornography and prostitution are now being discussed and treated within social and legal frameworks is due, in large measure, to the strong pressures applied by the women's movement in the 1960s and 1970s. These are issues that the media sensationalize but they are only part of a fundamental shift in consciousness, a new awareness that women are discriminated against when it comes to jobs, pay, political rights and social arrangements.

The battle is long and tiring and relatively little ground has been gained. Most women

are still sharply aware that what they see and what they experience are not what 'should be'. Certainly they have succeeded in creating an awareness of the inequalities that exist, but in real terms they are not much further on. On average women's pay is still only 59 per cent of men's. Women are still performing their traditional roles. Women are still exploited as cheap labour; and with unemployment increasing, they are often first to be sent home to leave the workplace open to men. Men still control the power sources – governments, banks, industry, the armed forces. The land-slide victory that returned Britain's first woman Prime Minister to her second term of office in June 1983 again returned only a handful of women to Parliament. And the presidency of Ronald Reagan in the United States is deplored by the majority of women, who feel he is singularly unresponsive to their needs.

Modern contraceptives and fertility drugs, among the most important advances in modern medicine, have theoretically given women the freedom to become pregnant if and when they want to; I say 'theoretically' because even in advanced countries like Britain and the United States some 50 per cent of pregnancies are unplanned and about one in ten couples remains involuntarily sterile. Yet with this imperfect freedom has come increased social and economic pressure. Many women in the West today feel that they are expected to be high achievers at school, pursue a worthwhile career, bear and care for children, run a home... and on top of all that summon up the energy and inclination to be terrific in bed. Very few men experience this kind of pressure; they do not feel similarly obliged to be all things to all people. Nor is technology the boon it is often made out to be; labour-saving gadgetry has certainly changed the character of women's work but it has not reduced demands on their time or essentially changed their domestic responsibilities.

High-flying Superwomen make news, but the majority of women remain slaves to convention, although it is still debated whether the conventions are man-made, literally, or nature-given. More women have economic independence than in the past, but there are now so many more people on this planet vying for its finite resources that women are not, in overall terms, much better off. The role of women in the Third World is changing, but

'Her little padlock's lost and gone', *the cover of a French songsheet of 80 years ago. Women have indeed gained many freedoms, including the freedom to do paid work on top of all their traditional chores.*

Below *Superwoman copes again... just! How and how much can things change for the benefit of both sexes?*

how far will the changes go and in what direction? It is still too soon to say.

Reproductive freedom has certainly given women access to sexual liberties previously available only to men, whether one is talking about liberties within marriage or outside it. Clinical and personal reports, and surveys of EMS and other sexual activities, support the view that more women have begun to take advantage of their reproductive freedom. But the majority of women have not made it an excuse for promiscuity or felt pressured into promiscuity because of it. Rather they have treated it as an extension of available options.

The new sex industry

In the West today most adults of both sexes take the view that sexuality is an important part of their personal indentity, an important tool to. self-realization, an important motivating force in their own lives and the lives of others. More is expected and demanded of sex than in the past. Sex excites more interest for its own sake than it did in the past. Magazines such as *Playboy*, *Hustler*, *Ms*, *Cosmopolitan*, *Forum* and *Sexology Today* deliver sexual information, fantasy, humour and other notabilia month in, month out. Sexual curiosity can be satisfied by reading sex manuals, or sending away for sex aids, or attending sex workshops – you can spend a weekend trying to locate your G-spot, or learning how to make one orgasm last half an hour or more, or how to be multiply orgasmic. Also on offer are an increasing variety of sex therapies – counselling, drugs, massage, nudity, groups – and problems can even be aired and discussed on television and radio with a professional counsellor on tap to advise or mediate.

Even though the intent behind much of the comment that gushes forth from newspapers, magazines, books, television, radio, movies, audio and video cassettes, is to shock and titillate rather than sensibly inform, I see increased willingness to talk about sex unashamedly and look for ways to 'make it better' as an encouraging trend. Men and women are learning to understand and appreciate their bodies better; they are learning to identify and ask for what they want in sexual relationships. As this knowledge becomes less esoteric and more sophisticated I hope that fewer people will glibly assume that sexual problems can be solved simply by pushing the right button, finding the right technique. The fact is that sexual problems are more often psychological than physical. In fact there is still considerable debate among counsellors and therapists, and indeed among the public at large, as to what constitutes a 'sexual' problem and what constitutes a 'solution' or 'cure'. For example, is learning to achieve orgasms the 'solution' to not being able to achieve orgasms? Or is it learning to find greater pleasure in other phases of the response cycle? Or is it learning not to care a damn because the rest of the relationship is good? Or is it finding a partner specifically to provide orgasms, much as one might find a partner specifically to play tennis? Dilemmas like this are very much part of the contemporary sexual scene.

Various companies, most run by women for women, market sex aids in the home. They sell every sex toy except men themselves.

Right and below
*Neither sexy telephone
tapes nor blue videos are
'imposed' on a reluctant
public. These and other
services are offered because
a sector of the public votes
for them with its wallet.*

New media sex

The sudden explosion of the home video
market has made X-rated movies available to
all. A video store in any respectable small town
or suburb usually carries a good stock of 'adult
movies'. Though not always on open display,
'porn flicks' account for approximately 50 per
cent of the video rental market. As one American publisher commented: 'People want to
look at the forbidden. They're not buying
these [video] machines to look at Superman.
What's the point of that?' The forbidden can be
yours for only a few dollars or pounds a week.
In some respects the video market merely
expands existing possibilities – a video version
of *Playboy* was launched in 1981.

Among the more bizarre developments in
the United States are pay and cable TV quiz
games that offer you the chance to pick up a
date, strip, or act out sexual fantasies on screen;
other shows are 'no holds barred' counselling
sessions in which couples thrash out their most
private and intimate problems in full view of
millions of people 'just like themselves'. Not
slow to spot the commercial potential of the
telephone, there are now various firms, and
not just in the United States, that play sexually
suggestive tapes down the phone, or even
provide live and very sexy conversationalists
at the other end of the line.

Rock music has punched a good hole in
traditional tight-lipped moralism too. In the
early 1970s, even the most obliquely suggestive songs were banned on radio or television.

A naturist supermarket in the south of France. To naturists nudity has little to do with titillation. It is merely comfortable, natural and honest. Why do so many of us feel threatened by nudity?

Now they come across the airwaves making no bones about their messages; explicit sexual references and loudly uttered obscenities are quite common. Afternoon TV soap operas show 'musical beds' situations regardless of whether the kids might be watching. Nudity and simulated sex quite frequently appear on stage, though even in the early 1980s British morality choked on a simulated homosexual rape scene at the National Theatre in London. Art galleries of course have always broken rules in the name of art, but now the graphics visible in any high street or main street contain a variety of overt sexual come-ons.

Not surprisingly all this has been met with gusty oppostion – from parents and teachers concerned about the corruptibility of the young, evangelists concerned about people's immortal souls ('sex rots your soul quicker than candies rot your teeth') and the Moral Majority concerned that 'media attitudes towards erotica seem to imply that sex is as easy and as pleasurable as having a good meal' and, I might add, less expensive.

Sexual consumerism

It is mainly through the news media that we gauge how typical we are in our own preferences and practices. In general the centralized media, as opposed to fringe or specialist TV channels or publications, cater for a relatively conservative slice of the population, supposedly the majority. It is in their interests to make an accurate assessment of public taste: to be too conservative is to risk boring consumers; to be too sensational or radical is to risk alienating them. Though some editors and producers take the occasional risk for the sake of highlighting a particular issue or making a quick killing in sales or audience ratings, most media items are carefully pitched at, or only slightly ahead of, an average level of public acceptance. There is very rapid, and ferocious, feedback if they go too far. We, the consumers, have great influence. Whatever we want will become or continue to be available. And whatever battles develop between consumers and watchdogs, they are sure to be fascinating to watch □.

16

The new millennium

W e approach the year 2000. The date has a certain resonance. We cannot know what its historic significance will be, but it invites speculation. If there is one prediction that can be made with certainty it is that most predictions will turn out to be wrong! In 1939 psychologist Lewis Terman predicted that by the 1960s no American woman would be a virgin on her wedding day. At least 50 per cent of brides in the 1960s proved him wrong. Yet the 1960s marked the so-called sexual revolution: cohabitation became more open, contraceptive techniques improved, homosexuality came out of the closet, swinging couples became less coy about their activities, and communal lifestyles were experimented with. Jeremiahs by the score foresaw an end to 'civilized' moral codes. Now, in the 1980s, we can look back and say that the sexual revolution was not really a revolution at all; at most it was an evolution. Most of the behaviour trumpeted as 'new' in the 1960s was not really new at all and those behaviours which caused most stir – premarital and extramarital sex, swinging, homosexuality, divorce – have in fact levelled off in percentage terms. We have not, it turns out, descended into sexual anarchy or risen to sexual heaven.

Nevertheless, since World War II, choice in matters sexual has broadened enormously. That does not mean, of course, that everyone enacts the possibilities open to them – the possibility of sleeping around, protected by the pill and antibiotics, does not make every adult promiscuous, nor does the legality of same-sex sex mean that more people are homosexually active. Broader choice in sexual matters is a trend that can be expected to continue. And when choice is available, consumers generally become more discriminating, more demanding, and surer of what they want.

Nuclear threat

Are we likely to reach the year 2000? The date is meaningful in that it is sufficiently near to be relevant in terms of personal planning, whether that planning concerns marriage, family, career or retirement. My question is not frivolous, for fear of nuclear war, of the virtual extinction or perhaps the hopeless vitiation of our species, is something that many people feel even if they do not openly articulate it.

The best-selling author of the 1970s was not Shere Hite, Jackie Collins or any other chronicler of our sexual mores. By a gigantic margin

Satisfying human relationships depend crucially on at least some degree of optimism about the future, some shared view of what is going to be good about it. Most of us live with at least some free-floating anxiety about the state of the world we live in, and the spectre of nuclear war is part of it.

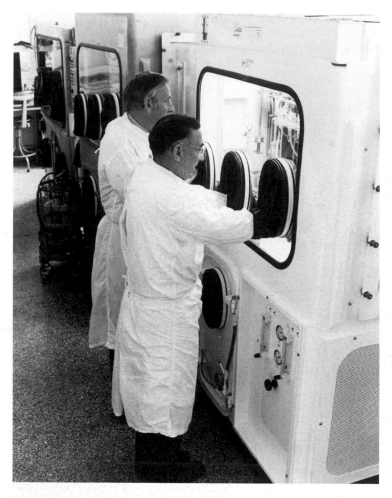

Medical research on VD. Infected animals are treated in a sterile environment through sealed portholes fitted with gloves. Scientists hold out the hope that sexual activities will be able to be indulged in safely.

perceived threat. Anxiety inhibits all kinds of pleasure, especially sexual, and has a direct bearing on important decisions such as whether to marry, divorce or bring children into the world.

Advances and checks in medical science

In the last few decades the social consequences of coitus have been greatly modified by medical science. That modification is not reversible. In fact the methods we use to control reproduction are likely to become even more efficient. Safer and easier-to-use contraceptives are sure to arrive, although the main burden of responsibility for using them will, I believe, continue to rest with women. Abortion and sterilization are simpler than ever before. Already we have home pregnancy testing kits and before the end of this decade home abortion drugs will become available, probably in suppository form. Infertility is no longer a barrier to parenthood. Almost daily there appear new diagnostic and therapeutic procedures that ensure safer pregnancy and earlier detection of foetal abnormalities, and the possibility of pregnancy in situations that even five years ago would have been hopeless.

The speed with which medical research can tackle herpes, and AIDS, the one incurable and the other almost inevitably fatal, will be a decisive factor in future attitudes to sexually transmitted diseases and to sexual encounters in general. We have got used to living rather carelessly, relying on antibiotics and other medical miracles to get us out of trouble. However, public awareness of herpes and AIDS has modified the sexual behaviour and lifestyles of large groups of people. Among heterosexual as well as homosexual populations these diseases have begun to discourage casual sex and bring about a return to old-fashioned dating behaviour; people want to get to know each other better before they jump into bed.

Initially, in the West, AIDS claimed the majority of its victims from among the male homosexual community. Fear of AIDS has infected social and sexual exchanges among homosexuals; sex has become less casual, less anonymous.

There is no doubt in my mind that by the end of the 1980s AIDS will be a significant concern for almost everyone who is sexually active with a large number of partners. Unless

of sales – 15 million copies worldwide – the spokesman of our time was Hal Lindsey in his book *The Late Great Planet Earth*, an apocalyptic prophecy of the final conflict. Dismiss such well paid doom-mongering if you like, but it is less easy to dismiss the growing memberships of peace movements in every industrialized country in the world. A very large number of people are not so sure about their chances of being alive a year from now, let alone in the year 2000.

Reaction to threat can take many forms, with hedonism at one extreme and total withdrawal at the other. In sexual terms these extremes might translate into unbridled sexual activity regardless of the consequences, or religious celibacy or disabling guilt about sexual activity. The in-between reaction, the reaction typical of most of us, is to carry on more or less as normal, more or less afflicted by anxiety, unable to absorb or deflect the a medical breakthrough occurs soon – and from now until the end of the century is not long in terms of medical research – AIDS will taint many sexual relationships. Anyone who intends to be virginal until marriage or until a relationship is established, and to be monogamous thereafter with a monogamous partner, will not have to worry. But statistics show that such lifestyles are becoming increasingly rare.

Women, work and power

It now seems fairly clear that Superwoman, the image of womankind erected by various radical sectors of society, is no longer the model that most women, or most men, feel comfortable with. It also seems that the super-macho male, in North America and Europe at least, has had his day. Economic recession and new technology are obliging both sexes to re-evaluate their social status and

A poster advertising the World Conference on the United Nations Decade for Women in 1980. It offers the view of women as the eternal safety net for male ambitions. One of the costs of change has been that women are now beginning to suffer from many of the stress-related diseases that accompany high-wire achievement.

roles. However, I do not see the male/female balance, or rather imbalance, of power changing much, unless men suddenly become more willing to take on more tasks in the home.

It is often said that the new technologies advantage women rather than men – certainly physical strength becomes academic as soon as machines and microchips take over. Present-generation computers require keyboard skills, precisely the skills possessed by more women than men. But the typewriter, the telex machine and the telephone switchboard have propelled very few women, as a proportion of the total female workforce, into positions of power. I see no reason to expect computer skills *per se* to radically alter this state of affairs.

Sophisticated computing and telecommunications equipment will, it is often said, eventually lead to a dispersal of office work; more work will be done via terminals in the home. This will be welcomed by a minority of men. Though some women may also welcome the opportunity of combining their work with looking after babies and children, in a sense the combination is retrograde, a reversal of freedoms that many women have fought hard for since World War II. It is also said that full-time, well-paid jobs will become increasingly scarce and substantially replaced by work that has traditionally suited women better than men.

Overall the world of 2000 and beyond is a world that men may find more difficult to adjust to than women. Overall I see an era of male readjustment rather than female conquest, an era in which the battle for survival will be more important than the battle of the sexes. We must train our children for an economic world rather different from the one we ourselves occupy, and the most realistic target we can aim for is to make the fullest possible range of choice available to everyone. No one should be debarred from any work, paid or unpaid, part-time or full time, in the home or out of the home, on the grounds that not many members of his or her sex do that work.

Sex ratios and the search for sexual satisfaction

A trend now emerging with ever greater insistence is the preponderance of females over males in Western populations. Inevitably this will affect sexual mores. The ratio of adult males to females has been falling since the 1940s. At birth the ratio between the sexes is about equal, or even slightly weighted in favour of males, but as time goes on the situation changes. More men than women die young, in their twenties and thirties, from accidents and injuries. In their middle years men are more vulnerable than women to life-threatening diseases, especially heart disease. Add to this the fact that women live longer and the imbalance is not difficult to explain.

How will the high-tech societies of centuries to come deal with the differences between woman and man? Will they draw them into sharper and more equal opposition? Or will they regard the differences as trivial compared with the similarities? This illustration by Alan Craddock seems to envisage sharp opposition.

244

By 2000 women in their late twenties and early thirties will find a shortage of men for sexual relationships, at least for the long-term sexual relationships that most people, straight or gay, aspire to. There is no reason to assume that marriage will be knocked off its pedestal. For a percentage of women marriage and long-term partnerships will not be options in the strictly statistical sense. The odds against a woman remarrying after divorce or the death of her husband will be even greater.

It is unlikely that bigamy or polygamy will suddenly become socially acceptable. But for emotional, economic, erotic and reproductive reasons many women will be obliged to consider, and society will tacitly accept, mate sharing. This sharing may take the form of a man openly having both a wife and a mistress, as is traditional in China and Japan, where such triangular arrangements are not furtive or morally reprehensible. Or it might take the form of a man and two women sharing a home and openly acknowledging the sexual component of both relationships. Alternatively women may have to get used to short-term sexual relationships with men but satisfy their emotional needs through other relationships; multiple friendships would take the place of marriage. Some women might seek sexual satisfaction in lesbian relationships – coitus with a man is no longer a precondition for pregnancy if artificial insemination is available. My own feeling is that few women will choose the lesbian option since personal and social taboos against homosexual behaviour are still strong. Another mechanism of adjustment might be that more marriages will take place across the divides of generation, race, ethnic ties and religion. The convention of looking for a partner of roughly the same age and social group will simply become less and less practical.

People, people and yet more people

I have little doubt that by the year 2000 many of the dire predictions about over-population in the Third World will be coming to pass. Technological and medical advances available to those of us in industrialized and modern societies will not be available to all. Many countries will react to overpopulation pressures with unprecedentedly stringent attempts to control reproduction and sexual activities. Moves to force sterilization on the populations of India and China are only a first

sign of this. More laws controlling sexual relations – marriage not allowed until after the age of 25, for instance – will be another sign. Contraception and abortion will increasingly be seen as socially beneficial and responsible.

For related and other reasons population pressures will be accompanied by increasing lack of privacy. Marriage, pregnancy and birth will be subject to more public scrutiny. The anonymity of large urban centres will be compromised by the proximity of neighbours and more crowded living conditions.

On the other hand, the press of numbers will offer increased sexual opportunities; the greater the number of people one encounters the more likely one is to meet another person who is sexually compatible and willing. And, significantly, sex as a legitimate recreation and reducer of stress will replace the primacy of sex for reproduction.

Divorce and the marriage ideal

Far from representing a crumbling of the institutions of marriage and the family, the high divorce rates we are seeing today mirror the high hopes, perhaps unrealistically high, that most people have of marriage. Those who bewail the fact that one in three marriages in the United States end in divorce would do well to reflect that two in three marriages manage to survive the pressures of twentieth-century life. And in any case the 'one-in-three' statistic is not the universal norm. It is not true, for example, of Japan, where only one in fifteen, or Italy, where one in fifty marriages ends in divorce. Divorce rates in the United

A poster in the Chinese city of Guanzhou. It says: 'Change your lifestyle and help the five modernizations. Plan Births. Just have one child.'

States and Britain have already begun to level off and for economic reasons alone, as times get harder, the rate is likely to drop. Marriage and family will continue to provide the area of greatest satisfaction in most people's lives.

Sex teaching

A change I would very much like to predict is better sex education in schools and homes. Many Western societies pretend that childhood sexuality does not exist, and keep children damagingly ignorant of their own bodies, their physical development and sexual potential. More open and matter-of-fact attitudes to sex would help to prevent unwanted pregnancies and high divorce rates among those who marry young. The teaching of sex techniques in the classroom is still a long way off although there is a good deal of straightforward biological and social information that could be more thoroughly presented within present educational frameworks. Ideal sex education should teach individuals how to make personally relevant decisions rather than hold up models to be copied. Sexual decision making is not a skill that is easily taught or a freedom that is easily granted. Even conservative countries such as those of the Soviet bloc will come to realize the need for better sex education for their children.

Untying the knots

Therapies and counselling services for sexual problems are becoming more numerous and more widely used, and I see no reason why this trend should not continue. It represents a more liberal climate towards sexuality and higher personal expectations of sex. Nevertheless, as I have said before, greater tolerance does not automatically translate into changes in sexual practice. Telecommunications, global travel, contacts with immigrant groups, are giving us new perspectives on our own sexual behaviour and helping to dissolve rigid customs and conventions. The direction of this tide of change – from less to more liberal – will not easily be reversed. Of course there will always be exceptions, Iran for example, where liberal influences were extinguished in a matter of months by a return to Islamic fundamentalism. About-turns are not unusual in countries where democracy is weak or non-existent. But, lest we be too complacent, it is worth musing that, as of the early 1980s, several of the most powerful democracies in the West have governments of a conservative hue; a succession of conservative governments might conceivably redirect the tide of change, but if they did it would probably not be with the mandate of their electorates.

We should also be wary, in this post-Freudian age, of replacing one collection of inhibitions with another. Many authors have pointed out how we in the West have exchanged concepts like 'sin' and 'shame' in sexual matters for 'neurosis' and 'immaturity'. We are still liable to make judgements about ourselves and each other that may unnecessarily inhibit sexual behaviour, but this tendency is decreasing.

In terms of personal sexuality the outlook is bright. Many options exist and appear to be expanding. We have tacitly accepted the needs of the unmarried adult, and we are learning to recognize the sexual needs and potential of the sick, the disabled and the old, even if fashion and advertising continue to be targeted at the young and able-bodied. We accept that many people prefer partners of their own sex, or that others do not want a partner and have other ways of satisfying their needs. Instead of having one standard of sexual behaviour for all we are increasingly tolerant of a flexible array with a great deal of choice.

What all this means is that fewer people are prepared to put up with second best, with situations that are frustrating, disappointing or unwanted. Though romance will never be totally abandoned, nor should it be, I think we will get better at tailoring our expectations to the relationships on offer, better at distinguishing between erotic excitement and the pleasures of companionship, and better at looking for reflections of the different facets of ourselves in different people, because all these things will relieve us of the search for unreachable ideals, and of the burden of unreasonable expectation we place on ourselves and our partners. If these things come to pass we will indeed have a more joyous world in which to live, love and sexwatch□.

References

Chapter 1

EPSTEIN, L. M., *Sex Laws and Customs in Judaism*, 1948, New York: KTAV Publishing House Inc.

BULLOUGH, V. and BULLOUGH, B., 'Why the hostility to sex?' *Sin, Sickness, and Sanity: A History of Sexual Attitudes*, 10-23, 1977, New York: a Meridian Book

BOSWELL, J., *Christianity, Social Tolerance, and Homosexuality*, 1980, Chicago: University of Chicago Press

MANTEGAZZA, P., *The Sexual Relations of Mankind* (translated by Samuel Putnam), 1935, New York: Eugenics Publishing Co

HAEBERLE, E.J., 'The Jewish contribution to the development of sexology' *Journal of Sex Research*, 18(4), 305-23, 1982

FREUD, S., *Three Essays on the Theory of Sexuality*, 1905 (translated by J. Strachey) 1969, New York: Avon

BLOCH, I., *The Sexual Life of Our Time*, 1912, New York: Allied Book Co.

MOLL, A., *Die Konträre Sexualempfindung*, 1891, Berlin: H. Kornfeld

MOLL, A., *Untersuchungen über die Libido Sexualis*, 43-4, 1897, Berlin: Fischers Medizinische Buchhandlung

MOLL, A., *The Sexual Life of the Child*, 1909 (translated 1912), New York: Macmillan Publishing Co.

BARNES, H. J., Introduction, in: Calverton, V. C., *Sex Expression in Literature*, 1926, New York: Boni & Liveright

EXNER, M. J., *Problems and principles of Sex Education: A Study of 948 College Men*, 1915, New York: Association Press

ABERLE, S. and CORNER, G., *Twenty-five Years of Sex Research*, 1953, Philadelphia: Saunders

ELLIS, H., *Studies in the Psychology of Sex*, 1942, New York: Random House (Lifetime Library)

KINSEY, A. C., POMEROY, W. B. and MARTIN, C. E., *Sexual Behavior in the Human Male*, 1948, Philadelphia: Saunders

KINSEY, A. C., POMEROY, W. B., MARTIN, C. E. and GEBHARD, P. H., *Sexual Behavior in the Human Female*, 1953, Philadelphia: Saunders

HITE, S., *The Hite Report: A Nationwide Study on Female Sexuality*, 1976, New York: Macmillan Publishing Co.

TAVRIS, C. and SADD, S., *The Redbook Report on Female Sexuality*, 1979, New York: a Dell Book

WOLFE, L., *The Cosmo Report: Women and Sex in the 80s*, 1982, New York: Bantam Books

Playboy Readers' Sex Survey, 1983
Part One, Jan., 108, 241-2, 244, 246, 250
Part Two, Mar., 90, 92, 178, 180, 182, 184
Part Three, May, 126, 128, 136, 210, 212, 215, 216, 219, 220
Part Four, Jul., 130, 132, 192, 193, 196-8, 200, 203
Part Five, Sep., 92, 94, 96, 182, 184, 185, 186, 187, 188

HITE, S., *The Hite Report on Male Sexuality*, 1981, New York: Alfred A. Knopf

Chapter 2

Playboy Readers' Sex Survey, 1983, op. cit.

JOY, K. and YOUNG, A., *The Gay Report: Lesbians and Gay Men Speak Out About Sexual Experiences and Lifestyles*, 1977, New York: Summit Books

DION, K. K., 'Physical attractiveness, sex roles and heterosexual attraction', in: M. Cook (ed.), *The Basis of Human Sexual Attraction*, 3-22, 1981, London: Academic Press

SCHACHTER, S. and SINGER, J. E., 'Cognitive, social and psychological determinants of emotional state' *Psychological Review p09*, 69, 379-99, 1962

BAILEY, R. C., CHOROSEVIC, P., WHITE, D. and WHITE, H., 'Physiological arousal and perceptions of a member of the opposite sex' *The Journal of Social Psychology*, 115, 271-6, 1981

DUTTON, D. G. and ARON, A.P., 'Some evidence for heightened sexual attraction under conditions of high anxiety' *Journal of Personality and Social Psychology*, 30(4), 510-17, 1974

DAVENPORT, W. H., 'Sex in cross-cultural perspective', in: Beach, F. A. (ed.), *Human Sexuality in Four Perspectives*, 115-63, 1976, Baltimore: Johns Hopkins University Press

STEINMAN, D. L., WINCZE, M. S., SAKHEIM, J. P., BARLOW, D. H. and MAVISSAKALIAN, M., 'A comparison of male and female patterns of sexual arousal' *Archives of Sexual Behavior*, 10(6), 529-47, 1981

HEIMAN, J. R., 'Women's sexual arousal' *Psychology Today*, 91-4, Apr. 1975

WOLFE, L., *The Cosmo Report: Women and Sex in the 80s*, 1982, New York: Bantam Books

DOTY, R. L., 'Olfactory communication in humans' *Chemical Senses*, 6(4), 351-76, 1981

BANCROFT, J., 'The relationship between hormones and sexual behavior in humans', in: J. B. Hutchison (ed.), *Biological Determinants of Sexual Behavior*, 1978, New York: Wiley

SALMON, U. J. and GEIST, S. H., 'Effect of androgens upon libido in women' *Journal of Clinical Endocrinology*, 3, 235-8, 1943

KAPLAN, H. S., 'Hypoactive sexual desire' *Journal of Sexual and Marital Therapy*, 3, 3-9, 1977

Chapter 3

COOK, M. (ed.), *The Basis of Human Sexual Attraction*, 1981, London: Academic Press

WALSTER, E., ARONSON, V., ABRAHAMS, D and ROTTMAN, L., 'Importance of physical attractiveness in dating behavior' *Journal of Personality and Social Psychology*, 4, 508-16, 1966

WALSTER, E. and WALSTER, G. W., *A New Look at Love*, 1978, Massachusetts: Addison-Wesley

DION, K., BERSCHEID, E. and WALSTER, E., 'What is beautiful is good' *Journal of Personality and Social Psychology*, 24, 285-90, 1972

PERRIN, F. A. C., 'Physical attractiveness and repulsiveness' *Journal of Experimental Psychology* 41, 203-17, 1921

WALLER, W., 'The rating and dating complex' *American Sociological Review*, 2, 727-34, 1937

BAR-TAL, D. and SAXE, L., 'Perceptions of similarly and dissimilarly attractive couples and individuals' *Journal of Personality and Social Psychology*, 33, 772-81, 1976

MILLER, A., 'Role of physical attractiveness in impression formation' *Psychonomic Science*, 19, 241-3, 1970

SIGALL, H. and LANDY, D., 'Radiating beauty: the effects of having a physically attractive partner on person perception' *Journal of Personality and Social Psychology*, 28, 218-24, 1973

GARNER, D., GARFINKEL, P. and MOLODOFSKY, H., 'Perceptual experiences in anorexia nervosa and obesity' *Canadian Psychiatric Association Journal*, 23, 249-63, 1978

SPITZ, R., *The First Year of Life*, 1965, New York: International University Press

SPADA, J., *The Spada Report: The Newest Survey of Gay Male Sexuality Today*, 1979, New York: a Signet Book, New American Library

DODSON, B., *Liberating Masturbation: A Meditation on Self-Love*, 1974, New York: Betty Dodson

FRANKFURT, E., 'Vaginal Politics', in: Dreifus, C. (ed.), *Seizing Our Bodies: The Politics of Women's Health*, 263-9, 1977, New York: Vintage Books

LANVAL, M., *L'amour sous le Masque*, 1946, Brussels: Le Laurier (English translation: *An Inquiry into the Intimate Lives of Women*, 1950, New York: Cadillac Publishing Co. Inc.)

HITE, S., *The Hite Report: A Nationwide Study on Female Sexuality*, 1976, New York: Macmillan Publishing Co.

WOLLMAN, L., 'Female Circumcision' *Journal of the American Society of Psychosomatic Dentistry and Medicine*, 20(4), 130-1, 1973

DICKINSON, R. L., *Human Sex Anatomy*, 1933, Baltimore: Williams & Wilkins

LOWRY, T. P., LOWRY, T. and SNYDER, M. A., *The Clitoris*, 1976, Missouri: Warren H. Green Inc.

LOWRY, T. P. (ed.), *The Classic Clitoris: Historic Contributions to Scientific Sexuality*, 1978, Chicago: Nelson-Hall

GRAFENBERG, E., 'The role of the urethra in female orgasm' *International Journal of Sexology*, 3, 145-8, 1950

LADAS, A. K., WHIPPLE, B. and PERRY, J. D., *The G Spot: and Other Recent Discoveries About Human Sexuality*, 1982, New York: Holt, Rinehart & Winston

HARTMAN, W. E. and FITHIAN, M. A., *Treatment of Sexual Dysfunction: A Bio-Psycho-Social Approach*, 1972, California: Center for Marital and Sexual Studies

KINSEY, A. C., POMEROY, W. B. and MARTIN, C. E., *Sexual Behavior in the Human Male*, 1948, Philadelphia: Saunders

JAY, K. and YOUNG, A., *The Gay Report: Lesbians and Gay Men Speak Out About Sexual Experiences and Lifestyles*, 1977, New York: Summit Books

HUNT, M., *Sexual Behavior in the 1970s*, 1974, New York: a Dell Book

SHEIKH NEFZAOUI, *The Perfumed Garden*, 1964, New York: Lancer Books

Chapter 4

DIAMOND, M. and KARLEN, A., *Sexual Decisions*, 1980, Boston: Little, Brown & Co.

KOLODNY, R. C., MASTERS, W. H. and JOHNSON, V. E., *Textbook of Sexual Medicine*, 1979, Boston: Little, Brown & Co.

KAPLAN, H. S., *The New Sex Therapy: Active Treatment of Sexual Dysfunctions*, 1974, New York: a Brunner/Mazel Publication

LASHET, U., 'Antiandrogens in the treatment of sex offenders', in: Zubin, J. and Money, J. (eds.) *Contemporary Sexual Behavior: Critical Issues in the 70s*, 311-20, 1973, Baltimore: Johns Hopkins University Press

DOUGLAS, N., *Paneros*, 74-5, 1932, New York: Robert M. McBride & Co.

Chapter 5

KINSEY, A. C., POMEROY, W. B. and MARTIN, C. E., *Sexual Behavior in the Human Male*, 1948, Philadelphia: Saunders

KINSEY, A. C., POMEROY, W. B., MARTIN, C. E. and GEBHARD, P. H., *Sexual Behavior in the Human Female*, 1953, Philadelphia: Saunders

MASTERS, W. H. and JOHNSON, V. E., *Human Sexual Response*, 1966, Boston: Little, Brown & Co.

DIAMOND, M. and KARLEN, A., 'The Sexual Response Cycle', in: Lief, H. (ed.), *Sexual Problems in Medical Practice*, 37-51, 1981, Chicago: American Medical Association

HITE, S., *The Hite Report: A Nationwide Study on Female Sexuality*, 1976, New York: Macmillan Publishing Co.

TAVRIS, C. and SADD, S., *The Redbook Report on Female Sexuality*, 1977, New York: a Dell Book

WOLFE, L., *The Cosmo Report: Women and Sex in the 80s*, 1982, New York: Bantam Books

SINGER, I., *The Goals of Orgasm*, 1973, New York: Schocken

PFEIFFER, E., VERWOERDT, A. and WANG, H.-S., 'Sexual behavior in aged men and women: observations on 254 community volunteers' *Archives of General Psychiatry*, 19(6), 753-8, 1968

Chapter 6

DIAMOND, M., 'Sexual identity and sex roles', in: Bullough, V. (ed.), *The Frontiers of Sex Research*, 39-56, 1979, Buffalo, Prometheus Press

DIAMOND, M., 'Sexual identity and sex roles' *The Humanist*, 16-19, March-April 1978

DIAMOND, M., 'Human sexual development: biological foundations for social development', in: Beach F. A. (ed.), *Human Sexuality in Four Perspectives*, 1977, Baltimore: Johns Hopkins University Press

PHOENIX, C. H., GOY, R. W. and RESKO, J. A., 'Psychosexual differentiation as a function of androgenic stimulation', in: Diamond M. (ed.), *Perspectives in Reproduction and Sexual Behavior*, 33-49, 1968, Bloomington: Indiana University Press

CALDERONE, M. S., 'Fetal erection and its message' *SIECUS Report*, 9-10, May-July 1983

KALLMAN, F. J., *Heredity in Health and Mental Disorder*, 1953, New York: W. W. Norton & Co.

DIAMOND, M., 'Sexual identity, monozygotic twins reared in discordant sex roles and a BBC follow-up' *Archives of Sexual Behavior*, 2(2), 181-6, 1982

DIAMOND, M., 'A critical evaluation of the ontogeny of human sexual behavior' *Quarterly Review of Biology*, 40, 147-75, 1965

MONEY, J., HAMPSON, J. G. and HAMPSON, J. L., 'Hermaphroditism: recommendations concerning assignment of sex, change of sex and psychologic management' *Bulletin of the Johns Hopkins Hospital*, 97, 284-300, 1955

MARTINSON, F., *Infant and Child Sexuality: A Sociological Perspective*, 1973, St. Peter, Minnesota: Gustavus Adolphus College Press

KINSEY, A. C., POMEROY, W. B. and MARTIN, C. E., *Sexual Behavior in the Human Male*, 1948, Philadelphia: Saunders

KINSEY, A. C., POMEROY, W. B., MARTIN, C. E. and GEBHARD, P.H., *Sexual Behavior in the Human Female*, 1953, Philadelphia: Saunders

MARSHALL, D. S., 'Sexual behavior on Mangaia', in: Marshall, D. S. and Suggs R. C. (eds.), *Human Sexual Behavior*, 103-163, 1971, New York: Basic Books

MESSENGER, J. C., 'Sex and repression in an Irish folk community', in: Marshall, D. D. and Suggs, R. C. (eds.), *Human Sexual Behavior*, 3-37, 1971, New York: Basic Books

SCHOFIELD, M., *The Sexual Behaviour of Young Adults*, 1973, London: Allen Lane

ZELNICK, M. and KANTNER, J. F.,
'Sexual activity, contraceptive use and
pregnancy among metropolitan-area
teenagers: 1971-1979' *Family Planning
Perspectives* 12(5), 230-7, 1980
*Sexual Activity of Youth: A Survey Report
on High School and College Students in Japan*,
1981, Tokyo: The Japanese Association for Sex Education
RABOCH, J. and BARTAK, V., 'Changes
in the sexual life of Czechoslovak
women born between 1911 and 1958'
Archives of Sexual Behavior, 9(6),
477-94, 1980

Chapter 7

DIAMOND, M., 'Sexual identity and sex
roles' *The Humanist*, 16-19, March-
April 1978
FREIDL, E., *Women and Men: An
Anthropologist's View*, 1975, New York:
Holt, Rinehart & Winston
SCOTT, H., *Does Socialism Liberate
Women?*, 1974, Boston: Beacon Press
YOUNG, M. B. (ed.), *Women in China:
Studies in Social Change and Feminism*,
1973, Ann Arbor: University of
Michigan Press
BLUMSTEIN, P. and SCHWARTZ, P.,
American Couples: Money, Work, Sex,
1983, New York: William Morrow
Survey: Attitudes of Married Men, 1980,
New York: Benton and Bowles
Research Surveys
SYMONS, D., *The Evolution of Human
Sexuality*, 1979, Oxford: Oxford
University Press
DAHLSTRÖM, E. and LILJESTRÖM, R.,
'The family and married women at
work', in: Dahlström, E. (ed.), *The
Changing Roles of Men and Women*, 19-58,
1971, Boston: Beacon Press
GILLIGAN, C., *In a Different Voice: Psycho-
logical Theory and Women's Develop-
ment*, 1982, Cambridge, Massachusetts:
Harvard University Press

Chapter 8

BELL, A. P. and WEINBERG, M. S.
*Homosexualities: A Study of Diversity
Among Men and Women*, 1978, New
York: Simon & Schuster
BOSWELL, J., *Christianity, Social Tolerance,
and Homosexuality*, 1980, Chicago:
University of Chicago Press
FORD, C. and BEACH, F. A., *Patterns of
Sexual Behavior*, 1951, New York:
Harper & Row
KINSEY, A. C., POMEROY, W. B.,
MARTIN, C. E. and GEBHARD, P. H.,
Sexual Behavior in the Human Female,
1953, Philadelphia: Saunders

BELL, A., WEINBERG, M. S. and
HAMMERSMITH, S. K., *Sexual Preference:
Its Development in Men and Women*, 1981,
Bloomington: Indiana University Press
TRIPP, C. A., *The Homosexual Matrix*,
1975, New York: McGraw-Hill
KARLEN, A., *Sexuality and Homosexuality*,
1971, New York: W. W. Norton & Co.
HUMPHREYS, L., *Tearoom Trade:
Impersonal Sex in Public Places*, 1975,
Chicago: Aldine
ACKROYD, P., *Dressing up: Transvestism
and Drag: The History of an Obsession*,
1979, New York: Simon & Schuster
WHITAM, F. L., 'Childhood indicators of
male homosexuality' *Archives of Sexual
Behavior*, 6, 89-96, 1977
BENJAMIN, H., *The Transsexual
Phenomenon*, 1966, New York:
Julian Press
DIAMOND, M. and KARLEN, A., *Sexual
Decisions*, 1980, Boston: Little, Brown
& Co.
OVERZIER, C. (ed.) *Intersexuality*, 1963,
London: Academic Press
GEBHARD, P. H., GRAGNON, J. H.,
POMEROY, W. B. and CHRISTENSON,
C., *Sex Offenders*, 1965, New York:
Harper & Row

Chapter 9

ELLIS, A. *The Art and Science of Love*, 1960,
New York: Lyle Stuart Books
JECKER, J. and LANDY, D., 'Liking a
person as a function of doing him a
favour' *Human Relations*, 22 (4),
371-8, 1969
HARLOW, H., *Learning to Love*, 1974,
New York: Aronson
PRESCOTT, J. W., 'Alienation of
Affection' *Psychology Today*, 124,
December 1979
GUYON, R., *The Ethics of Sexual Acts*
(translated by J. C. and I. Flugel), 1934,
New York: Alfred A. Knopf
LEE, J. A., *Colours of Love: An Exploration
of the Ways of Loving*, 1973, Toronto:
New Press
TENNOV, D., *Love and Limerence: The
Experience of Being in Love*, 1979, New
York: Stein & Day
DE ROUGEMONT, D., *Love in the Western
World* (translated by M. Belgion), 1966,
New York: Fawcett
WALSTER, E. and WALSTER, W. G.,
A New Look at Love, 1980, Reading,
Massachusetts: Addison-Wesley
RUBIN, Z., *Liking and Loving*, 1973, New
York: Holt, Rinehart & Winston
SOLOMON, R. C., *Love: Emotion, Myth
and Metaphor*, 1981, New York:
Anchor Press
BUSCAGLIA, L. F., *Love*, 1972, Thorotare,
New Jersey: Charles B. Slack

Chapter 10

Playboy Readers' Sex Survey, Part Four,
July 1983, 130 & passim
KINSEY, A. C., POMEROY, W. B. AND
MARTIN, C. E., *Sexual Behavior in the
Human Male*, 1948, Philadelphia:
Saunders
KINSEY, A. C., POMEROY, W. B.,
MARTIN, C. E. and GEBHARD, P. H.,
Sexual Behavior in the Human Female,
1953, Philadelphia: Saunders
French Institute of Public Opinion,
Patterns of Sex and Love, 1961, London:
Panther Books, Cox & Wyman Ltd
GORER, G., *Sex and Marriage in England
Today*, 1971, London: Nelson
HUNT, M., *The Affair: A Portrait of
Extramarital Love in Contemporary
America*, 1969, New York: a NAL Book
McWHIRTER, D. and MATTISON, A.,
The Male Couple, 1983, Englewood
Cliffs, New Jersey: Prentice-Hall Inc.
SHINGU, F., *The Swappers* (in Japanese),
1981, Tokyo: Yagenbura Sensho
THOMPSON, A. P., 'Extramarital sex: a
review of the research literature' *The
Journal of Sex Research* 19(1), 1-22, 1983
GILMARTIN, B., 'Swinging: who gets
involved and how', in: Libby, R. W. and
Whitehurst, R. N. (eds.), *Marriage and
Alternatives*, 161-85, 1977, Glenview,
Illinois: Scott, Foresman
SPANIER, G. and MARGOLIS, R., 'Marital
separation and extramarital sexual
behavior' *Journal of Sex Research*, 19(1),
23-48, 1983
MASTERS, W. H. and JOHNSON, V. E.,
The Pleasure Bond, 1975, Boston: Little,
Brown & Co.
BARTELL, G. D., *Group Sex*, 1971, New
York: New American Library
GUTTENTAG, M. and SECORD, P. F., *Too
Many Women: The Sex Ratio Question*,
1983, Beverly Hills: Sage Publications
SKINNER, B. F., 'Origins of a behaviorist'
Psychology Today, 22-33, September
1983
PIETROPINTO, A., *Husbands and Wives*,
1979, New York: Times Books

Chapter 11

RICH, A., *Of Woman Born: Motherhood as
Experience and Institution*, 1976, New
York: W. W. Norton & Co.
GRAHAM, H., *Eternal Eve: The Mysteries of
Birth and the Customs that Surround It*,
1960, London: Hutchinson
NIHELL, E., *A Treatise on the Art of
Midwifery Setting Forth Various Abuses
Therein, Especially as to the Practice with
Instruments*, 1760, London
SEMMELWEIS, I. P., 'The etiology, the
concept and the prophylaxis of childbed
fever' *Medical Classics*, 5(5), 357-417,
1941

EHRENREICH, B. and ENGLISH, D., *Complaints and Disorders: The Sexual Politics of Sickness*, 1973, New York: Feminist Press

FORD, C. S. and BEACH, F. A., *Patterns of Sexual Behavior*, 1951, New York: Harper & Row

DICK-READ, G., *Childbirth Without Fear*, 1959, New York: Harper & Row

LEBOYER, F., *Birth Without Violence*, 1975, New York: Alfred A. Knopf

NEWTON, N., 'Interrelationships between sexual responsiveness, birth and breast feeding', in: Zubin, J. and Money, J. (eds.), *Contemporary Sexual Behavior: Critical Issues in the 1970s*, 1973, Baltimore: Johns Hopkins University Press

LAMAZE, F., *Painless Childbirth* (translated by L. Celestin), 1970, Chicago: Regnery

Chapter 12

'A report on Bucharest' *Studies in Family Planning*, 5(12), December 1974

WESTOFF, C. F., 'Trends in contraceptive practice: 1965-1973' *Family Planning Perspective*, 8(2), 54-7, March-April 1976

GRISWALD v. Connecticut 381 U. S. Y79, Y. E. Y., (Physicians & Contraceptives, Supreme Court Decision)

GRAY, M., *Margaret Sanger: A Biography of the Champion of Birth Control*, 1979, New York: R. Moreck

'Periodic abstinence: how well do new approaches work?' *Population Reports* I(3), 1981

'Update on condoms – products, protection, promotion' *Population Reports* H(6), 1982

'The diaphragm and other intravaginal barriers – Review' *Population Reports* H(4), January 1976

'Injectable progestogens – official debate but use increases' *Population Reports* K(1), July 1975

'IUDs: an appropriate contraceptive for many women' *Population Reports* B(4), July 1982

'Oral contraceptives in the 1980s' *Population Reports* A(6), May-June 1982

WHEELER, R. G., DUNCAN, G. W. and SPEIDEL, J. J. (eds.), *Intrauterine Devices: Development, Evaluation, and Program Implementation*, 1974, New York: Academic Press

APPLEZWEIG, N., 'Will there be enough pills to go around?' *People*, 2(1), 10-12, 1975

FEN, C. C., GRIFFIN, D. and WOOLMAN A. (eds), *Recent Advances in Fertility Regulations*, 1981, Geneva: Atar S. A. (Symposium, Beijing 1980)

'Periodic abstinence: how well do new approaches work?' *Population Reports* I(3), September 1981

'Vasectomy reversibility – a status report' *Population Reports* D(3), May 1976

RICHART, R. M. and PRAGER, D. J., *Human Sterilization*, 1972, Springfield, Illinois: Charles C. Thomas

'Tubal sterilization – review of methods' *Population Reports* C(7), May 1976

'Uterine aspiration techniques' *Population Reports* F(3), June 1973

'The use of prostaglandins in human reproduction' *Population Reports* G(8), March 1980

'Menstrual regulation – what is it?' *Population Reports* F(2), April 1973

STEINHOFF, P. and DIAMOND, M., *Abortion Politics*, 1977, Honolulu: The University Press of Hawaii

Chapter 13

POHLMAN, E., *Psychology of Birth Planning*, 1969, Cambridge: Schenkman

TOTH, A., LESSER, M. L., BROOKS, C. and LABRIOLA, D., 'Subsequent pregnancies among 161 couples treated for T-mycoplasma genital-tract infection' *New England Journal of Medicine*, 308(9), 505-7, 3 March 1983

PARKER, P. J., 'Motivation of surrogate mothers: initial findings' *American Journal of Psychiatry*, 140(1), 117-18, January 1983

ROBERTSON, J. A., 'Surrogate mothers: not so novel after all' *The Hastings Center Report*, 28-34, October 1983

Chapter 14

DIAMOND, M. and KARLEN, A., 'Sexually transmitted diseases', in: Lief, H. (ed.) *Sexual Problems in Medical Practice*, 307-22, 1981, Wisconsin: American Medical Association

Playboy Readers' Sex Survey, 1983 Part One, Jan., 108, 241, 242, 244, 246, 248, 250

British Medical Association, *Sexcare Digest*, 1, March 1983

FELMAN, Y. M. and NIKITAS, J. A., 'Herpes genitalis' *Cutis*, 30 (4), 442, 446-8, 452-4, October 1982

'Herpes: Truth and consequences' *Sexual Medicine Today*, 6, 7, 12, 15 June 1983

Medical Tribune World Service, 'World AIDS toll growing, now totals over 3,200' *Medical Tribune*, 2, 17, 28 December 1983

LEO, J., 'The real epidemic: fear and despair' *TIME*, 56-8, 4 July 1983

Chapter 15

Federal Bureau of Investigation, *Uniform Crime Report*, 1977, Washington D.C: U.S. Government Print Office

SARREL, P. and MASTERS, W., 'Sexual molestation of men by women' *Archives of Sexual Behavior*, 11(2), 117-32, April 1982

STORASKA, F., *How to Say No to a Rapist and Survive*, 1975, New York: Warner Books

GROWTH, N. A., *Men Who Rape*, 1979, New York: Plenum Press

SANDAY, P. R., *Female Power and Male Dominance: On the Origin of Sexual Inequality*, 1981, Cambridge: Cambridge University Press

KRONHAUSSEN, E. and KRONHAUSEN P., *Pornography and the Law: The Psychology of Erotic Realism and Pornography*, 1959, New York: Ballantine Books

The Report of the Commission on Obscenity and Pornography, 1970, New York: Bantam Books

HOLBROOK, D. (ed.), *The Case Against Pornography*, 1973, Open Court, Illinois: The Library Press

KINSEY, A. C., POMEROY, W. B. and MARTIN, C. E., *Sexual Behavior in the Human Male*, 1948, Philadelphia: Saunders

WINICK, C. and KINSIE, P. M., *The Lively Commerce: Prostitution in the United States*, 1971, Chicago: Quadrangle Books

Data prepared by Women's Bureau of Employment Standards Administration, U. S. Dept. of Labor, 1975, Bureau of Census. U. S. Dept. of Commerce

DIAMOND, M., Abortion and Sexual Behavior', in: Shachdev, P. (ed.), *Abortion: Reading and Research*, 193-208, 1981, Toronto: Butterworths

POGREBIN, L. C., GLEDEN, L. V. and MICOSSI, A. L., 'Can women really have it all?' *Ms*, 47-51, 72-3, March 1978

Chapter 16

LINDSEY, H., *The Late Great Planet Earth*, 1970, Grand Rapids, Missouri: Zondervari

GOCHROS, H., GOCHROS, J. and FISCHER, J., *Helping the Sexually Oppressed*, 1984, Englewood Cliffs, New Jersey: Prentice-Hall Inc.

DIAMOND, M., 'Sexuality and the Handicapped' *Rehabilitation Literature*, 35(2), 34-40, February 1974

GUTTENTAG, M. and SECORD, P. F., *Too Many Women: The Sex Ratio Question*, 1983, Beverly Hills: Sage Publications

Medical Tribune World Service, 'World AIDS toll growing, now totals over 3,200' *Medical Tribune*, 28 December 1983, (data from WHO headquarters meeting 1983)

Index

Picture credits